Derek V. Ager

Imperial College, London

Paleoecology

An introduction to the study of how and where
animals and plants lived in the past

McGraw-Hill Book Company, Inc.

New York   San Francisco   Toronto   London

TO RENÉE

Principles of Paleoecology

Library of Congress Catalog Card Number 62-21239

00535

Ancient and modern trails. *Top,* trail in the Yoredale series (Lower Carboniferous), Wensleydale, Yorkshire, England. $\times 5\!/\!8$. (D. J. Shearman collection.) **Bottom,** trail in the *Globigerina* ooze on the floor of the western part of the Pacific Ocean. $\times 1\!/\!10$. (From Vyalov and Zenkevich, 1961; by courtesy of Academician Vyalov.)

Preface

Fossils were once animals and plants that lived and breathed, fed and bred, moved and died. Their lives were a continuous battle with their environment. Their story is the essential prelude to the fleeting present and the unknown future.

The object of this book is to show how we can study these fossils as once-living things and not simply as dry lumps of stone in a museum. Unfortunately a dichotomy has developed in paleontology, with the morphological systematists on one branch and the ecologists on the other. The former commonly regard the latter as impractical theorizers who are unable or unwilling to read the vast mountain of relevant literature, while the latter commonly regard the systematists as hopelessly old-fashioned museum paleontologists, who only think of fossils as specimens in drawers. In my opinion a training period of purely morphological work is essential to every paleontologist, but there is no need for this to have a fossilizing effect on the student of fossils. If paleontology is to progress beyond the level of stamp collecting, we must consider fossils as living organisms. The museum and the library are excellent places to study paleontology, but so are the laboratory, the cliff, and the quarry —and so, it may be added, is the whole world of living nature.

It would be quite impossible for one man in one book to write a comprehensive account of the ecology of all the different fossil groups or all the different kinds of fossil assemblages. The literature is at the same time too vast, too scattered, and too inadequate. It is therefore my intention in this book to approach the subject by way of the methods which have been and can be used in its study. After the introductory Part 1, which deals with the necessary generalities, Parts 2 and 3 consist essentially of examples chosen to illustrate the various possible approaches. The examples have been taken from as wide a field as possible, but obviously they come from my own experience and reading. Inevitably my choice has been prejudiced by my special interests, so the British Mesozoic and Cenozoic and the phylum Brachiopoda may seem to be somewhat overrepresented, but these examples are meant as illustrations and nothing more.

I have a strong distaste for the mountains of theoretical paleontology, especially in the field of evolution, which are built up of millions of words about very few observations. It would be easy to do the same for paleoecology, but it seems to me far preferable to quote actual examples than to pursue abstract principles. It also seems to me highly unsatisfactory, especially in a subject of this sort, to present the material *in vacuo* and leave the reader groping for the original sources. In the chapters which follow, it may be understood that anything not attributed to a particular author is from my own research or imagination, unless it is so well known as to need no authority.

Some of the examples are a little farfetched, and I do not necessarily believe everything I quote. Such examples are included to suggest possible methods of paleoecological research, even if the work quoted was unscientific in execution and overladen with imagination in presentation. Very often in scientific research, the pioneer gets the right answer for the wrong reason, and the brilliant theorist is years ahead of the careful experimenter. I only wish to show the sort of study which has been and can be made. There are doubtless many better examples of some of the principles and methods, and I shall be pleased to hear of them. This is the first textbook on paleoecology in the English language, and my hope is that critics will either do better themselves or suggest improvements for possible later editions. To write the perfect book on paleoecology, one would need to be a specialist in every group of fossils and in every aspect of modern ecology and a first-rate sedimentologist and geochemist besides. I certainly cannot pretend to be all these.

My simple aim is to introduce present and future paleontologists to a field of study which is wide open for research and which promises unlimited scope for rewarding work and exciting discoveries.

CONVENTIONS

I have attempted a compromise in the way I use geologic terms. Generally speaking I have followed American usages and spellings for such terms as *pelecypod* and *Paleozoic*, but I have followed the national customs of the original authors with such terms as *Pennsylvanian* and *Upper Carboniferous*. I have used the metric system and Celsius (centigrade) temperature scale throughout, as altogether more reasonable and more international.

There are probably many points of detailed taxonomy, distribution, and the like which are not completely up to date, but I am unrepentant in this, since it is quite impossible for one person to be fully acquainted with the latest literature on every group. My principle has been, except in obvious cases, to use the names and information employed in the work cited. I have also deliberately omitted authors of specific names quoted in the text, partly in the interest of readability and partly because of the vast amount of unrewarding search necessary to find and check them. There are no systematic principles involved and the original source, if different from the paleoecological work quoted, rarely adds anything to the matter under discussion.

ACKNOWLEDGMENTS

This book depends so much on the work of others that it is impossible to acknowledge them all adequately. The sources of the observations and illustrations, where not original, are indicated, but the sources of many of the ideas are often hidden in my subconscious. I must therefore thank without name my many friends in Europe, North America, and other parts of the world who have helped in endless discussions and lengthy correspondences. I have made a special point of taking examples from the work of personal friends wherever possible, since I have thus been able—in my cases—to discuss them firsthand.

I should like to thank specifically Prof. John Sutton of Imperial College, for his continuous help and encouragement, and Prof. George W. White, whose invitation to spend a year at the University of Illinois made the start of this long-thought-of work possible. I benefited considerably from the comments of Dr. Robert R. Shrock and Dr. Joel W. Hedgpeth, but they are in no way responsible for the many inadequacies of my text. Dr. R. F. Gekker of the Paleontological Institute in Moscow very kindly assisted me with the Russian literature, including copies of his own great contributions to paleoecology.

I am particularly grateful to my research assistant, Miss Mary E. Pugh, who drew all the original figures, helped considerably with bibliographic matters, and forwarded the work in many other ways, including the immense labors of the proof checking and the index. Mr. J. A. Gee and Miss Janet Taylor took the photographs and reproduced many of the figures with great care and proficiency. My wife helped in the innumerable different ways that only a wife can.

Derek V. Ager

Contents

PART ONE

Introduction

ONE

The subject

THE NATURE OF PALEOECOLOGY

Every scientific specialization is a search for the answers to certain fundamental questions. The study of fossils may be subdivided in terms of a series of such questions.

WHAT? What are fossils? This question is the business of *morphological paleontology*, that is, the straightforward study and description of fossilized remains. This study includes such modern diversions as quantitative paleontology with the application of statistical methods to morphological description. It is the primary discipline of paleontology and must not be avoided.

WHEN? When did a particular fossil live? This is the business of *stratigraphical paleontology*, which is the chief line of contact between paleontology and the rest of geology. In a sense, this study is "applied paleontology," since it is the study of fossils not for their own sakes but for their use in dating the rocks.

WHENCE AND WHITHER? In other words, what were the ancestors of a particular fossil and what were its descendants? This is the business of *evolutionary paleontology*—the tracing of fossil lineages through the rocks—which is intimately linked with the two previous specialties.

WHO? Who wrote about particular fossils in the past hardly forms a specialty, but often forms a major part of paleontological study and so is a question that no young paleontologist can afford to ignore.

There remain two further questions, which are the business of this book:

HOW AND WHERE? How and where animals and plants lived in the past is the concern of paleoecology. In other words, paleoecology is the

3

study of the habits and habitats of living organisms from the time they first appeared on the earth up until yesterday.

Paleoecology and Biology

Botany and zoology are merely the study of the fleeting present moment in the long history of life that is paleontology. Ecology is the study of the relationship between organisms and their environment to-day—of the how's and the where's of ephemeral modern life—while paleoecology seeks to answer the same questions for the whole of the living record.

Paleoecology, then, is clearly the main subject of which ecology is but a tiny aspect. Yet it is ecology which has the status of a science, and paleoecology is just beginning to take the first hesitant steps beyond the mists of guesswork and supposition. We are always told in text-books that the term *ecology* was first introduced by the German zoologist Haeckel in 1875; but it was recently pointed out that Henry D. Thoreau, that ascetic dweller by Walden Pond and an excellent naturalist, used the term in correspondence nearly twenty years earlier. However, ecology did not really begin to develop as a separate study until the beginning of the present century, its growth coinciding with that of such speciali-zations as biochemistry and genetics. To a certain extent it is true to say that ecology became the refuge of those who were interested in animals and plants as living things rather than in chemistry and mathe-matics. It is the province of the old "field naturalist" and is closest in spirit to the work of the field geologist.

The modern ecologist studies a living population like this year's auto-mobile—as a working machine. The paleoecologist studies a whole parking lot full of abandoned earlier models extending back to the first horseless carriage—all stationary, but containing within themselves the evidence of how this year's model came to be what it is. The ecologist's automobile is dynamic in space but static in time; the paleoecologist's automobiles are static in space but dynamic in time.

Paleoecology and Paleontology

When we turn from the biology of the present to the biology of the past, we immediately encounter great difficulties. The physiological ac-tivities of our fossils have long since ceased, and no one has yet found a fossilized chromosome. We are still essentially in the descriptive stage of our subject, and it is difficult to see how we shall ever proceed far beyond it. There are thought to be about 1.5 million different species on earth today. If we allow, following Zeuner (1946), half a million years' existence for each species, we have about 1.5 billion potential fossil species since the beginning of the Cambrian. So we have an overwhelming mass of morphological description still to be done. Unfortunately many young paleontologists find this prospect irksome and dull, so paleoecology and such heady delights as quantitative paleontology have become something of a refuge and an escape, especially in the absence of a good library. I would be the last to wish to encourage such a tendency. I maintain strongly that every young paleontologist should have fundamental training in the careful examination and description of fossils. This is essential not only for altruistically taking one's share of the vast task still before us but also because there is no other way of getting to know fossils properly. By all means let the Ph.D. candidate combine a paleoecological study with a revision of the fauna or flora concerned, but he should not think that he can just sample the cream and leave the very nourishing milk to someone else.

Perhaps the most exciting aspect of paleoecology, in relation to general paleontology, lies in the field of evolution. The doctrine of the survival of the fittest is basically an ecological matter, since those fittest to survive are those best adapted in terms of habit and habitat. Unfortunately the vast majority of evolutionary studies in paleontology have been of simple morphological successions quite unrelated to any thought of contemporary environments. Generalizations have been made, of course, such as the correlation of the evolution of grazing mammals with the spread of a close grass cover on the earth's surface, but remarkably little has been done in the way of detailed studies. There are immense possibilities in straightforward studies of lineages correlated with changes in the enclosing sediments or in the associated fauna and flora.

Paleoecology and Geology

The place of paleoecology in geology as a whole is so obvious it hardly requires discussion, for every geologist wants to know as much as he can about the environments represented in his rocks. The interest of the general geologist tends, however, to be concentrated on what may be termed "applied paleoecology"; that is, he is concerned with what the fossils can tell him about the conditions under which the sediments were deposited. On the other hand, there is what may be called "pure paleoecology," in which the reverse process of reasoning operates: the concern is with what the sediments can suggest about the conditions under which the fossils lived.

The overwhelming bias of paleontology in geology has been toward the elucidation of stratigraphy, but it is becoming increasingly apparent that a great part of stratigraphical paleontology is meaningless without sufficient consideration of paleoecological factors. Many cases could be quoted of false or inadequate correlations which have resulted from a lack of concern for considerations of environment. A good example is the long controversy over the dating of the Shenley limestone in the Cretaceous of Bedfordshire, England. This consists of highly fossiliferous limestone lenticles which were found apparently above Aptian sands and below Albian clays, but with a fauna which appears exactly to match Cenomanian, i.e., post-Albian, faunas elsewhere. Almost in desperation, glacial overturning of a large tract of country was postulated to explain this apparently anomalous succession, and a long and bitter argument ensued. The solution was simply that the Shenley limestone was in fact lower Albian in age and the Cenomanian aspect of the fauna was nothing more than coincidence of facies.

PREVIOUS GENERAL WORKS

It is usual in a textbook of this sort to trace the history of the subject from its earliest beginnings, with the inevitable references to the ancient Greeks and Leonardo da Vinci. I do not propose to travel this well-trodden path, since any observant man who ever said, "This is a sea shell, so the sea must once have covered this place," was in fact a paleoecologist. There are many great names which should be mentioned—Forbes, Petersen, Kovalevsky, Vaughan, Richter, and many others—but it is hoped that most of these will receive their due acknowledgment elsewhere in this book.

A brief history of the subject, and very much more besides, will be found in the monumental *Treatise on Marine Ecology and Paleoecology*, published in two volumes by the Geological Society of America. There will be many references to the *Treatise* in the chapters which follow, for it is the only attempt that has been made to reach a synthesis in the English language. The *Treatise* is not, however, a textbook in any sense, and it is for reference rather than reading. The first volume, edited by J. W. Hedgpeth (1957), deals with modern marine ecology. It comprises a valuable series of articles on various aspects of present-day environments and associations; it should be studied by anyone concerned with the fossils in marine sediments. The second volume, edited by H. S. Ladd (1957a), deals with paleoecology, and consists largely of a series of papers on local items of North American stratigraphy written with an ecological bias. The *Treatise* followed an earlier series of reports on marine ecology and paleoecology (National Research Council, 1941–1951). All the above works are indispensable for their annotated bibliographies. It should be borne in mind, however, that they are entirely restricted to marine environments.

The only other important book on paleoecology as a separate subject is the *Introduction to Paleoecology* by R. F. Gekker (1957), in Russian. This was the culmination of a long series of valuable papers and guides on paleoecological matters by Dr. Gekker (whose name is often transliterated as Hecker) and his associates. This book will also be frequently quoted here, though it is somewhat different in approach and intent from mine. It has recently been translated into French by Dr. J. Roger.

There are also a number of general works on paleontology, for example, J. Piveteau's superb *Traité de Paléontologie*, which include some brief consideration of paleoecological matters. Apart from these (and several excellent paleobotanical syntheses), the paleoecological literature is extremely scattered. There is a vast number of papers in geological and allied literature which may be regarded as paleoecological in theme. There are an almost infinitely larger number of papers in which incidental reference is made to matters of paleoecological interest. No attempt will be made here even to begin to cover the whole field of study.

FUNDAMENTAL PRINCIPLES

Underlying both ecology and paleoecology are certain fundamental principles which it is necessary to bear in mind from the start. I propose, however, to introduce them in only a very brief way here and to expand upon them later.

Adaptation to Environment

Every organism, both living and dead, has become adapted to a certain environment, which may be as wide as a continent or as narrow as the intestine of a mouse.

The British race of the beautiful swallowtail butterfly recently almost became extinct in our country, partly because of the depredations of collectors, but largely because of the increasing scarcity of the hogs'-fennel, or milk parsley, which provides the food for its caterpillars.[1] This plant is now very restricted in distribution and very scarce where it is found, because of shading out by the alder buckthorn, the sallow, and other shrubs.

This is a good example of a species restricted by a very limited habitat. It also illustrates another fundamental principle of ecology,

[1] In captivity they will eat the leaves of carrot, but this is probably not a native plant, and under natural conditions they are restricted to the hogs'-fennel.

that every species is directly dependent on several others in a complex interrelationship. The insect depends on the flower, which is controlled by other species—the shrubs.

An interrelationship of a different type is illustrated by the deer of the Kaibab National Forest south of the Grand Canyon. The killing of predatory animals in the area during the early years of this century brought about a tremendous increase in the numbers of this species. This led to great depredations on the local flora, and this in turn led to mass winter starvation for the deer until they were reduced to a tenth of their peak population.

The aquatic faunas, which particularly concern paleontologists, include many examples of restricted environments and curious interrelationships, such as the clown fish of the Indian Ocean, which are adapted, species by species, to life between the stinging tentacles of particular species of sea anemones, and the elongated urchin fish, which swim in a vertical position between the erect spines of certain echinoids. Often, unusual environments have curiously specialized inhabitants. Thus there are the remarkable faunas adapted to life in the strange conditions of caves, such as the blind fish in Mammoth Cave, Kentucky.

Contrasting with these examples of very restricted habitats and therefore restricted distributions, there are other forms which are tolerant of a wide range of environments. Perhaps the most tolerant of all species at the present day is man himself. To quote myself (Ager, 1961*a*):

Probably no other animal of similar size (and certainly not a single species) has spread and become so abundant in so many different environments. His habitat ranges from the hottest tropical rain-forest to the coldest arctic deserts, from the arid hearts of continents to remote oceanic islands, from the lowest river-side marshes to the high mountain plateaux. Perhaps the most remarkable environment of all to which he has become adapted is that of modern cities, living in boxes, travelling in tunnels and utterly dependent for his food on people he never sees and who may live on the other side of the world.

Adaptation to Mode of Life

Every organism is adapted to a certain mode of life. Thus many different groups of animals are adapted to a swimming habit (Figure 1.1) and so have come to resemble each other superficially. On the other hand, closely related forms may differ from each other because of adaptation to different habits. The most famous example of this is "Darwin's finches" on the Galapagos Islands, which, though closely *long beaked feed on pollen shubby beaked nuts!*

related, differ in beak characters and other features because of different feeding habits.

Not only are species of animals and plants adapted to certain habitats and habits, but individuals may be directly modified by their physical environment. The hawthorn bush on the edge of a cliff may grow asymmetrically as a result of the prevailing wind. Similarly, sponges tend to develop into irregular encrusting forms in strong currents, but into tall symmetrical shapes in quieter waters.

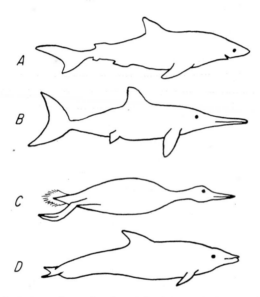

FIGURE 1.1 Adaptation of unrelated vertebrate groups to a swimming mode of life. *A,* shark (living fish); *B,* ichthyosaur (fossil reptile); *C, Hesperornis* (fossil bird); *D,* dolphin (living mammal). Not to scale.

Ecological Limitations

Every organism is restricted in its distribution by the limitations of the environment to which it is adapted. Although man is the most widespread of animals on land, he is restricted to a terrestrial environment and cannot live at the bottom of the sea. This is very obvious, but other restrictions are more subtle. An elf owl in the southern United States is restricted to the abandoned holes made by certain woodpeckers in certain giant cacti. Theoretically therefore, if the giant cacti and the woodpeckers have different distributions, it is only where these two distributions overlap that the elf owl can make its nest. In other words there are two restrictive factors operating on its distribution. In fact, there are probably dozens of others as well, such as temperature, humidity, and food supply.

Every organism is delimited by a whole range of environmental factors, only one of which needs to be deficient to make life impossible for the organism concerned. This is Leibig's *law of the minimum*, which, more exactly, states that the determining factor in the limitation of the distribution of a species is that which is present in minimum amount. An organism is no stronger than the weakest link in the chain of its ecological requirements.

Dependence on Other Organisms

Every organism is directly or indirectly dependent on most or all other members of the same community. No highly evolved organism can live in a biological vacuum, but forms part of a complex net of relationships. One often reads of a certain "plant community," but there is really no such thing, since every living community is an extremely complicated organization involving many different kinds of plants and animals. A very simple example is the *food web* shown in Figure 1.2. Even in this diagram many organisms have been lumped together for convenience, and many larger animals (and a multitude of microorganisms) have been omitted.

LIMITATIONS OF THE EVIDENCE

Every word spoken on paleoecological matters must be echoed by the phrase *limitations of the evidence*. It is hardly possible to overemphasize the limitations with which one is beset in the study of paleoecology. They were well summarized by Wilson (1951) and Ellison (1955) and are all well known, but the following is a brief restatement of the main points:

Limitations of fossilization

1. The remains of most organisms are removed after death by scavengers, saprophytes, and bacterial decay.

2. The parts of an organism which do escape these processes are still very unlikely to be preserved as fossils.

3. Those that are preserved are likely to be removed by later erosion.

4. Only a minute proportion of those that survive are likely to be exposed at the surface or to come to the notice of a paleontologist.

Limitations of interpretation

5. Only certain environments are at all likely to be represented in the rocks.

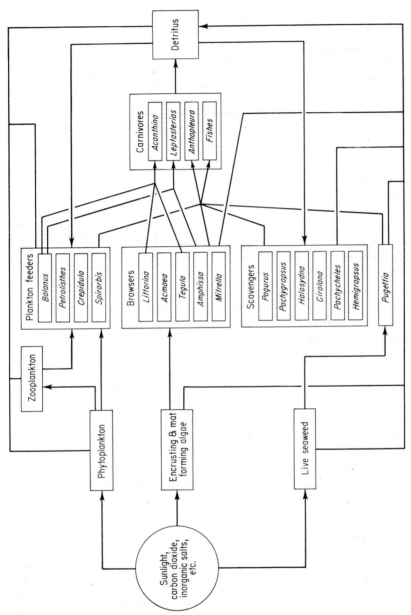

FIGURE 1.2 Simple food web of organisms on protected littoral rocks at Cabrillo Point, Monterey Bay, California. (After W. G. Hewatt, 1937; by courtesy of *American Midland Naturalist*.)

6. Many, if not most, fossils are preserved in environments other than those in which they lived.

7. It is impossible to make provable deductions about the ecology of organisms which are now extinct.

8. The uniformitarian approach of interpreting past environments in the light of modern ones may not be valid, since geographical factors may have changed.

9. Similarly, the organisms themselves may have changed their habits and habitats with time.

In paleoecology we often pile assumption on assumption and use circumstantial evidence in a way that would never get by in any court of law. In a few cases the evidence is very clear and indisputable —as when we find the boring pelecypod buried in the fossil coral, or the grass still clenched between the teeth of the frozen mammoth—but in the majority of our deductions this is not so, and we must make our constantly repeated reservations.

ECONOMIC APPLICATIONS

The best economic geology is simply the best geology, and paleoecology takes its place as an essential part of any geological investigation which involves fossiliferous rocks. Often we find that the paleoecological picture only became apparent long after the discovery of the valuable commodity concerned, but in a few cases paleoecology has been used as a tool in the original search. Potentially it could, and it should, be used a great deal more. This aspect of the subject has also been admirably summarized by Ellison (1955).

Oil

The most obvious and best-known application of paleoecology in economic geology is in prospecting for oil. The study really became fashionable among oil geologists with the discovery of oil accumulations associated with reefs, first in New Mexico and Texas (Lloyd, 1929) and later around the Great Lakes (Lowenstam, 1950) and in western Canada. The association of oil fields with Pennsylvanian and Permian reef belts in the classic area of Texas and New Mexico is illustrated in Figure 1.3.

One of the most promising areas for the use of paleoecology in prospecting for oil is in the underground Devonian reefs of southern Alberta and Saskatchewan. Here both fringing and isolated reefs are well developed and are capped by Late Devonian shaly formations. A typical mode of oil accumulation is shown diagrammatically in Figure 1.4.

The sedimentary and paleontological features of the reefs are mostly obscured by dolomitization, but a few do give some very interesting information, notably the Redwater reef complex described by Andrichuk (1958). He showed that the reefs migrated in a southwesterly direction, probably because of a prevailing wind from the northeast. They also

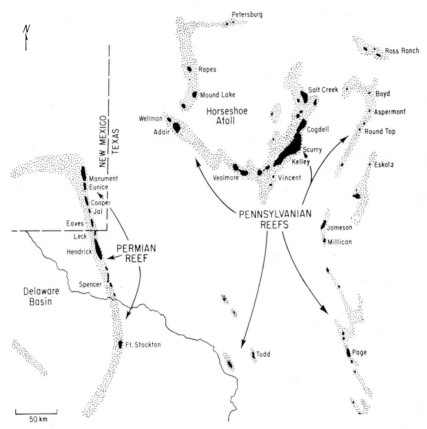

FIGURE 1.3   Relation of oil and gas fields (black) to reef belts (stippled) in Texas and New Mexico. (From Ellison, 1955, after King, 1942, and Bartley, 1951; by courtesy of *Economic Geology*.)

grew upward, and at each stage in growth he could distinguish an outer zone of calcareous algae and an inner zone of corals and stromatoporoids, which he compared with the zonation of modern reefs. Andrichuk went on to show how these belts coincided with the margin of oil accumulation (Figure 1.5) and suggested methods of exploration by which such accumulations might be detected by paleoecological methods.

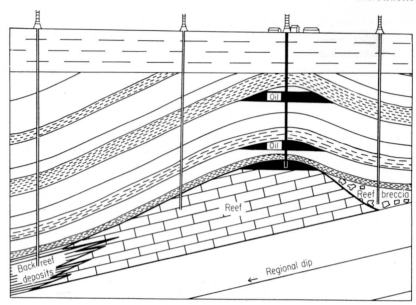

FIGURE 1.4 Idealized section showing the relationship of oil accumulations to a reef.

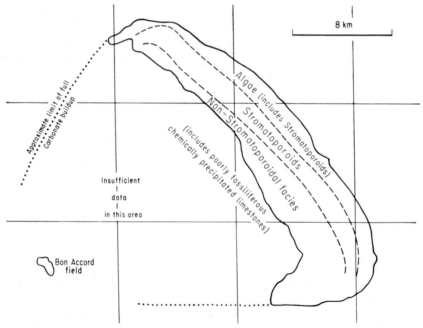

FIGURE 1.5 Biofacies of the top part of the Leduc reef in the Redwater reef complex of Alberta. The solid line shows the limits of the oil field. (From Andrichuk, 1958; by courtesy of the American Association of Petroleum Geologists.)

The procedure may be summarized as follows:

1. Delineation of the shoals which acted as foundations for the reefs by finding the highest calcarenite ratios.

2. Delineation of the reefs themselves by finding the highest ratio of potential frame-building organisms.

3. Delineation of incipient reef fronts by study of the distribution patterns of the different organisms and their comparison with known reefs.

Other types of oil accumulations may also be explored by paleo-ecological methods. Hoffmeister (1955) suggested a method of study of microfossil distributions which would be applicable to the finding of accumulations in strandline sediments. It would be applicable, for example, in the Pennsylvanian oil fields in Kansas described by Bass (1936). Here the oil is related to thin "shoestring" sands, which represent shoreline bars between fully marine deposits and continental or lagoonal deposits.

A similar type of study is that of accumulations in interdigitating marine and nonmarine deposits on the Gulf Coast of the United States. Here quantitative studies of the ecological distribution of foraminifera are particularly useful in predicting the proximity of facies margins.

Apart from looking for possible oil traps by paleoecological methods, there is much potential value in looking for likely source rocks through the study of such matters as fossil ecological zonation, fossil distributions on a world-wide scale, fossil evidence of contemporary climates, and possible modern analogues of fossil assemblages.

Coal

Coal exploration is the most direct application of paleoecological studies to economic matters, since it is the fossils themselves which are sought, and their whereabouts usually depends directly on the environment they required in life. It would be stretching the point a little to suggest that paleoecology has ever been used directly in the finding of coal, but it is very much involved in the necessary building up of knowledge about the general framework of paleogeography and cyclic changes. Feofilova (1959) has shown how this can be done in a study of the Donetz coal field in the U.S.S.R. Detailed distribution and association studies have considerably refined the paleontological view of the cycle of sedimentation. This will be discussed later.

On this basis it may be possible to correlate cyclothems on paleo-ecological grounds, even where the sediments and the environments have changed laterally. Thus the all-important, though thin, marine bands of the Upper Carboniferous coal cycles of western Europe, with their varied faunas of goniatites, crinoids, brachiopods, pelecypods, and the rest, are often represented laterally by bands yielding only *Lingula*. The latter still represent the same horizon, but in a less marine environment.

Mineral Deposits

No two things may seem farther apart in geology than paleoecology and the search for metallic minerals, but there are several cases where the one has had an important bearing on the other.

The syngenetic ironstones are particularly amenable to this approach, for most of them clearly represent deposition in very unusual environments. The famous Middle Silurian Clinton iron ores of the Appalachians are always cited for the effect of the sedimentation on the fossils they contain (see page 271), and they occupy a distinct nearshore position in Middle Silurian paleogeographies. A similar environmental position is occupied by Cambrian iron ores in New Mexico.

In Britain, I was able to demonstrate (Ager, 1956*a*) lateral faunal changes in the Lower Jurassic which coincide with the passage from a ferruginous limestone in southwest England to a valuable iron ore in Oxfordshire (see Plate 1).

With quite a different type of mineral problem, Ohle and Brown (1954) showed that the presence or absence of algal "rolls," or reefs, controlled the emplacement of lead-ore bodies in Cambrian limestones in southeast Missouri (Figure 1.6). Apparently the permeable reef structures provided easy passageways for the ore solutions.

Ellison (1955) has given many other examples of mineral deposits of all kinds whose emplacement was controlled by contemporary environments and whose discovery may therefore be sought by paleoecological means.

TERMINOLOGY

It is very easy and even tempting in a book such as this to produce a large number of new terms for paleoecological phenomena, but I am strongly opposed to this tendency, and most of the matters I wish to discuss can be described in everyday English. There are already enough monstrosities in the literature, such as "psephonecrocoenosis," which add nothing to our knowledge or ease of communication. There are some terms, however, which are both useful and necessary, and a glossary of these is given as Appendix 1. Most of these are common in the ecological literature, but may not be familiar to all paleontologists; others require careful definition; and a few are used here in a restricted sense.

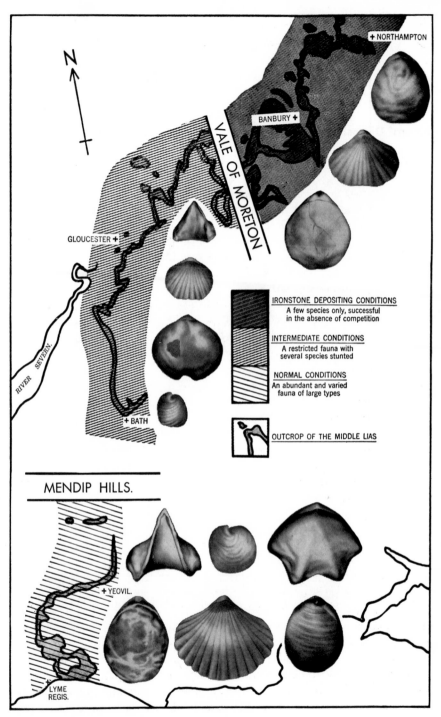

PLATE 1 **Lateral changes in a brachiopod fauna.** Relationship between certain brachiopods of the Lower Jurassic *spinatum* zone and the enclosing sediments. (From *Research Report of the Royal College of Science*, 1953; data in Ager, 1956*a*.)

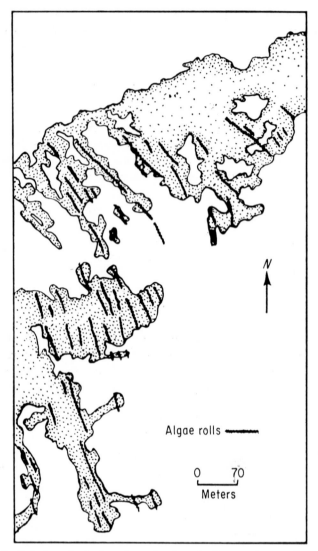

Algae rolls ━━━━━

0   70
Meters

Figure 1.6 Relation of algal reefs to lead-ore bodies in the Cambrian of southeast Missouri. (From Ellison, 1955, after Ohle and Brown, 1954; by courtesy of *Economic Geology.*)

Divisions of the Subject

There has been much argument among neontologists about what is and what is not ecology, but there is no point in extending this academic argument to paleoecology, which is defined here simply as the study of how and where animals and plants lived in the past. The more conventional definition of ecology as the study of the relationship between organisms and their environment gets us into difficulties over the definition of "environment," especially when we extend it to encompass the vast scope of the geological record.

A great deal of work, in both neontology and paleontology, has been done on the geographical distribution of animals and plants, and this is often regarded as a separate subject from ecology (chorology, or biogeography). But obviously the geographical distribution of any organism is an ecological matter on a grand scale; an organism will only live where the conditions suit it, so this study cannot be separated from ecology—a point that has been well argued by P. V. Wells (1959). We can study the distribution of seaweed on a beach, or we can discuss why poison ivy is so painfully common in North America but hardly known in Europe. There is no critical scale which delimits our subject. Also, many fascinating aspects of present-day distributions, such as those of the redwoods and the elephants, depend directly on studies of past distributions for their interpretation.

Merely to bring a little order into an extremely diffuse and disorganized subject, then, I think it is desirable to recognize in this book two major subdivisions of the subject.

First there is the study of the ecology of the individual organism or small taxonomic group. This subject—ecology in the original strict sense—has been called *autecology*. The paleontological equivalent is here called *paleoautecology*, and this is the concern of Part 2 of this book.

Secondly there is the study of the ecology of communities as a whole. This is often called *synecology*, and the fossil version is therefore *paleosynecology*, which is the concern of Part 3 of this book.

Obviously we cannot draw a rigid line between the individual and the community, but synecology is essentially the synthesis of what we know of the autecology of all the individual species making up the community. It is therefore logical and desirable to deal with the individual first and the communities second.

TWO

The nature and classification of environments

GENERAL PRINCIPLES

Before I go on to discuss the fossils, it is necessary to present certain basic ideas about the world in which they lived and in which their descendants continue to live as our present ephemeral population. Much of this chapter is therefore general knowledge, but this is included for the sake of completeness. The reader is advised to study also one of the more general ecology textbooks, such as that of G. L. Clarke (1954) or that of C. Elton (1956), bearing in mind that both the paleontologist and the neontologist are prejudiced, in their different ways, about the organic world.

Attention has already been drawn to the glossary of paleoecological terms (Appendix 1), but it is desirable to consider in more detail some of the names we give to different environments and to the different environmental regions of the world.

The environment of a particular organism may be divided into:

1. Its physical environment
2. Its chemical environment
3. Its biological environment

The various factors of each category have been aptly and exhaustively listed by Ellison (1955) as follows (list slightly modified and shortened):

PHYSICAL
Temperature
Light conditions
Radiation
Pressure
Gravity
Sound
Depth of water
Viscosity and diffusion of air and water
Atmospheric conditions
Water movements
Land-surface conditions, including kind and thickness of soil
Geomorphology of land surface and sea floor
Bottom sedimentological conditions
Distance from shores
Geographical shape of water body
Geographical conditions of adjacent lands
Latitude and longitude

CHEMICAL
Salinity of water
Hydrogen-ion concentration
Chemical buffers
Trace elements
Colloids
Carbon dioxide content of air and water
Nitrogen content of air and water
Oxygen content of air and water
Hydrogen sulfide content of air and water
Oxidation-reduction potentials
Other chemical factors, e.g., calcium content
Organic-carbon content of air and water

BIOLOGICAL
Associated organisms: number, size, and kind
Symbiotic relations with other species, including mutualism and commensalism
Antagonistic relations with other species, including antibiosis, exploitation, and competition
Mobility
Birth and mortality rates
Rate of population increase or decrease

Obviously many of these factors stand no chance whatever of being recognizable from fossil evidence, but we must still bear them in mind as possible contributory factors in any situation.

As paleoecologists, we approach environments in a necessarily very biased and distorted way. Although we are, or ought to be, concerned with the actual environment in which a fossil organism lived, we are directly concerned only with the environment in which it was buried.

We therefore need to remember the following duality carefully: the living environment is that of the ecologist; the burial environment is that of the sedimentologist. Thus it is always necessary to be clear what we mean when we use a term such as "sublittoral." Do we use it in an ecological sense and refer only to organisms which lived on (or just under) a certain part of the sea floor? Or do we apply it also to all those other organisms which lived in the sea or sky above that part of the sea floor, or even drifted there from elsewhere after death? Figure 2.1 illustrates the problem, which always faces us in paleoecology, of dealing with organisms of many different habits and habitats which may accumulate at one level.

These remarks, of course, exemplify the perennial and almost unconscious bias of the paleoecologist toward marine environments and so suggest the first environmental subdivision I must make—into marine and nonmarine environments.

NONMARINE ENVIRONMENTS

The great majority of ecological studies so far published have been concentrated on nonmarine environments, by reason of facility of study, variety of interest, and economic importance. A great deal is therefore known about just those environments about which the paleoecologist is least able to speak.

Some ecologists make great use of the term *biome,* which is defined as a major natural region characterized by certain groups of communities. So far as land environments are concerned, several world-wide biomes are recognized:

Permanent snow and ice
Tundra
Coniferous forest (taiga)
Temperate deciduous forest
Grassland, including prairie and steppe
Arid desert
Temperate rain forest
Tropical rain forest

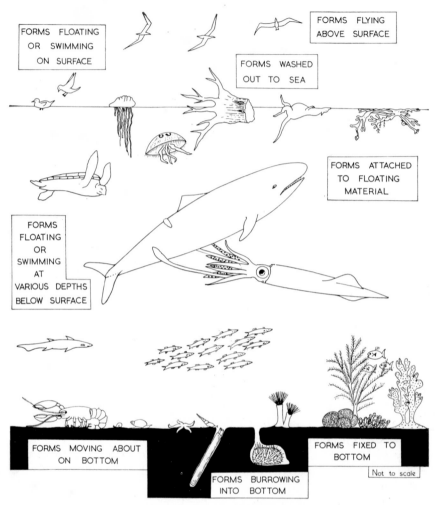

FIGURE 2.1 The variety of organisms with very different habits and habitats which may accumulate as fossils in one layer of sediment on the sea floor. (Drawn by Miss Mary E. Pugh.)

A useful way of thinking about these is in terms of temperature and moisture, which are the two main controlling factors (Figure 2.2).

The distribution of these biomes on the land surface is complicated by factors such as topography and ocean currents. Mount Kenya in East Africa has its base in tropical rain forests and its summit in the zone of permanent snow and ice, and the San Francisco Peaks in Arizona have their summits in the tundra zone and their base in the arid desert.

Altitude is as effective downward as upward. The rims of the Grand Canyon are covered with Canadian-type coniferous forests; the floor is a Mexican-type desert.

The differences in biotic zonation due to ocean currents are particularly apparent in England, which is in the same latitudes as Labrador. Human history would have been very different if the cold Labrador Current had not flowed down the west side of the North Atlantic and the warm Gulf Stream had not swept across to the eastern shores.

These matters may seem to have little application in paleoecology, but in fact they have an important bearing on the interpretation of the past. They remind us that biotic distributions do not necessarily parallel the equator. We cannot assume that because an area was once an arid desert, it was necessarily in the tropics, or that because an area was once glaciated, it was necessarily near one of the poles.

The classification above is mainly based on plant types. Other classifications of terrestrial environments have been based on altitude, temperature, and climate as a whole, but these are matters about which we can only hypothesize in paleoecology. To geologists, land surfaces are principally areas of erosion, and there are only limited circumstances under which sediments, and therefore fossils, may accumulate under continental conditions. These may be classified as follows:

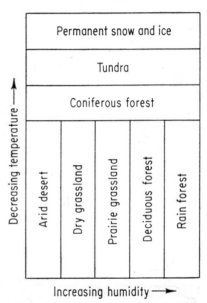

FIGURE 2.2 Idealized representation of the relationship of temperature, humidity, and environment in a continental area.

TERRESTRIAL ENVIRONMENTS
Inland basins (which also include the other categories)
Eolian deposits, such as loess and sand dunes
Soils (in special circumstances)
Volcanic ashes and similar deposits
Glacial deposits

FLUVIAL ENVIRONMENTS
Piedmont
River deposits, including levees and flood plain sediments
Deltas
Estuaries

PALUDAL ENVIRONMENTS
Swamp deposits of various kinds: lake, backwater, paralic, etc.

LACUSTRINE ENVIRONMENTS
Fresh water (various categories)
Saline
Lagoons

CAVE DEPOSITS AND FISSURE FILLINGS

It should be noted that this is in no sense a classification of all non-marine environments but only of those in which sediments and fossils may accumulate. All of these environments have distinctive ecological conditions and therefore potentially distinct fossil assemblages all through the stratigraphical record.

In the limbo between marine and nonmarine conditions are the environments usually referred to as "brackish water." There are many differences of opinion as to what is meant by this term and, in fact, as to how saline water has to be before it is fully marine. A man who works in the Baltic is likely to have different views on this from a man who works in Hawaii.

One of the most commonly used classifications based on salinities is as follows:

SALINITY, ‰	TERM
<0.5	Infrahaline (fresh water)
0.5–3.0	Oligohaline (brackish water)
3.0–16.5	Mesohaline (brackish water)
16.5–30.0	Polyhaline (brackish water)
>30.0	Ultrahaline (sea water)

The average concentration of sea water is about 35‰. In special circumstances—as in shallow lagoons connected with the sea, under conditions of high evaporation—very high salinities may occur and the term *hypersaline* is used.

MARINE ENVIRONMENTS

The majority of sediments and fossils are of marine origin, and it is in the sea that we have the greatest difficulty in classifying environments. Compared with conditions on the land, conditions in the sea are remark-

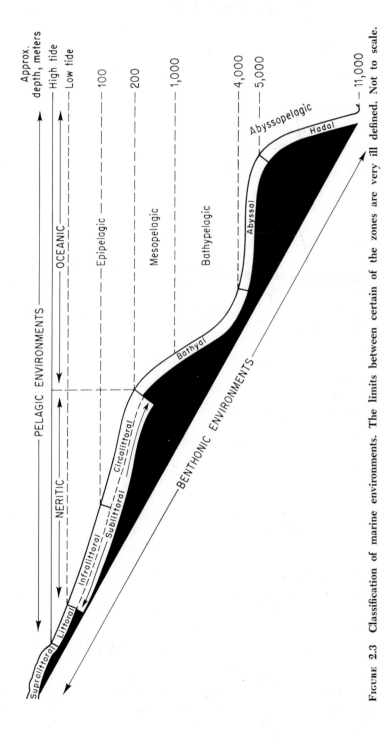

FIGURE 2.3 Classification of marine environments. The limits between certain of the zones are very ill defined. Not to scale.

ably uniform and constant. The temperature varies only very slightly, there is no shortage of water, and plants do not have the controlling influence on animal life that they have on land.

Whereas the main controlling physical factors in terrestrial environments are temperature and humidity, the main controlling factors in fully marine environments are temperature and depth. The latter has probably been overemphasized; but of course, temperature itself is in part dependent on depth, as is the other very important factor of light penetration.

Several terms relevant here have been included in Figure 2.3. Apart from these, there are the two very useful terms *photic zone* and *aphotic zone*. The photic (or euphotic) zone is that depth of water penetrated by sunlight and therefore available for photosynthesis. Its depth varies according to the salinity, impurities, and other characters of the water but is generally about 100 m in the open ocean. The aphotic zone constitutes the larger part of the oceans, and is virtually without light. Some workers distinguish an intermediate *disphotic zone*, in which there is enough light to see but not enough for photosynthesis. This varies according to the organism concerned; thus a man can distinguish light at a slightly greater depth than a fish and a crustacean at a much greater depth than either.

So far as the mode of life of marine organisms is concerned, we need to distinguish three main categories:

Planktonic, or floating
Nektonic, or swimming
Benthonic, or living on or in the sea floor

The first two may be grouped together as *pelagic* (though that term has been variously used). Sometimes a fourth, intermediate category—*nektobenthonic*—is used by paleontologists for forms which both crawl on the sea floor and swim just above it. Many organisms change their habits during their lifetime, from planktonic or nektonic in the early stages to sessile benthonic in adulthood. We may also usefully follow Schäfer (1956) in subdividing the benthos into *epibionts*, which live *on* the sea floor, and *endobionts*, which live *within* the bottom sediments. These correspond to the *epifauna* and *infauna* of Petersen, but those terms have been used in other ways and by implication omit the flora.

When we try to produce a bathymetric, as distinct from a habitat, classification, we find many more difficulties, since nearly every term has been used in different ways. Thus "littoral," though so well known, has remarkably contradictory usages in the literature. The upper limit is generally accepted as the high tide level, but the lower limit has been defined in various ways, ranging from low tide level to the edge of the continental shelf. The use of such terms is particularly difficult in regions such as the Mediterranean, where there is practically no tidal rise and fall. There is therefore a great need to be generally careful in the use of terms and to be sure of the meaning attached to a particular term in a particular context.

Fortunately the Committee on Marine Ecology and Paleoecology which prepared the *Treatise* went into this matter thoroughly over a period of years by means of international questionnaires and discussions. It is therefore clearly better to use their terms than to confuse the issue further by more discussion, even though several variants are in common use. The *Treatise* is the chief source of the terms used in Figure 2.3. There are two other systems, however, which should be mentioned.

The first is the classification of benthonic environments agreed on by the Commission Internationale pour l'exploration de la Mer Méditerranée (Pérès, 1957). Their system is close to the *Treatise* system, but their terms *infralittoral* and *circalittoral* are certainly preferable (being more international) to the terms *inner sublittoral* and *outer sublittoral* of the *Treatise*.

Secondly, Zenkevich (1951, 1959) has outlined the depth zones used by Soviet investigators, and these are included in Table 2.1 for com-

TABLE 2.1 *Classification of marine benthonic environments*

Treatise	*Mediterranean Commission*	*U.S.S.R.*	
Supralittoral	Supralittoral	Supralittoral	
Littoral	Mesolittoral	Littoral	Upper or surface zone
Sublittoral {Inner / Outer	Infralittoral / Circalittoral}	Sublittoral	
		Transition zone	
Bathyal	{Epibathyal / Mesobathyal		
Abyssal	Infrabathyal	Abyssal {Upper / Lower	
Hadal	Hadal	Ultra-abyssal	

parison. It should be pointed out that the term *neritic* (which has been used in many different senses) is applied in this book to pelagic environments of the continental shelf corresponding with *sublittoral* in the bottom environments.

The infralittoral zone extends approximately to the limit of large algae and reef corals, both of which are dependent on light (the latter through their symbiotic algae); this limit therefore corresponds with the limit of the photic zone. The bathyal zone, usually thought of as corresponding to the continental slope, goes down approximately to the average depth of the oceans (about 3,800 m), below which the temperature is never above 4°C. This seems to be a useful dividing line, but it cannot be emphasized too strongly that the depth limits (such as that between bathyal and abyssal) given in Figure 2.3 are very approximate. This reflects the fact that, in the deeper waters, the pelagic fauna is much better known than the benthonic.

Special attention has been paid by marine ecologists to the littoral zone, partly by reason of its accessibility and partly because of the extreme abundance of its benthonic life. It has been subdivided in various ways, notably into the *Littorina, Balanus,* and *Laminaria* zones of many ecologists. These zones are remarkably widespread, in varying forms, in many parts of the world.

It is worthwhile saying a little more at this stage about coastal environments generally, since coast-line concepts figure so largely in the geological literature. Shorelines, especially wave-battered rocky shorelines and the seaward side of reefs, may seem harsh and inhospitable places to live, but in fact they sustain the richest and most varied populations in the sea. Gorvett (1958) recorded as many as 1,756 individual animals, all visible to the naked eye, on 25 sq cm of wave-beaten rocky surface on the island of Oronsay off Scotland. Such abundance of life results from the plentiful supplies of nutrients and oxygen in the turbulent waters, which are thereby made eminently suitable for any organism which can hang on and stand the competition.

Unfortunately for paleoecology, the rocky shoreline is almost the least likely place for sedimentation, so that this environment is underrepresented in the fossil record. This is also why we rarely see fossil limpets or barnacles or their past equivalents. The circumstances under which this environment may be preserved exist only when we have the deposits of a transgressive sea. Thus where the Upper Cretaceous sea flooded Precambrian ridges in southern Sweden, there are rocky bluffs and boulders covered with cemented mollusks. Even here, forms such as limpets, which depend on their muscles for attachment in the surf, must have become detached and smashed as they would be on a modern rocky beach.

What is far more commonly preserved in the geological record than the actual cliff-and-boulder line is the smooth wave-cut platform on solid rock just offshore. Such clearly defined surfaces are often found marking unconformities in shelf-sea deposits; in Mesozoic and later rocks they are usually encrusted with oysters and perforated by borings (Plate 4, *top,* and Figure 7.7). Gekker (1960) discussed the fossil associations of more ancient rocky sea floors in a well-illustrated paper on this general theme. He included examples from areas and ages as diverse as the Ordovician of Estonia, the Devonian on the Russian platform, and the Paleogene of the Fergana depression in Turkestan.

PART TWO

Paleoautecology

*T*HIS *part of the book (Chapters 3 to 11) concerns the ecology of fossil organisms as individuals or as small taxonomic groups, but not fossil assemblages as a whole. Each chapter will deal with a particular approach or method in the study of paleoautecology. I do not suggest for one moment that it is possible to separate rigidly the study of individuals from the study of assemblages, and it is certainly not possible to draw sharp lines between the various methods used in their study. Any worthwhile paleoecological study will consider both the individual and the assemblage of which it is part; it will also inevitably use several different lines of approach to any particular problem. The division into parts and into chapters is made only for convenience and to emphasize the many different facets of paleoecological research.*

THREE

Comparison with living representatives

Uniformitarianism—the main method and basis of geological reasoning—is equally applicable to paleoecology. Just as we can interpret the inanimate past by reference to the natural geological processes going on today, so we can interpret past life by comparison with life today. We can make inspired guesses as to the environment and mode of life of a fossil from our knowledge of these things in living representatives.[1] We know that reef corals only grow in tropical waters within a very restricted range of tolerances at the present day, and we can assume that comparable forms lived under similar conditions in the past; but we immediately come to the obvious reservation that corals may have changed their habits with the passage of time.

Natural processes such as rain and frost and river erosion can hardly have changed through the ages, but animals and plants may, within

[1] As a corollary to this, it may even be possible, in some cases, to reverse the process and interpret the fleeting present organic world in the light of the inexpressibly longer fossil record. Present-day distributions of animals and plants, recorded for a few hundred years at the most, may seem very fixed at the moment under natural circumstances, but the fossil record may suggest that they are merely passing phases which would not even be recorded in the rocks.

33

limits, have changed a great deal. Thus it may be reasonable to suppose that Tertiary reef corals lived under conditions similar to those of modern reefs, but we must be skeptical when we go back to the Mesozoic and more skeptical in the Paleozoic.

The inadequacy of our record adds to the difficulties. Thus the creatures which made the two trails shown in the frontispiece are equally unknown, although one lived on a Carboniferous delta and the other on one of the deeper parts of the floor of the modern Pacific Ocean.

Another important reservation in comparisons of ancient and modern is that, although the physical environment may have remained constant, the organic environment certainly has not. Evolutionary changes in one group may have had a profound effect on many of its contemporaries and even on the physical world. The outstanding example of this is the evolution and spread of grass at the end of the Mesozoic and in early Tertiary times. Besides providing a new type of foodstuff for land animals, grass must have retarded considerably the rate of subaerial erosion over the area where it provided a close ground cover. Since grassland constitutes approximately 24 per cent of the land surface at the present day, this was no inconsiderable geological phenomenon.

A comparable, though less dramatic, change in the marine environment may have been occasioned by the appearance of the oysters at the beginning of the Mesozoic; thereafter oysters formed a major element in the shallow-water fauna, and so must have considerably affected the balance of life when they appeared.

Thus uniformitarianism has its limitations when applied to the fossil record.

"Paleontology of the Present Day"

The first and most essential prerequisite, if we are to compare our fossils with living representatives, is that we should know something about these living representatives. This may seem very obvious, but paleontologists are always being surprised by the lack of information about particular living forms when they come to look into the neontological literature. This is especially true about knowledge of the habits and habitats of certain marine forms, such as the brachiopods, which particularly concern the paleontologist; much of the ecological literature is concerned with land plants, land vertebrates, and land arthropods.

We therefore often need to study the present-day ecology of the forms which interest us before we can make deductions about the fossils.

One of the chief pioneers of this approach was Rudolf Richter, who, as a paleontologist, made detailed studies of shallow-sea faunas off the German coast of the North Sea. In several of his early papers (e.g.,

1920*b*, 1927*a*, 1927*b*) he described the habits of various marine "worms" and the structures they produce in modern sediments; he then compared these with sedimentary structures known in rocks of all ages. Thus he wrote of large, flat-topped "reefs" which are seen at low tide on the west coast of Holstein and which are formed entirely of the tubes of the annelid *Sabellaria alveolata*. This form he found to be limited to sea floors of pure sand which lack practically all other forms of life. He compared these modern annelid-ridden sands with bored sandstones in the Lower Devonian of Germany and with the *Scolithus* borings which form the pipe-rock of the Lower Cambrian, well known in Britain and around the Scandinavian and Canadian shields. Later, Fenton and Fenton (1934*c*) disagreed with this interpretation of *Scolithus*, which they preferred to compare with modern phoronids—slender wormlike creatures of uncertain affinities. The interpretation is different, but the principle is the same.

An annelid "reef" of another kind is shown in Plate 2. This is a mass of tubes of *Rotularia bognoriensis* from the lower Eocene of Bognor Regis in Sussex, England. They are probably in life position, since the majority show a consistent orientation and the long, distal free portions of the tubes, though fragile, commonly occur unbroken. They were found by Mr. H. E. Taylor, forming patches less than 10 cm thick, usually devoid of other fossils (though there is a huge fauna hereabouts), and clearly comparable with some of the modern flat-topped annelid "reefs."

We can learn a lot from such simple comparisons. Our studies of this kind cannot, however, simply be a matter of matching our observations on fossils with what is already known about present-day life. We must also study what has been called "the paleontology of the present." This was first emphasized by Richter (1928), who called this study "Aktuopaläontologie." An important part of such work is to observe carefully how the hard parts of animals and plants accumulate as potential fossils, especially on the sea floor, and how they are buried in the sediment.

An institute was founded by Richter at Wilhelmshaven, Germany, in 1928 with the precise object of studying the "Aktuopaläontologie" of the neighboring North Sea. A magnificent survey involving more than thirty years' work by this institute has been published by W. Schäfer (1962).

The study of how the remains of animals and plants are buried has been called *taphonomy* (Efremov, 1940, 1950), and much work has been done recently on this subject. Thus Sartenaer (1959*a*) made a detailed study, using an aqualung, of the way a particular species, the gastropod *Turritella tricarinata communis*, lives on the sea floor and is buried as a potential fossil in the muds of the Gulf of Fos on the west side of the Rhône delta.

Adopting a similarly paleontological approach to the present day, Elliott (1958) attempted to find a modern analogue for certain Cretaceous calcareous rocks from Iraq, Oman, and the Hadhramaut which

PLATE 2 A fossil worm "reef." Slab largely composed of the serpulid worm *Rotularia bognoriensis* from the lower Eocene of Bognor Regis, Sussex, England. X⅓. (Collected and presented by Mr. H. E. Taylor.)

abound in algal debris. The algae concerned belong to several different groups and are all related to forms which live in warm, very shallow littoral or lagoonal environments today.

A number of different modern sediments are known to contain algal debris, particularly in the vicinity of tropical reefs. Elliott came to the conclusion, however, that no known modern combination of circumstances matched those of the usual interorogenic Mesozoic shelf sea.

Apart from actual observations of what goes on under natural circumstances, a few people have also made experiments on these matters. Menard and Boucot (1951) described a series of laboratory experiments on the movement of shells by water. They demonstrated, for instance, that brachiopod shells may be buried in a particular way due to the undercutting action of moving water (Figure 3.1). Similar scour effects have been noted in the Triassic Moenkopi formation of the Grand Canyon area in Arizona.

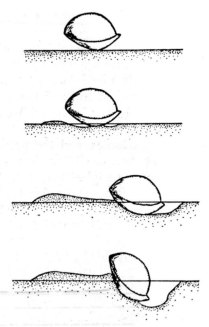

R. G. Johnson (1957) pursued this theme with what he called "crude experiments" on the transport of shells near the mouth of Tomales Bay, California. He found that 40 per cent of pelecypod valves placed near the bottom of the beach at low tide were moved before the next low tide, and of those so moved, 90 per cent had originally been placed concave upward. On the other hand, those placed concave downward were more commonly buried in the same position. He followed this with flume experiments involving twenty-four different combinations of shell kind, size, and orientation. Ten of the combinations resulted in the shells' burial in their original position; twelve combinations resulted in transportation. Johnson's general conclusion was that current scouring is induced by the presence of shells resting on a movable substratum, and that this is an effective mechanism for their burial. The original

Figure 3.1 A terebratuloid brachiopod, *Terebratulina septentrionalis*, being buried in sand as a result of scour by moving water. In all stages the water is moving from right to left at a constant velocity. (From Menard and Boucot, 1951; by courtesy of *American Journal of Science*.)

orientation of the shells seemed to be the most important factor controlling their ultimate disposition.

The most important consideration for paleoecologists which comes out of this work is the proposition that organic remains may be buried without sedimentation.

Uniformitarianism within a Species

The actual comparison of ancient and modern forms can be done at different taxonomic levels, depending on the geological longevity of the group concerned. If we restrict ourselves within a species, then we can hardly go beyond the Pleistocene; but this is still paleoecology, and paleoecology of a very exact kind.

In the deposits of an earlier Thames River in Trafalgar Square in London, Kerney (in Franks et al., 1958) identified three species of fresh-water mollusks which are no longer natives of Britain. These are two pelecypods, *Potomida littoralis* and *Margaritifera auricularia,* and a minute gastropod, *Belgrandia marginata.* These three are all characteristic of warm, swiftly flowing, and highly calcareous rivers in the south of Europe at the present day, and are evidence (confirmed by many other fossils) of similar conditions in the Thames of the last interglacial.

Similarly, we have in the interglacial Cromer Forest bed of eastern England abundant fruits of the Water Chestnut (*Trapa natans*). This plant will still grow in England at the present day, but it does not fruit in Europe north of about the Seine. It is a warm-water plant suited to continental climates, and the presence of its fruits in British deposits suggests warmer conditions than we have today. In Scandinavia, where it turns up in postglacial deposits, it is one of the lines of evidence for a climatic optimum there after the last glaciation, with an average temperature about 2.5°C warmer than at present.

Conversely, evidence of harsher conditions at other times in the Pleistocene is provided by the remains of plants such as the dwarf birch (*Betula nana*) and the White Dryas (*Dryas octopetala*), both of which are confined at the present day to high mountains and the Arctic Regions of Europe, Asia, and North America.

Uniformitarianism within a Genus

Species are very fleeting things from the point of view of the paleontological taxonomist, so that it is not often possible to apply uniformitarianism to a particular fossil species. On the other hand there are a number of genera which are generally accepted as being of ancient vintage. The best known of these is that oldest of all genera—the inarticulate brachiopod *Lingula.* This genus is the epitome of conservatism, in the sense that it "got into its rut," both literally and figuratively, in Ordovician times, and has stayed there ever since.

Craig (1952) summarized what was known about the ecology of the living *Lingula* (and its close relation *Glottidia*) and compared it with what he had observed himself in the Carboniferous of southern Scotland. The modern forms are confined to tropical and subtropical seas, generally at less than 40 m depth. They inhabit all kinds of littoral sediments, especially the more argillaceous ones. The animal lives in a vertical burrow, attached at the bottom by its massive pedicle. It is distributed in a free-swimming larval stage and, though essentially marine, it can survive in brackish water.

So far as can be judged, all these characters fit in with the paleoecological evidence of the same genus. Fossil examples are commonest in shaly sediments and are quite often found still in a vertical position with the anterior end uppermost. Craig even recorded a specimen in this position with what seemed to be a pyritic infilling of the pedicle tube. His evidence also suggested that the brachiopods arrived as larvae less than 2 mm wide and were associated on a muddy sea floor with burrowing pelecypods. Reference has already been made to the extension of *Lingula* beyond the range of other marine fossils in the marine bands of the west European "Coal Measures." There is much other evidence in the stratigraphical column of *Lingula's* tolerance of brackish conditions. Thus we have the abundant *Lingulae* of the English Downtonian strata which are intermediate between the marine Ludlovian rocks of the Silurian and the continental Old Red Sandstone of the Devonian. *Lingula* also had the honor recently of being the first definite marine fossil to be found in the British Trias (below the Rhaetian) and may well represent the furthermost manifestation of the Muschelkalk sea, which extended as close to Britain as Heligoland. In North America, a similar example is provided by the Cretaceous of Minnesota, which represents the furthest extension of a transgressive sea and which has yielded only one kind of brachiopod—the tolerant *Lingula*.

Uniformitarianism within Larger Groups

In only a very few cases before the Tertiary can we make direct comparisons between fossil and living members of the same genus. There are certain groups, however, which are restricted as a whole to limited environments and which are therefore particularly suitable for comparative studies of this kind. The corals are the outstanding example of such a group, and much valuable work has been done on the comparison of ancient and modern representatives, most notably through the work of T. W. Vaughan and J. W. Wells. Another group which has received considerable attention has been the Foraminifera, not because of a limited environment for the whole group, but because of their abundance in sediments, their convenience for study in borehole samples and their particular application in oil-field geology. These two groups will therefore be specially considered.

Corals Corals today are very fussy creatures, and it is tempting to suppose that they always were so. They are closely controlled and delimited by their physical environment (Figure 3.2), though, compared

with other organisms, they are not much affected by their organic environment. In other words, they have few enemies.

The big snag about the corals from the paleoecological point of view
is that the modern forms belong to the orders Scleractinia and Alcyo-
naria which only appeared in Mesozoic times, and our deductions about
them do not necessarily apply to the Rugosa and Tabulata of the
Paleozoic.

Modern corals fall naturally into two ecological groups: the "hermatypic" types, which live in colonies and form reefs, and the "ahermatypic"

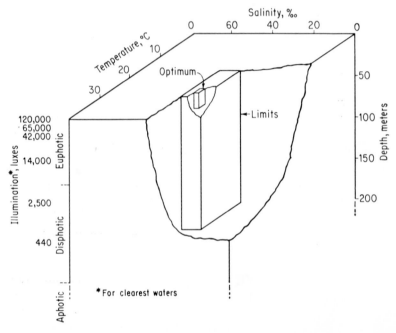

FIGURE 3.2   Physical factors limiting the distribution of hermatypic corals. (From
J. W. Wells, 1957a; by courtesy of the Geological Society of America.)

types, which are solitary in habit and do not form reefs. I am only concerned here with the hermatypic types.

At the present day, hermatypic corals range from the surface to a
maximum depth of about 90 m, but they only flourish as reef builders
at less than half that depth. In fact the vast majority live in the shallower waters, with few below 20 m; most reef builders grow best at
15 m or less. Hermatypic corals can live in the warmest sea water known
(about 36°C), and their average minimum temperature is about 22°,
though a few can stand 17 or 18° for a short time. Their optimum temperature seems to be between 25 and 29°C. Temperature is certainly
the main controlling factor in the distribution of reef corals at the pres-

ent day. This restricts them in the main to the latitudes between 30° N and 30° S, but there are many local variations due to ocean currents and other causes. Thus there are no reefs on the Galapagos Islands because of the cold Humboldt Current which sweeps up the west coast of South America.

All corals are marine, of course, and they cannot stand very much freshening of the water or increase in salinity. Corals are best developed at salinities within one part per thousand of the average salinity of sea water (about 35‰). Hermatypic corals also require strong sunlight for vigorous reef growth. This is directly connected with the symbiotic relationship existing today between corals and associated algae.

A few other major factors delimit coral distribution at the present day. Thus, most corals can stand short periods of exposure to air, but not more. They depend for their food on particles carried in the water, so good water circulation is essential for their growth. This is also necessary for the removal of sediment, since, though they can remove a certain amount themselves, foreign particles very soon smother them if allowed to settle. For this reason there are gaps in the Great Barrier Reef of Australia opposite the mouths of rivers bringing down sediment. Sediment also tends to inhibit coral growth by reducing the amount of sunlight penetrating the water.

This is a brief summary of the physical limitations on reef growth today. Let us now consider how such knowledge may be applied to the fossil record. Some of the factors are likely to be recognizable in the past; others are not. We can, for instance, argue that the general absence of fossil compound corals from argillaceous rocks supports the contention that they have always been susceptible to smothering by sediment in suspension. On the other hand, we have no sure way of knowing how long the presence of symbiotic algae has necessitated strong sunlight.

J. Wyatt Durham (1942) more conclusively discussed Eocene and Oligocene coral faunas of the state of Washington and compared them with their modern equivalents. His observations on the middle Eocene Crescent formation may be tabulated as follows:

GENUS	PRESENT HABITAT
Agaricids	Normally in reefs—tropical
Archohelia	Extinct, but closely related to *Oculina*, which is widespread today in the tropics, usually in reefs
Astreopora	Pacific reefs—tropical
Colpophyllia	Reefs around Florida, absolute minimum temperature 18.15°C
Leptophyllastraea	Extinct
Madracis	Hawaii, etc., 74–459 m depth, 10–22.8°C
Montipora	Hawaii, etc., 0–74 m depth, 22.8–25.6°C
Turbinolia	West Indies, varying depths—tropical

From this we may draw the general conclusion that the coral fauna of the Crescent formation represents a tropical reef environment. The occurrence of *Madracis* and *Montipora* together in this formation is interesting, since at the present day, e.g., around Hawaii, they are segregated by depth and temperature. Durham concluded that the conditions must have been just about the dividing line between the two genera; that is, the depth of water must have been about 74 m, and the temperature must have been about 22.8°C. This fits in with the known facts about other genera present.

The present 20°C winter isotherm just skirts the southern tip of the peninsula of Lower (Baja) California. Durham therefore postulated that in middle Eocene times the thermal environment at about 48° N in Washington was similar to that now existing more than 28° farther south on the Mexican coast. He made similar comparisons for other faunas up to the late Oligocene, with similar results. Such hypotheses are obviously dangerous, since we cannot be sure that one genus or indeed all the genera have not changed their habits since the Eocene; but such hypotheses are justified if, as in this case, the theory is supported by several independent lines of evidence.

If we now move back to the Mesozoic, we have the famous work of W. J. Arkell on the Jurassic coral reefs of northwest Europe. In an early paper (1928) he compared the successive coral reefs developed in the English Upper Jurassic with Pleistocene and modern coral reefs in the Red Sea. Later (1935) he made a detailed study of Jurassic reefs in the vicinity of Oxford and discussed their nature, origin, and climatic significance in the light of our knowledge of their modern counterparts.

In the first place, Arkell was able to state, from a number of different lines of evidence, that the Jurassic reefs around Oxford did not live at anything like the maximum depths of modern reefs. Though many of the delicately branching corals and some of the associated fauna evidently lived in quiet conditions, in other parts of the reefs there was ample evidence of wave action. Similarly, Arkell (1935, p. 102) stated, and summarized all the evidence for the belief that "there was a more uniform climate over most parts of the globe, and that the regions that are now cold or temperate were considerably warmer." Apart from the corals themselves, the large reptiles, the cycadlike plants, and the richness and variety of the molluskan life all point to a tropical climate. Nothing is proved, but the circumstantial evidence is strong. Arkell went on to show that the Oxford reefs are comparable, not to barrier reefs or atolls, but to modern fringing reefs growing on a very gently shelving sea floor, which become broken up into irregular patches over large areas.

As we move farther back in geological time, my comparisons become less certain; and the problems become doubly difficult in the Paleozoic, when we are dealing with extinct orders. However, most of the leading students of Paleozoic corals, notably Vaughan (1911, 1940), J. W. Wells (1957*b*), Hill (1938), and Ma (1933, 1937), seem to have come to the general conclusion that most Paleozoic compound corals lived in conditions similar to those of modern reef forms.

An interesting sideline here is that many workers have noted the almost complete absence of reef corals from Paleozoic rocks in the present tropics. This may be due merely to the nonpreservation of suitable sedimentary facies in that region, but Cailleux (1951) suggested that the absence might be due to the sea temperatures there having been too high in Paleozoic times. Modern corals live in the warmest water available, but their upper limit is thought to be about 36°C. If we consider (as many paleontologists do) that the world as a whole was warmer in the past than it is now, then we must presume that the equatorial regions had higher temperatures than are known anywhere today. This may have had two effects on the paleontological record. First, the equatorial regions may have been too hot for certain forms (as is postulated in this case); secondly, forms may have become adapted to these higher temperatures and then become extinct when the regions cooled down. The latter contingency might be an explanation of the disappearance of the rudist pelecypods at the end of the Cretaceous. Others have argued that a general increase in temperature would merely have improved the circulatory system of winds and currents, so that no great warming up at the equator would be necessary to warm the polar regions. These matters will be discussed further in Chapter 10.

Foraminifera   From the economic viewpoint, some of the most valuable paleoecological work so far published has been on the present-day distribution of Foraminifera. This is immediately applicable in the interpretation of related foraminiferal faunas in Tertiary oil-bearing sediments. The most outstanding work of this nature has been in the United States—around the Gulf of Mexico and in southern California. Natland's work in the latter area (1933) soon became a classic of paleoecological research. Studying modern forams off California, he was able to distinguish five temperature/depth zones, which he was then able to apply to the fossil forams of late Cenozoic age in Hill's Canyon, California. This was a wonderful demonstration of faunal facies, since Natland was able to show that contemporaneous fossil assemblages differ considerably because of ecological factors, and conversely, similar assemblages do not necessarily imply contemporaneity.

From the wealth of now-available literature with a similar approach, I may cite two examples which give a clear picture of the lateral distribution of forams at the present day in the Gulf of Mexico and its coastal plain. These are the papers by Lowman (1949) and Phleger (1951). Lowman showed that it is possible to distinguish a number of different faunal associations in fresh-water, brackish, and marine environments (Figure 3.3). These include three divisions in the benthonic faunas of the continental shelf which, though rather vague, have been found applicable in Tertiary studies. He noted that the most striking faunal change occurred at about 100 m depth, and this was confirmed by Phleger, who was concerned chiefly with the deeper-water facies.

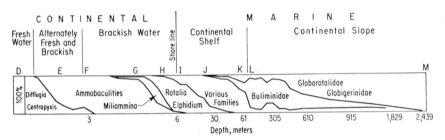

FIGURE 3.3 **Distribution of Foraminifera in the Mississippi delta region and the Gulf of Mexico.** (From Lowman, 1949; by courtesy of the American Association of Petroleum Geologists.)

Phleger observed six benthonic-foram depth facies in the Gulf of Mexico, with boundaries as follows:

80 to 120 m
180 to 220 m
500 to 750 m
1,000 to 1,300 m
1,800 to 2,000 m

He also noted certain subfacies.

Phleger suggested that at all levels, temperature was the prime ecological factor affecting the distributions. Thus the main break at 80 to 120 m marks (among other things) the lower limit of any pronounced seasonal temperature variation. The usual bottom temperature at 100 m depth is about 18°C (Figure 3.4), but may reach as low as 15.5°C in winter. The latter temperature may be significant, as will be pointed out later (see pages 154, 155).

For obvious reasons, the benthonic forams are the main facies indicators, as is always the case in paleontology, whereas the pelagic ones are more independent of facies and therefore more useful for stratigraphical purposes. However, because of the decreasing abundance of benthonic faunas seaward and the slower sedimentation, a great abundance of pelagic forams in the bottom sediments is characteristic of the deeper-water areas in the Gulf of Mexico.

While the offshore distributions are controlled chiefly by temperature, near- and onshore distributions are related chiefly to salinity. Besides the main divisions mentioned above and shown in Figure 3.3, there is also a distinctive assemblage on the floors of foul, brackish-water marsh pools; this is composed of forms tolerant of poorly oxygenated waters.

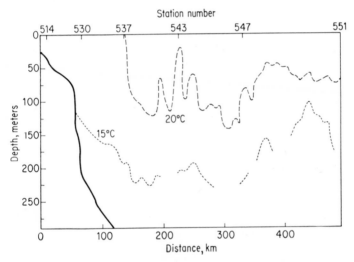

FIGURE 3.4 Distribution of water temperature along an offshore traverse in the Gulf of Mexico, south of New Orleans. (Modified from Phleger, 1951.)

In another paper, Parker, Phleger, and Peirson (1953) demonstrated the effect of island barriers on foraminiferal distributions in the Gulf area (Figure 3.5). They also showed how seasonal variations were caused by the increase and decrease of the amount of fresh water running off from the land into the lagoons along the Texas coast.

The paleoecological application of this type of work is exemplified by Phleger's paper (1951). He noted that the foraminiferal faunas at the bottom of cores taken from the seabed in the Gulf indicate conditions of shallower water than that existing in the same location today. The implication is a change in sea level of 40 to 50 m in the last few thousand years. Such work can be applied in the search for oil through paleoecological interpretations of the Tertiary strata in the immediate vicinity, where there is a constantly oscillating interdigitation of

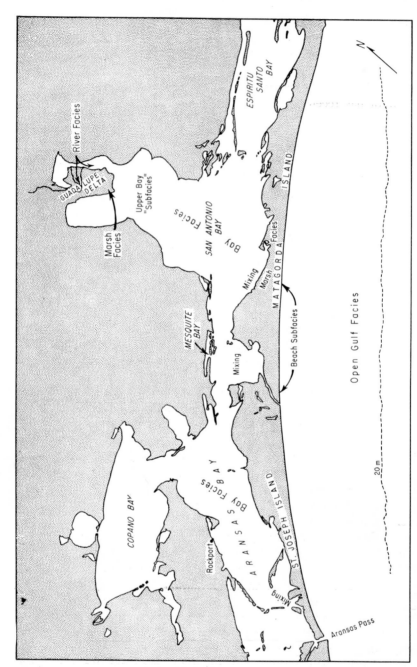

FIGURE 3.5 The effect of island barriers and fresh water on foraminiferal distributions in the Gulf area. (After Parker, Phleger, and Peirson, 1953; by courtesy of the Cushman Foundation.)

shallow marine and nonmarine sediments. Oil traps occur in sands which pinch out in a shoreward direction, and anything which can indicate where these are likely to occur is obviously useful to the oil seekers.

A general survey of existing knowledge of the ecology of living Foraminifera has recently been published by Phleger (1960) and is of great value, from the uniformitarian point of view, to the paleoecologist.

COMPARATIVE ANATOMY

But there is much more to the comparative approach in paleoecology than the simple identification of fossils with living forms, followed by the assumption that they had similar environmental requirements. Quite apart from the direct comparison of species with species and group with group, we can learn a great deal from comparative anatomy.

Thus, in a study of the extinct cave bear, *Ursus spelaeus*, Mlle. M. Friant (1952) compared its dental anatomy with that of members of the same genus living today. This comparison was based on skeletons from La Grotte du Pech-Merle in southwest France. From the teeth and the structure of the mandibular condyle, Mlle. Friant concluded that the cave bear was less carnivorous in its eating habits than any of the other European bears.

One of the most detailed comparisons of this type in recent years was that in which Nichols (1959) studied the well-known Upper Cretaceous echinoid *Micraster*. He interpreted the habits and habitat of this form by means of detailed comparative anatomy, using seven living species in which function could also be observed. The comparison was particularly interesting because *Micraster* had been the subject of one of the classics of evolutionary paleontology (Rowe, 1899) and lived in what seems to have been a remarkably constant environment (the Chalk) for a very long period of time.

Nichols demonstrated a progressive increase in the number of pore pairs in the petaloid part of the ambulacral areas of *Micraster* and of the closely related subgenus *Isomicraster*. By comparison with such living echinoids as *Echinocardium cordatum*, he interpreted these changes as an increase in the number of respiratory tube feet which enabled the successive populations to burrow more and more deeply in the chalk mud. Other changes, interpreted by similar analogies, suggested an increasing reliance on the use of ciliary currents rather than the tube feet for feeding. A clear story was worked out on this basis, in which an early lineage of shallow burrowers (*M. leskei*) gave rise to divergent stocks of shallow burrowers (*M. corbovis*) and deeper burrowers (*M. cortestudinarium*). The former stock died out, and the surviving stock burrowed even more deeply (*M. coranguinem*).

An entirely different lineage of Chalk echinoids shows a similar trend in a simpler form (Figure 3.6). This is the *Infulaster-Hagenowia* group, which shows an excessive development of the front part of the test. Nichols found that the pores in this group were like those of the living

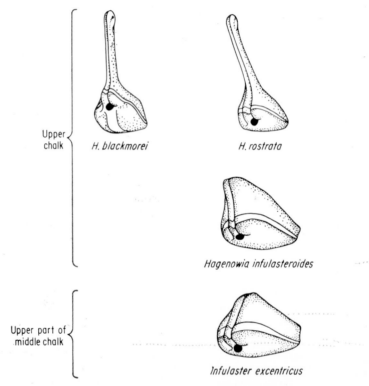

Upper
chalk   *H. blackmorei*   *H. rostrata*

Hagenowia infulasteroides

Upper part of
middle chalk

Infulaster excentricus

FIGURE 3.6   Evolution in the *Infulaster-Hagenowia* group of Cretaceous echinoids, showing elongation of the front part of the test as an adaptation to a deeper burrowing habit. (From Nichols, 1959; by courtesy of the Royal Society.)

echinoid *Spatangus purpureus* and presumably gave rise to similar wholly sensory tube feet. Deeper burrowing in this group was therefore achieved by elongation of the rostrum, which raised the apical disc above the surface of the sediment.

We can use the technique of comparative anatomy even for forms which are completely unrelated. The phenomenon of homeomorphy is well known in paleontology; the same morphological types turn up again and again in different stocks and presumably imply similar modes of life. Yet we cannot always guess the function of a particular modification.

We can deduce from modern comparisons (and from common sense) that any elongated, thin-shelled pelecypod with posteriorly gaping valves was probably a burrowing form, and this applies to long-extinct forms like *Orthonota* of the early Paleozoic just as well as it does to members of still-living genera. We even know, from Iredale's account (1942) of a borehole in the Great Barrier Reef, that such burrowing forms may quickly lose their thin shells by solution, as is so commonly the case with fossils which are thought to have lived in the same way.

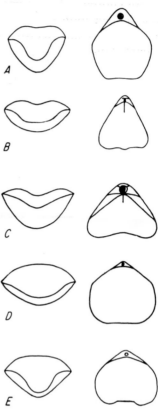

The brachiopods also abound in anatomical repetitions. A classic case is that claimed by Buckman (1906) for the unusual Mesozoic terebratulids *Pygope*, *Pygites*, and *Antinomia*. In these there is a central perforation which developed—allegedly independently—in three distinct stocks. The function in this case is far from clear, but we may presume that the three were adapted to a similar mode of life. We are limited here by the lack of a comparable living species.

In a similar example, but one I believe more strongly, I have recorded (Ager, 1960) homeomorphy between members of three different families of Mesozoic brachiopods. In one case, the three families simultaneously produced forms with sulcate anterior commissures (Figure 3.7). As is not the case with Buckman's example, there are here modern analogies in two unrelated brachiopods which have the same unusual structure. The function is again unknown, but it may be significant that both the living genera are abyssal in habit and that the fossils are restricted to the Alpine region.

FIGURE 3.7 Convergent structures in three families of Alpine Triassic brachiopods, compared with two living abyssal forms. A, *Propygope hagar*, a Triassic terebratulid; B, *Norella geyeri*, a Triassic rhynchonellid; C, *Cruratula endora*, a Triassic zeilleriid; D, *Neorhynchia strebeli*, a Recent rhynchonellid; E, *Abyssothyris wyvillei*, a Recent terebratulid.

This type of comparison applies to details of anatomy as well as to general form. Thus the theropod dinosaurs disappeared in the Cretaceous Period, but it is completely logical to deduce that their large, sharp, curving teeth were used for tearing flesh, as are the comparable teeth in modern carnivorous mammals. Similarly, the sauropod dinosaur *Brachiosaurus* has its nostrils set in a peculiar upward-projecting process on top of its skull (Figure 3.8). It is reasonable to make comparison with the arrangement and use of the nostrils in the living alligator and hippopotamus and to deduce that *Brachiosaurus* frequently submerged itself in water with only its nostrils protruding above the surface.

There are innumerable examples of homeomorphy among fossils where the same kind of argument can be used. To remain with the chordates,

FIGURE 3.8 Reconstruction of the head of *Brachiosaurus*, showing the presumed function of the nostrils in an elevated process on the top of the skull.

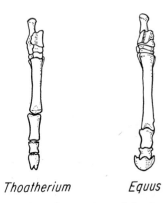

FIGURE 3.9 Comparison of the forelimb of the litoptern *Thoatherium* (Miocene) with that of the true horse *Equus* (Quaternary).

we have one of the most remarkable examples of all in the South American group of primitive Tertiary mammals known as the Litopterna. In these the limbs are adapted in the same extreme way as in the horse, with the reduction of the digits and the elongation of the bones (Figure 3.9). Clearly this was an earlier adaptation to a fast-running mode of life in open country, like that of the horse. In fact the litopterns were not related to the horses at all, but belonged to an early group of primitive hoofed mammals which reached South America before that continent was isolated at the beginning of the Eocene. They flourished in the absence of competition from more advanced types but rapidly died out when land contact was reestablished with the rest of the world in late Tertiary times. *Thoatherium*, the extreme form of the Litopterna, was in fact "more horse-like than any true horse" (Romer, 1945), since its digits were more reduced than those of *Equus;* but in other characters, notably its teeth, it was nowhere near as efficient as the horse and so did not survive.

COMPARATIVE PHYSIOLOGY

As H. L. Hawkins has observed, the paleontologist can never be a midwife—he can only be an undertaker. We can never bring our fossils to life; we can never study their physiology, only their anatomy. We can, however, make some deductions about the way our fossils "worked" by comparison with living forms. This is obvious when the fossil and the living organism are closely related, but, bearing in mind the inevitable relationship between form and function, we may extend our analogies to organisms which are completely extinct.

Orton (1914) observed that the living inarticulate brachiopod *Crania* draws in laterally two streams of water which serve for aeration and to carry food particles. It also has a single median exhalant stream which serves to carry away the waste. He suggested a relationship between this arrangement of three water streams and the trilobate shell which is characteristic of such brachiopods as the rhynchonelloids. It would presumably be an advantage for the brachiopod to separate the inhalant and exhalant streams as much as possible, so that the waste would not be drawn once more into the shell. This may well be the explanation of the repeatedly seen trend in the rhynchonelloids toward an extreme trilobation of the shell with an exaggerated development of the median fold, for example, in *Pugnax, Homoeorhynchia,* and *Rhynchonella* s.s. (Figure 3.10).

Extrapolation

Once such comparisons of fossils with living forms have been made, there are almost no limits to the piling of hypothesis upon hypothesis with apparent validity. There is no doubt that in many cases this is amply justified, both by the general nature of the evidence and by the mere fact that it is the only possible line of approach. It is not my intention, then, to dispute the examples which follow; but we must remain aware the whole time of exactly what we are doing, and we must be constantly on the lookout for other lines of evidence which may confirm or deny the main hypothesis.

An example of brilliant extrapolation of this kind is the much-quoted work of A. E. Trueman (1940) on the mode of life of ammonites. The fundamental assumption of this work was that the unfossillized ammonite body was exactly comparable to that of the only living tetrabranchiate cephalopod, *Nautilus*. For a whole series of ammonites, Trueman studied the size of the body chamber and compared it with the size of the unoccupied chambers behind. Assuming that the specific gravity of the ammonite body was the same as that of *Nautilus* and that the unoccupied chambers were filled only with air, he was able to calculate the buoyancy of the shell and the position in which it floated.

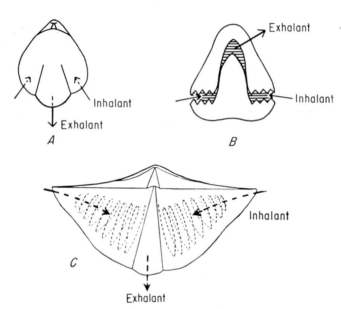

Figure 3.10 Possible relationship between water streams and trilobation in brachiopods.
A, in modern rhynchonellid (dorsal view); *B*, in fossil rhynchonellid with exaggerated fold (anterior view); *C*, in fossil spiriferid with exaggerated lateral extremities (dorsal view).

Many "ordinary-looking" ammonites turned out to have a calculated specific gravity very close to that of *Nautilus* and of modern sea water, i.e., about 1.026. Unlike the modern organism, however, many ammonites had shells which were themselves made heavier by ribs, tubercles, and other processes. Trueman was also able to determine the center of gravity and the center of buoyancy of each shell (Figure 3.11). Thus the mean density of the Middle Jurassic ammonite *Ludwigia* came out at about 1.03. Its calculated attitude in the water was also very like that of *Nautilus*.

Another Middle Jurassic ammonite, *Sigaloceras*, appears to have had the same attitude in life, but a lower density—about 0.9. This seems

to imply that, unless some other factor is involved which cannot be observed, *Sigaloceras* must have floated at the surface.

It will be seen from Figure 3.11 that the three genera so far mentioned all have their center of gravity and center of buoyancy set well
apart, so that their attitude was, presumably, fairly stable. The living
Nautilus can change its position by gripping the sea floor with its
tentacles, but it always floats as shown in the figure and cannot turn

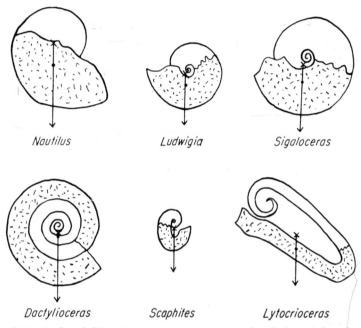

FIGURE 3.11 Deduced life orientations of some typical coiled cephalopods. Cross,
center of buoyancy; dot, center of gravity; stipple, body chamber. (After Trueman,
1940; by courtesy of the Geological Society of London.)

right over. In many evolute ammonites, however, the two centers were
much closer together, so that *Dactylioceras*, for example, must have been
much less stable in the water and able to change its position easily,
even turning upside down.

Considerable interest has always been taken in the mode of life of
the heteromorphic "uncoiled" ammonites. It has often been suggested
that they crawled about on the sea floor, though it is difficult to see
how. Trueman investigated a few of these, notably the Upper Cretaceous
Scaphites, and found that the aperture must have been directed upward
(Figure 3.11).[2] He also suggested, though could not prove, that they

[2] For an example of confirmatory evidence from a completely different viewpoint,
see p. 91.

were lighter than sea water and floated at the surface feeding on microplankton.

COMPARATIVE LIFE HISTORIES

So far in this chapter I have used the uniformitarian approach in the comparison of ancient and modern organisms, both as whole individuals and in their detailed anatomy and physiology. Finally I wish to consider the rare cases in which we can compare the whole life history of a fossil species with that of some living form. This approach has great possibilities for the statistically minded paleontologist, but there are, as yet, few examples which can be quoted.

In one of the rare papers on the life, as distinct from the anatomy, of living brachiopods, Percival (1944) demonstrated the extremely high rate of infant mortality in the living New Zealand brachiopod *Terebratella inconspicua* by means of a growth curve that was very much skew to the left. Veevers (1959) has demonstrated somewhat similar size-frequency distributions in Devonian brachiopods from Western Australia (Figure 3.12). The fossils were silicified, and were obtained by the solution of the limestone matrix in acid, so are much more likely to be a true sample than are collections made by ordinary hand picking. Rudwick (in Hallam, 1962) said that Percival's curve was highly abnormal in showing no peak for larger shells such as he himself had found in collecting from a much larger area. He suggested that Percival's sample might have included a very dense patch of shells from the most recent spatfall. Both Percival's and Rudwick's samples came, of course, from living populations which did not include the generations of adult dead which would most commonly be found in a fossil assemblage. The skewness of the curves might be exaggerated by this process or by scavengers; and the adult figures themselves would be controlled by other factors such as the mode of growth. Hallam himself suggested (1962) that the irregular character of the curves he obtained for British Jurassic brachiopods might be due to the effect of successive broods. These matters will be discussed again in Chapter 12.

More acceptable as a true study of mortality rates and age was the study by Kurtén (1958) on the life and death of the Pleistocene cave bears (*Ursus spelaeus*) found in caves around Odessa in the southern U.S.S.R. Kurtén concluded that the bears had died in the caves during winter hibernation, with a mortality peak at the end of each winter. The mortality rate M for each year of age was determined by the equation

$$M = \frac{a}{b}$$

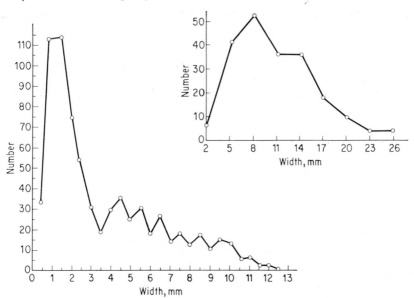

FIGURE 3.12 **Comparative size-frequency curves for (*top*) the Devonian brachiopod *Schizophoria stainbrooki* (after Veevers, 1959) and (*bottom*) the living brachiopod *Terebratella inconspicua* (after Percival, 1944).**

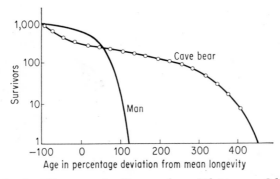

FIGURE 3.13 **Survivorship curves for *Ursus spelaeus* (Pleistocene, Odessa, U.S.S.R.) and *Homo sapiens*, (Recent, white males continental United States). (From Kurtén, 1958; by courtesy of the author.)**

where *a* is the total number of teeth in a given age group, and *b* is the sum of these and all older homologous teeth.[3] Juvenile mortality could be estimated from the milk canines. On this basis, life tables comparable to those of an actuary, that is, showing the expectation of life of all the various age groups, were worked out. These showed the usual sigmoidal

[3] *M* is the sum of all the teeth from skulls of a certain age divided by the sum of these and all the teeth from skulls of later age groups.

survivorship curve, like that of man, with high infant mortality, stable rates for bears in their prime, and increasing rates again in old age (Figure 3.13). An even better comparison might have resulted if Kurtén had chosen a less fortunate human population than white males in the continental United States.

An interesting point about the bears was that they showed strongly differential mortality rates for different variations, suggesting the rapid operation of natural selection. Other intimate details of the bears' lives were revealed in the same study, notably the fact that the female bears appear to have chosen easily defendable caves and managed to keep out the males during winter hibernation!

FOUR

Deductions from morphology

In the last chapter I was concerned with the paleoecological deductions which could be made from the comparison of fossils with living forms. In this chapter I am concerned with the deductions that can be made from fossil morphology when no comparisons are possible with present-day organisms. In other words, I wish to consider what we can learn without the use of uniformitarianism (or at least without its direct use). We are then immediately wading into a sea of hypotheses, where we may be concerned, for example, with the mode of life of a completely extinct group, like the trilobites, or with some anatomical structure, like the rostrum of a belemnite, which is unlike anything known today.

Sometimes even the paleontologist's capacity for hypothesis fails, and we are left with fossil remains which are a complete ecological mystery. There are, for instance, a whole series of inexplicable mammals in the Tertiary of South America—the Astrapotheria. One of these is *Astrapotherium*, which was a large animal, about 3 m long, with a strange truncated skull. There were no upper incisors, but very long canine teeth; the nasal openings were slitlike and placed on top of the head; there were very strong forelimbs but very weak hind limbs. Romer (1945) concluded: "All in all, the creatures' mode of life is beyond reasonable conjecture."

DEDUCTIONS ABOUT FUNCTION

If we can find out how the various parts of an organism function, we go a long way toward understanding its mode of life. If we had never watched a duck paddling about in a pond, we might still make some reasonable guesses as to its habits from the observation that its webbed feet would function very well as paddles.

Among fossils we have the example of the reptile *Dimetrodon* and its relations in the Permian of Texas, with their remarkable dorsal crests. Nothing comparable to this structure is known in modern animals, and various suggestions have been made about its possible function. The most likely explanation seems to be that its function was simply that of providing a large surface area for rapid heat loss to regulate body temperature. Overheating when on land is a great problem for reptiles and amphibians, which lack the delicate thermostatic control of the warm-blooded animals. The *Dimetrodon* crest, therefore, may have been an extremely beneficial device for such an animal living on dry land, especially in the arid-desert conditions which are suggested by the local rocks. We may, indeed, suppose that *Dimetrodon* and its relations were enabled by the crest to live a more free-moving life than their crestless but otherwise comparable contemporaries, which were mainly restricted to lakes and swamps. Conversely, it is difficult to imagine the mode of life of fossils in which a vital function was performed by some unfossilizable organ.

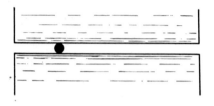

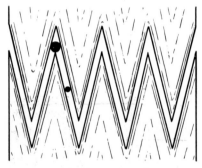

FIGURE 4.1 Plication of the commissure in brachiopods and its effect in excluding unwanted particles. The large particle in the upper diagram can only enter the shell in the lower diagram at the bends in the zigzag commissure. Setae or spines may be developed in this position to exclude such particles.

It is debatable, for example, whether anyone would have guessed the form and function of the elephant's trunk if the last two species of this great family had become extinct before the beginning of human records. Much speculation might have been devoted to the problem of how these animals fed.

Turning to the invertebrates, a whole series of interesting deductions have been made about the function of various structures in certain fossil brachiopods. Herta Schmidt (1937) studied problems associated with feeding among brachiopods and the solutions displayed in their shells. There was clearly the need for excluding large solid particles from the food streams coming into the shell (Figure 3.10). This was in part solved by the development of a sharply folded anterior commissure (Figure 4.1), though overlarge particles could still get in at the bends in the zigzag junction. Dr. Schmidt described setae projecting from the mantle edges in certain German Devonian rhynchonellids which served to close this gap. She also described spines in other forms which

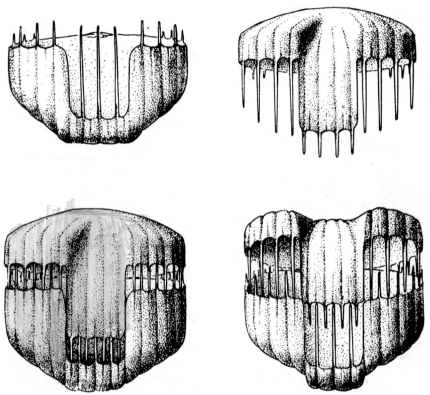

Figure 4.2 Protective sieve in the Devonian rhynchonellid *Uncinulus*. (From H. Schmidt, 1937; by courtesy of the author.)

must have performed the same function, and she showed how, in one species, these spines formed a protective sieve when the shell was wide open (Figure 4.2). This theme was developed by Rudwick (1958) in various ways. He described sieve devices in a number of different brachiopod groups and later (1961*a*) described the extreme version in *Prorichthofenia uddeni* from the Texas Permian. In this species, a system of branching and anastomosing spines formed a continuous mesh across the shell cavity which must have effectively excluded particles larger than a certain size.

Turning to an entirely different group, there have been endless discussions about the many strange morphological modifications seen in the trilobites. Early deductions about form and function were made by Dollo (1910) and Staff and Reck (1911). They decided, chiefly on the basis of the form of the eyes, cephalon, and pygidium, that there were many different modes of life among the trilobites and merostomes. They concluded, for example, that the trinucleids, with their shovel-shaped, eyeless cephala, were burrowing forms in the aphotic zone.

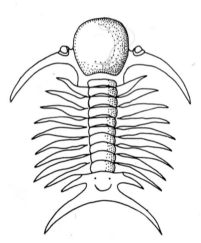

The ideas of Dollo and of Staff and Reck were criticized by Richter, who wrote a long series of careful and detailed papers (1915, 1919, 1920a, 1923a, 1923b, 1925, 1926, 1934, 1937) on the probable mode of life of a whole series of trilobites. His general conclusions were that most of the trilobites were rather poor swimmers, and normally crawled on the sea floor. Many other paleontologists have written on this intriguing subject, most notably Raymond (1920), but only brief examples can be quoted here. For instance, Delo (1935) discussed the locomotive habits of the phacopid trilobites and concluded that they were not true burrowers (as had been thought because of the shape of their head shields) but probably plowed along in soft sediment, with their large eyes just above the surface. They too were probably not very efficient swimmers, and swimming could only have been a secondary means of propulsion.

FIGURE 4.3 Reconstruction of the supposedly pelagic trilobite *Deiphon.* (After Barrande and Whittard, 1934.)

From their morphology, therefore, it seems that few trilobites can have been pelagic rather than benthonic in habit. One possible exception was the remarkable creature *Deiphon* of the Silurian (Figure 4.3) which was discussed by Whittard (1934). He suggested that the swollen glabella of this genus may have been filled with a liquid of low specific gravity which enabled the animal to float, probably in a sloping attitude at the surface of the sea.[1] Buoyancy was assisted by the extreme reduction of the skeleton to little more than spines, which in themselves would tend to retard sinking. The position of the eyes also supports this

[1] An earlier suggestion that the glabella contained gas bubbles for the same purpose had been rejected by Richter (1923a).

hypothesis, since they would have provided a wide field of vision if the body were oriented in this way.

One of the best examples of good deductive reasoning from morphology concerns the orthocone nautiloids. Many of these have curious

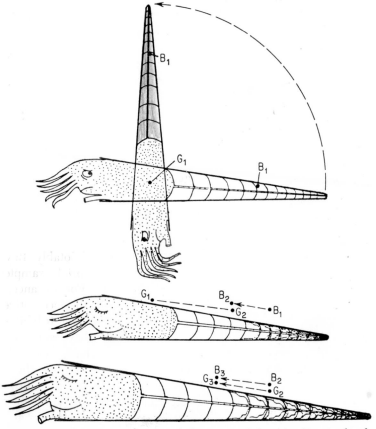

FIGURE 4.4 **Hydrostatic function of secondary cameral deposits.** *Top,* in the absence of such deposits, the orthocone nautiloid shell would assume a vertical position unsuitable for swimming or for bottom living. *Bottom,* with the progressive development of cameral deposits, a horizontal position is maintained during growth. In each case, G_1, G_2, etc., and B_1, B_2, etc., indicate the successive positions of the center of gravity and the center of buoyancy respectively. (From Flower, 1957; by courtesy of the Geological Society of America.)

secondary deposits around the septal necks, and it has been argued that these served to increase the weight of the shell proportionately with growth and so allowed the creature to swim or crawl in a horizontal position instead of floating vertically. Flower's delightful illustration of this device (1957) is reproduced in Figure 4.4. This seems to be completely valid and indisputable, at least for a large proportion of the orthocones. As an example of bad paleoecological reasoning, on the other hand, we have Buckman's remarks on the same subject (1919): "The early Orthocones utilising the gas effusion which resulted from temporary indigestion under the nervous apprehension of danger, found that a cone thus made more buoyant was a help in rapid retreat from foes." This imaginative explanation was hardly based on observation or on physiology.

We may contrast the postulated mode of life of nautiloids having such "loaded siphuncles" with the mode of life of the straight Upper Cretaceous ammonite *Baculites*. This had no such counterbalance and, according to Trueman (1940), must have floated in a vertical position.

The problem of keeping on an even keel was solved in another way by some nautiloids. These developed asymmetrical chambers in which

FIGURE 4.5 Hydrostatic device in a Paleozoic nautiloid. Asymmetrical chambers developed in the adult shell of *Ascoceras* after an earlier "normal" shell which is usually shed; Silurian, Czechoslovakia.

pockets of air were retained on the upper side. This was taken to an extreme by *Ascoceras* in the Silurian of Czechoslovakia (Figure 4.5). *Ascoceras* was remarkable in that it changed the form of its shell halfway through life. After having a fairly "normal" gently curved shell in early life, it suddenly grew a bulbous adult shell with strongly asymmetrical chambers and usually shed the earlier portion. Such a change in morphology can only be interpreted as reflecting a change in habit, and it may be that *Ascoceras* became able to live a more active free-moving life.

Besides being able to guess at what an organism could do, we may also gain from its anatomy ideas about what it could not do. For example, J. W. Wells (1957*b*) pointed out that the Rugosa, unlike post-Paleozoic corals, had no edge zone, that is, no fleshy lobe hanging down round the outside of the corallite, thus they could not modify or add to the outside of their skeleton. This must have considerably restricted their powers of attachment and fixation, compared with those of their later relations. They could not increase the area of attachment at the base of each corallite, so that a simple rugose coral, as it grew, either sank into the sediment or toppled over. Many of the amazing variety of shapes seen in such forms simply result from this instability, since after falling over the coral grows upward again. One result of this has been a proliferation of names for morphological variants. It may be that because of this limitation, the Paleozoic Rugosa were unable to live in the rougher shallow water.

A similar problem faced the strophomenoid and productoid brachiopods after the evolutionary loss of pedicle attachment, and a whole series of strange modifications resulted, all apparently serving for attachment or stability on the sea floor. Some of these brachiopods, such as *Prorichthofenia* and *Chonetes*, developed spines, presumably to prop them up on the sea floor; specimens of the former are commonly found in this position. Others seem to have achieved stability by the development of a very large interarea. Many probably just lay on the sea floor and were slowly buried in sediment; and one modern articulate, *Neothyris lenticularis*, does in fact lie thus after the atrophy of its pedicle during ontogeny (Allan, 1937). This was presumably the mode of life of the large group of strophomenoids and productoids in which one valve was strongly convex and the other concave. It is usually thought that these lay in the sediment with the convex valve downward; then the problem seems to have been that of keeping their margins free of the mud for feeding. This may have led to the excessive development of the "trail," or anterior elongation of the shell, seen in forms such as *Proboscidella* and perhaps peculiar to areas of rapid sedimentation.

Limitations

Uniformitarianism has many drawbacks in its application to the geological record, and in paleoecology it may be actually misleading if we try too hard to deduce functions for fossil structures from modern analogues. This is exemplified in the contradictory conclusions which have been reached about the form and function of trilobite appendages. The typical limbs found on some trilobites consist of two branches, the lower one simply a series of jointed segments and the upper one bearing bladelike filaments. It has been common practice to equate these two branches with the endopodite and the exopodite, respectively, of the modern crustacean limb (Figure 4.6). From this it seemed to follow that the lower branch functioned primarily for walking on the sea floor, and the upper branch was a swimming organ or possibly a catching filter, as in the branchiopod crustaceans.

These comparisons were considered at length by Størmer (1940), and he disputed the supposed homology of the filament-bearing branch in the trilobites with the exopodite of the crustaceans. He showed that

it is in fact more comparable with the crustacean epipodite, which is a
simple or branched appendage (not jointed) serving as a gill. The
structure and position of the trilobite filamentous branches also strongly
suggest a respiratory function. It should be pointed out, however, that
trilobite appendages are as yet only known in about fifteen genera out

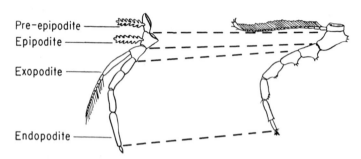

Figure 4.6 Thoracic appendages in (*left*) a modern crustacean and (*right*) a
trilobite. (After Størmer, 1940.)

of the fifteen hundred or so described to date (Harrington, 1959), so all
generalizations are quite inadequate.

Experimental Work

Paleoecology is essentially an observational science, unsuited to experimental treatment, but in a few cases it is possible to design experiments to test some aspect of functional morphology. An excellent example
of this type of study was done by Schmidt (1930) and later improved on
by Kummel and Lloyd (1955), on the relative streamlining of coiled
cephalopod shells. It had long been assumed that the more compressed
types—the oxycones—were more efficient swimmers than the more
globose types (Figure 4.8A and B). Swimming and flying organisms
(and man-made vehicles) tend to be much more graceful than their
pedestrian contemporaries which have to cope with the irregularities of
the land or sea floor. Kummel and Lloyd set out to test these assumptions
experimentally. They designed an apparatus (Figure 4.7) in which a
plaster cast of a cephalopod, coated with plastic, could be held in a
stream of water in such a way that its resistance to the water could
readily be determined. With this they studied twenty-one specimens of coiled nautiloids and ammonoids. In each case they calculated
a drag coefficient $C_{D'}$ as follows:

$$C_{D'} = \frac{2D}{V^2 A} \quad \text{when} \quad C_{D'} = \frac{C_D \rho}{N_R}$$

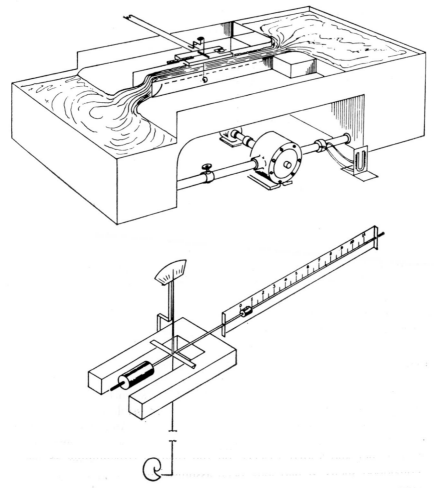

FIGURE 4.7 Apparatus for measuring the relative streamlining of coiled cephalopod shells. *Top,* stream table and flume; *bottom,* drag-measuring device. (From Kummel and Lloyd, 1955; by courtesy of the Society of Economic Paleontologists and Mineralogists.)

where D = drag force

V = velocity of fluid

ρ = density of fluid

A = cross-sectional area of specimen

N_R = Reynold's number (constant for the range of velocities employed)

From this it should be noted that the higher the coefficient, the greater is the resistance to the water and the poorer is the streamlining. The following is a selection of the results obtained:

ORGANISM	AVERAGE $C_{D'}$
Peltoceras	21.4
Gastrioceras	18.4
Dactylioceras	16.6
Douvilleiceras	16.4
Cravenoceras	16.0
Perrinites	15.4
"Nautilus"	14.8
Harpoceras	14.4
Perisphinctes	14.0
Spathites	13.8
Scaphites	13.0

Kummel and Lloyd concluded that, generally speaking, evolute forms were less well streamlined than involute ones. The size of the umbilicus proved to be very important, since two forms with similar cross sections can give different values because of the presence in one of a deep umbilicus (Figure 4.8*E* and *F*).

The experiments supported the idea that many ammonites changed their mode of life during development. Thus the young specimens of *Peltoceras* (Figure 4.8*C*) appear to have been more efficient swimmers than the adults. The most poorly streamlined forms proved to be depressed coarsely ornamented forms with a wide umbilicus. This is one of the frequent cases where the experiment has proved what had always been supposed from observation.

Another example of experimental work on fossil morphology is in the already-quoted work by Rudwick (1961*a*) on the Permian *Prorichthofenia*. In his introductory remarks he discussed the specific problem of this chapter, that is, the detection of adaptations in fossils for which no modern comparisons are possible. His stimulating approach was that of testing any supposed adaptation in a fossil against a model, or *paradigm*, which he defined as "the structure that can fulfil the function with maximal efficiency under the limitations imposed by the nature of the materials." The degree of approximation between the paradigm and the actual fossil structure is then a measure of the efficiency of that structure in performing the supposed function. Thence, by implication (and quite unprovably), it is also a measure of the probability that the structure concerned did perform that function.

In *Prorichthofenia*, the dorsal valve is reduced to a flat operculum within the conical ventral valve. A postulated function of this specialized dorsal valve was that it opened and shut rapidly to set up food currents into the ventral valve and the lophophore. Rudwick constructed

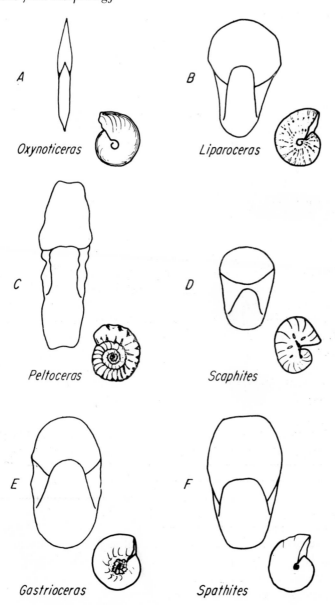

A   Oxynoticeras

B   Liparoceras

C   Peltoceras

D   Scaphites

E   Gastrioceras

F   Spathites

FIGURE 4.8 Cross sections and profiles of selected ammonoids, showing the relative streamlining of their shells.

working models of *Prorichthofenia,* and these were operated in a tank of water with very small oil droplets in suspension. The movement of the water currents could then be observed and photographed with a cinecamera. Figure 4.9 shows diagrammatically the water movements

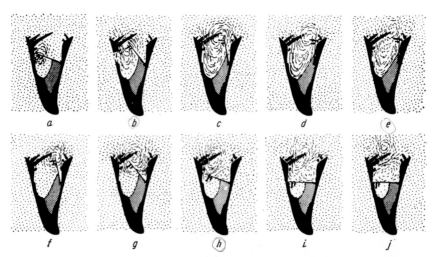

FIGURE 4.9 Reconstruction of feeding mechanism in *Prorichthofenia permiana,* showing successive positions of the dorsal valve and the relative movement of suspended particles. The shell is shown black and the visceral cavity by close regular stippling. (From Rudwick, 1961*a*; by courtesy of the author.)

observed. The efficiency of this mechanism makes it probable that this was, in fact, the function of the dorsal valve in *Prorichthofenia.*

DEDUCTIONS ABOUT HABIT

We can in some cases make direct deductions about the habits of past organisms from features of their anatomy without having to concern ourselves with presumed function.

Color Markings

Rare specimens of straight nautiloids from the Paleozoic are found from time to time with the original color pattern of the shell still preserved. The function of the color pattern is irrelevant; it may have been camouflage, mimicry, or sexual. The essential point about it is that it is usually asymmetrical. Ruedemann (1921) discovered such shells in the

Ordovician Trenton limestone with horizontal bands confined to the dorsal surface (Figure 4.10). This and other similar records were discussed by Foerste (1930) and Flower (1939). The immediate implication is that the shells were horizontal during life, though a few cases are known in which, for example, a zigzag pattern extends all round the shell.

Color markings on living animals are commonly darker and more pronounced on the upper surface. This is seen, for example, in the living

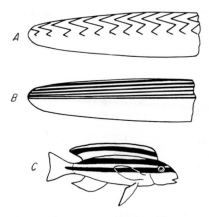

FIGURE 4.10 Two straight Paleozoic nautiloids with asymmetrical color banding (after Foerste, 1930, and Ruedemann, 1921) and a modern fish with comparable markings from Lake Nyasa (after Fryer, 1959).
A, *"Orthoceras" anguliferum;* B, *Geisonoceras tenuitextum;* C, *Pseudotropheus auratus.*

Nautilus and in many other aquatic animals, such as the fish from Lake Nyasa also shown in Figure 4.10.

Molting

Another category of fossilized remains which always causes complications in discussions of "life assemblages" and "death assemblages" is the exoskeletons of arthropods which have been cast off in molt stages. In the ostracods it is often possible to recognize these for what they are by simple measurement studies (Figure 4.11); the successive molt stages, or instars, show as clusters of points on a scatter diagram. It is, however, usually impossible to distinguish between a molted shell and one in which the creature died. The evidence suggests that the ostracods always had the molting habit, and this is also suggested by occasional exoskeletons of the extinct trilobites. Rare specimens are found which

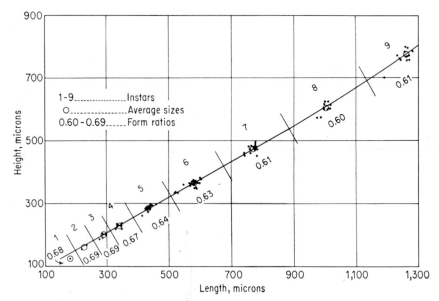

FIGURE 4.11 Scatter diagram of an assemblage of the ostracod *Bairdia oklahoma-ensis* from the Pennsylvanian of Illinois. (From Shaver, 1960; by courtesy of the Society of Economic Paleontologists and Mineralogists.)

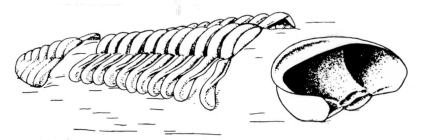

FIGURE 4.12 Molted exoskeleton of the trilobite *Nephranops* from the Upper Devonian of Germany. (From Harrington, 1959, after Richter, 1937, and Hupé, 1953; by courtesy of the Geological Society of America and the University of Kansas Press.)

seem, from their orientation, to have been cast off by a living animal (Figure 4.12), and different modes of molting have been distinguished. *Nathorstia transitans* of the Burgess shale fauna, which was described by Walcott as a "generalized trilobite" of uncertain affinities, was later reinterpreted by Raymond (1920) as the "soft-shell crab" of *Olenoides serratus*. In other words, it was merely the soft-bodied *Olenoides* caught by death in the interval between shedding one exoskeleton and growing the next.

Sexual Dimorphism

After eating, the most widespread habits among modern animals are those connected with sex, and there is no reason to suppose that this did not raise its allegedly ugly head millions of years before Freud. Clearly if we are to regard our fossils as once-living creatures, considerations of sex must arise, and many paleontologists have suggested sexual dimorphism to explain pairs of contemporaneous fossils with slight but nongradational morphological differences.

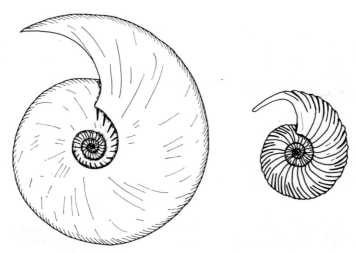

FIGURE 4.13 Possible sexual dimorphism in Upper Jurassic ammonites. *Left,* *Quenstedtoceras* (*Bourkelamberticeras*) *henrici; right,* Q. (*Quenstedtoceras*) *macrum.* X⅜. (After Makowski, 1962.)

Munier-Chalmas (1892) suggested that among the ammonites, small forms with lateral processes (lappets) on the aperture were males and larger forms without these structures were females. As an example he quoted *Normannites* and *Cadomites* of the French Bajocian (Middle Jurassic). Other workers compared the lappets with the male claspers of insects, but this analogy does not seem to be acceptable, and later ammonite specialists have suggested that the sexes were the other way round. The dimorphism is unprovable at this late stage, but remains an interesting possibility. Figure 4.13 shows a possible example from the Upper Jurassic of Poland.

Brachiopods are another of the less obvious groups in which sexual dimorphism has been claimed. Vandercammen (1959) has discussed it in his magnificent study of *Cyrtospirifer* in the Frasnian (Upper Devo-

nian) of Belgium. In many spirifer species he has found a fairly sharp
division into two groups. In a simple case, these may be narrow globose
forms and wide thin ones, but the divergent characters differ from species to species. Westoll (1950) suggested the same explanation for a
bimodal distribution in the terebratuloid *Dielasma elongata* in the English Permian.

DEDUCTIONS ABOUT HABITAT

The place in which a fossil lived, as well as the way in which it lived,
can sometimes be deduced from its morphology, even without the help
of modern relations. Thus we know that, because of the solvent power
of fresh water, nonmarine pelecypods are usually characterized by a very
thick periostracum. What is more, pelecypods and gastropods which
live in the more acid river waters characteristically lose that periostracum from the older parts of the shell, and the layers below are often
deeply etched. My colleague Dr. M. P. Kerney finds this frequently
among British Quaternary Mollusca, and Stenzel et al. (1944) noted
that all fresh-water mollusks were affected in this way in the Miocene
Fleming formation of Burkeville in eastern Texas.

Similarly—to return again to color markings—Forbes (1843) drew
attention to the fact that shells with clear color patterns are largely
confined to the better-lighted parts of the sea. It is reasonable to suppose
that these markings must be visible to have any function at all. So it
can be argued that the rare trilobites which have color patterns on their
skeletons prove, or help to prove, that these forms lived in shallow water.
For example, this argument was applied by Hudson and Jefferies (1961)
to mollusks from the Trias of Arabia. Plate 6A shows a pelecypod with
color bands from a short-lived and clearly shallow marine incursion in
the Oligocene of the Isle of Wight. It should be noted, however, that
a number of very-deep-water forms are now known to be brightly colored, and there is no apparent adaptive reason for this.

But color markings are only occasionally seen in fossils, and we must
normally depend on other characters, such as the general form of the
shell. Thus we know that most gastropods which live in the rough conditions of the littoral zone today have thick, heavy shells, often specially
adapted for clinging to wave-battered rock surfaces and offering the
minimum resistance to the sea. The limpet shape, for example, turns
up in every major division of the gastropods in forms which live in
such habitats. Farther out to sea, mollusk shells tend to become thinner
and more highly and delicately ornamented—for example, *Murex*, with
its long, fragile spines. Some gastropods and their relations, such as the
pteropods, are adapted for floating, having very thin, transparent shells.
There are exceptions to these generalizations, but they do provide a

rough guide to the understanding of fossil habitats. Thus the remarkable Miocene gastropod *Orthaulax*, found in Florida and the West Indies, has been interpreted as a reef-dwelling form because of its extremely thick and solid shell, which is clearly adapted to life in an area of constant battering by the waves.

So far, not much has been said about the fossil plants, though the paleobotanists have probably devoted more time and effort to ecological matters than all other specialists put together. In the present connection an interesting example is provided by the study of leaf shapes. W. N. Edwards (1936) pointed out that the nature of the leaf margin in dicotyledonous trees is an index of climatic conditions and that this could be applied to fossil floras even when the plants themselves have not been adequately identified. At the present day, there is a progressive increase in the percentage of trees with entire leaves as one approaches the tropics and a corresponding increase in dentate leaves toward the temperate regions. This is obvious in any visit to the hothouse in a botanical garden. Endo (1934) calculated that in Sakhalin, to the north of Japan, the percentage of trees with entire leaves is less than 8, in Hokkaido it is 13, and in southern Japan it is 56.

Edwards then showed how this could be applied to the interpretation of the Eocene flora of southern England. He found that 76 per cent of the genera represented in the London clay of the Isle of Sheppey and 86 per cent of the leaf species in the pipe clays of Alum Bay in the Isle of Wight had entire leaves (Figure 4.14, *top*). This evidence supported the general contention, reached from several other angles, that the flora of lower Eocene times in southern Britain was comparable with that of a modern rain forest (pages 192, 193). It is interesting to note the reduction in the proportion of entire leaves when we examine later Tertiary floras (Figure 4.14, *bottom*); this fits in with the general theory of a deteriorating climate. Tanai (1961) concluded from his work on Neogene leaf changes in Japan that there had been a gradual decline in temperatures there since the Miocene. Similar changes were observed in American Tertiary floras by Wolff and Barghoorn (1960). Clearly we must be sure that this is not an evolutionary effect before regarding the theory as proved, but the circumstantial evidence is strong.

My final example of the use of a fossil's morphology to make deductions about its habitat could equally well have been used to illustrate both the other kinds of deduction. Yochelson (1961) reexamined the Middle Cambrian fossil *Hyolithes carinatus* from the Burgess shale of British Columbia. Walcott had interpreted two structures at the apertural end of this shell as supports for fins like those of modern pteropods. Yochelson showed, however, that the structures in question were attached to the operculum and must have functioned as props to hold the operculum open during feeding. Thence he deduced that the animal could not have moved very much or the props would not have functioned. Yochelson therefore concluded that *Hyolithes* was virtually a sedentary benthonic organism, not planktonic as had formerly been sup-

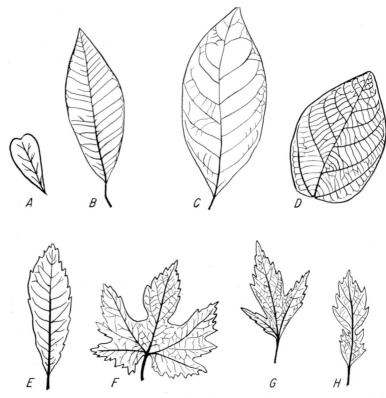

FIGURE 4.14 Fossil leaf shapes. *Top,* a selection of leaves with entire margins from the lower Eocene of Alum Bay, Isle of Wight, England. *Bottom,* a selection of leaves with dentate margins from the Miocene of the south of France (after Fritel, 1903). **A,** *Dalbergia;* **B,** *Ficus;* **C,** *Laurus;* **D,** *Apeiobopsis;* **E,** *Myrica;* **F,** *Vitis;* **G,** *Acer;* **H,** *Quercus.* Not to scale.

posed. So the deduction about function led to deductions about habit and habitat.

PALEOPATHOLOGY

Accident and disease are only too obviously a major facet of present-day life, and it is clear from the fossil record that it has always been so. Many papers have been written describing individual examples, and Moodie (1923) summed up all the evidence then available in a book entitled *Paleopathology.* The first volume of a large new work on the subject has recently been published by Tasnádi-Kubacska (1962). Well-known cases range from the dinosaur with rheumatoid arthritis to the trilobites whose dorsal skeletons were damaged and repaired between molts. We may also include here teratological specimens, or monstrosities —those specimens which are quite outside the normal range of variation of a species.

All these phenomena are very interesting in considerations of the life of the individual organism, but it is difficult to extract any generalizations other than the simple comment that they have occurred, very much as at present, since very early geological time. In terms of general paleoecology, the most important point about pathology and teratology is simply to remember that they may explain the occasional anomalous specimen. Serious misconceptions about the mode of life of particular fossils sometimes arise through the nonrecognition of such specimens.

The most surprising example of this is provided by Neanderthal man. This early man is always reconstructed as a clumsy, shuffling creature with a strongly curved back and a thrust-forward head. Cave (1959) has claimed that this picture is completely inaccurate, largely because of Boule's "insufficient recognition of the extensive spinal pathology" present in the La Chapelle-aux-Saints skeleton on which the conventional picture of the creature's posture was founded. Cave pointed out that the backbone, particularly in its cervical portion, is so distorted by osteoarthritis as to exclude any reliable estimation of its original curvature.

There are certain pathological conditions in modern times which can be related to factors of a particular local environment. For instance, goiter was so common in the limestone districts of Derbyshire, England, that it became known as "Derbyshire neck." Comparably, concentrations of pathological fossil specimens may have paleoecological significance. Examples of such concentrations are seen in the lenses of Shenley limestone near Leighton Buzzard in Bedfordshire, England. Many of the brachiopods here, notably the commonest form, *"Terebratula" capillata,* show signs of distortion during life; there is no obvious explanation of this, though the fauna is an unusual one for this horizon.

Besides disease, the organic world has always been burdened with a heavy toll of accidents, their victims ranging from the Siberian mammoth which slipped into a gully, down to the broken and repaired starfish of many ages. It is not often possible, however, to prove that the quite common specimens which can be shown to have been damaged during life were beset by purely mechanical accidents rather than attacked by not completely successful predators.

Catastrophic death of vast numbers of aquatic organisms is usually caused through organic agencies (as discussed in Chapter 15), but it may occur through directly physical causes. Popovici (1940) attributed the sudden death of thousands of the decapod *Upogebia littoralis* on the coast of Roumania to storms and a rapid drop in water temperature. A fossil example is provided by the thousands of *Holoptychius* and other fish on one bedding plane in the Old Red Sandstone of Dura Den near Cupar in southern Scotland. These seem to have died through the drying out of their lake home.

Accidents of a different kind are the forest fires which have been claimed on the evidence of fusain in sediments of various ages. Harris (1958) recorded Mesozoic forest fires in East Greenland, Yorkshire, and South Wales, all presumably caused by lightning. He pointed out that 2.9 fires per 100,000 acres (about 400 sq km) are caused by lightning in California every year.

FIVE

Orientation

ONE of the most important observations which paleontologists should make in the field is that of the precise orientation of each fossil in the rock. In such studies we are immediately faced with three alternatives:

1. Is it the natural position of the organism as it was in life?
2. Is it the natural position of the organism as it fell to the ground or to the sea floor on death?
3. Is it merely the position in which the dead body (or part of it) came to rest after movement by other agencies?

Clearly the majority of orientations will be more or less random, and it is only when a large majority of fossils are aligned or arranged in a certain way that observations of orientation may be significant. Though such conformable attitudes may appear to be obvious to the naked eye, it is easy to be subjective about such matters, and a statistical approach is very desirable.

The three alternatives presented above will be considered in reverse order.

MECHANICAL ORIENTATIONS

The mechanical arrangement of fossils by currents and other physical processes, though a popular topic with lecturers and writers on paleo-ecology, is hardly an ecological matter. Nevertheless, it must be considered here, since a paleoecologist who is not always aware of what may have happened through inorganic agencies may be tempted to attribute the results to organic causes. It is also necessary to remember here the possible movement of bodies by scavengers and other organic agencies after death.

   The simplest case of mechanical orientation is the parallel alignment
of elongated fossils on a bedding plane by water currents. Thus Kindle
(1938) described the supposed pteropod *Tentaculites* as oriented in this
way in the Gaspé sandstone of eastern Canada. Gekker (1957) has presented similar examples from the Svinord beds (Upper Devonian) of

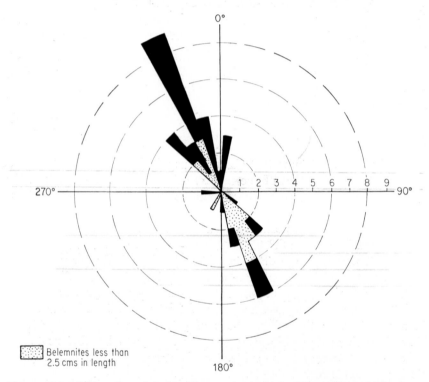

FIGURE 5.1   Orientation of belemnites on a single bedding plane of the lower
Kimeridgian (Upper Jurassic) near Brora, Sutherland, Scotland. The concentric
circles indicate numbers of specimens. The direction of the apex of the rostrum is
plotted in each case. It will be noted that the specimens less than 2.5 cm in
length and the larger specimens tend to point in opposite directions.

Russia, and I have found the same thing in the Longville flags (Upper
Ordovician) of Shropshire, England.
   Belemnite guards are also commonly found arranged in this way,
and it is a simple matter to show that they orient themselves very quickly
in a moving current with their apices upstream, though small specimens
do not always behave the same as large ones, depending on the current
and the nature of the bottom. Figure 5.1 shows the orientation of
belemnites on a bedding plane in the Upper Jurassic of eastern Scot-

PLATE 3 **Life and postmortem orientations.**
A, compound coral in life position, Bajocian (Middle Jurassic), near Ambléon (Ain), France. (Photograph taken by B. D. Evamy.) *B,* current-oriented belemnites, Toarcian (Lower Jurassic), near Hawsker, Yorkshire, England.

land, with the smaller specimens tending to point in the opposite direction from the larger ones. It is almost exceptional for abundant belemnites not to be lying parallel. I know of numerous examples of parallel alignment from all parts of the European Mesozoic. Plate 3, *bottom,* shows a typical case from the Lower Jurassic of Yorkshire, England.

Straight nautiloids behave in a similar way. Kay (1945) recorded two directions of orthocone orientation in the Ordovician of Saint Joseph Island, Ontario, and Rockwell Bay, Vermont. He suggested that the large shells had been oriented normal to the shoreline and the small ones parallel to it. Petránek and Kómárkova (1953) made simple quantitative studies on the orientation of orthocone nautiloids in the Silurian Budnany limestone and the Devonian Hlubočepy limestone of Czechoslovakia. They claimed that these orientations could be related to current directions and migration routes. Krinsley (1960) found a similar orientation in nautiloids on a single bedding plane in the Middle Silurian near Lemont, Illinois, and plotted it on a rose diagram. Flower has argued (1942*b*) that many such parallel orientations may be the result of the reworking of the sediments and not current action soon after death.

Many other groups of elongated fossils spring to mind—turreted gastropods, crinoid stems, productoid and echinoid spines and so on. Ruedemann (1897) found parallel orientation in the Utica shales of graptolites, sponge spicules, and bryozoa, besides straight nautiloids. There are almost endless possibilities in such studies, but it must be regarded as very doubtful that such orientations ever have more than strictly local significance.

It should also be borne in mind that some parallel orientations may be original life attitudes. Everyone has seen a bed of sunflowers all facing the same way, and certain marine organisms orient themselves in life in relation to the prevailing current. Crisp and Stubbings (1957) have demonstrated this in modern barnacles. They have shown, for example, that the barnacle *Coronula diadema* tends to attach itself to whales and ships with its rostrum pointing toward the direction of movement (Figure 5.2). Comparable examples are known in fan-shaped corals, sponges, and bryozoa.

The same thing has been postulated for a number of fossils. Thus it has been suggested that the L-shaped Silurian crinoid *Synchirocrinus* lay parallel to the current direction on the surface of a coral reef with its asymmetric branches elevated to catch food particles (Jaekel, 1918). Similarly, I have suggested (Ager, 1961*b*) a life orientation normal to currents for the dorsal valve of the Devonian brachiopod *Spinocyrtia iowensis;* and Richter (1929) showed by tank experiments that the Devonian coral *Calceola sandalina* was probably suited by its form to living in fairly strong currents, swinging like a weather vane with its calicular end toward the current. These three examples are shown in Figure 5.3.

So I have reached the general conclusion that, though most parallel orientations are probably mechanical, some of them could conceivably be natural.

Another familiar example of the mechanical arrangement of fossils is the tendency for the separated valves of bivalves to come to rest with their concave sides downward. This could hardly be mistaken for a

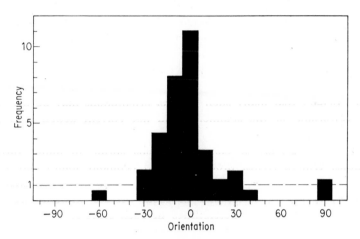

FIGURE 5.2 Histogram showing the orientation in relation to water currents of barnacles attached to a whale. Frequency is given as a fraction of the population per 10° sector × 36, so that unit frequency is the most probable value for a random orientation and is shown by the dotted line. (From Crisp and Stubbings, 1957; by courtesy of Blackwell Scientific Publications.)

natural orientation, though it might be in the case of other concave fossils such as trilobites. In a count of several hundred conical shells of the gastropod *Patella vulgata* on an exposed beach in east Sutherland, I found that 85.5 per cent were lying concave downward. Similarly, planoconvex bivalves and colonial organisms are often found lying on their flat sides, which is also their position of maximum mechanical stability.

Figure 5.4 shows a specimen of *Schizophoria* from the Lower Carboniferous of Yorkshire in which such an orientation is revealed by the partial infilling of the shell with sediment. Again, this may be a life orientation, but is more probably a mechanical one.

Fossil observations of this kind have often been suggested as possible "way-up" criteria in structural problems, though it is doubtful if many

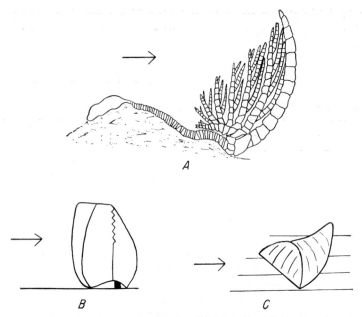

Figure 5.3 Supposed life orientations of fossils in relation to prevailing currents. *A,* Silurian crinoid *Synchirocrinus anglicus* (after Jaekel, 1918). *B,* Devonian brachiopod *Spinocyrtis iowensis* (after Ager, 1961*b*). *C,* Devonian coral *Calceola sandalina* (after Richter, 1929).

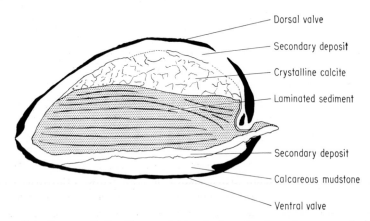

Figure 5.4 Lower Carboniferous Schizophoria, showing the accumulation of sediment, in two or more stages, in the lower part of the shell and the infilling of the space above with crystalline calcite. X1⅓. (Specimen collected by Prof. G. Bond from the D₂ zone, Swinden Knoll, Yorkshire, England.)

have been used in practice. They are commonly considered paleoecological matters, but it is difficult to see why, and they are better regarded as aspects of sedimentology.

DEATH ORIENTATIONS

When a free-moving organism dies, it naturally falls or comes to rest on the ground or the sea floor. The same is true of all sessile organisms, such as trees. The organism thus assumes what I call a "death orientation," and may be buried and fossilized in that position. We would hardly expect to find a man's body buried naturally in sediment in a standing position, but at Pompeii human bodies are found in the positions in which they fell to the ground and died when they were buried in the volcanic ash of Vesuvius. These are death orientations.

In the same category would come the bloated body of a mid-Tertiary rhinoceros which was engulfed and molded by pillow lavas as it floated in a lake (or lay on the shore) in the lower Grand Coulee, Washington (Chappell et al., 1951).

The way in which a fossil fell to the substratum on death may tell us a great deal about the mode of life of that organism. Rothpletz (1909) pointed out that some of the ammonites of the Upper Jurassic Solenhofen limestone of Bavaria have, beside them on the same bedding plane, the impressions made by their venters when they touched down on the sea floor. The animals had evidently been swimming about in the usual way before death. Presumably, the soft parts had been retracted into the shell (since they left no mark on the very fine-grained sediment), and the shells subsequently toppled over on one side. This single item of evidence proves three points about the life of the ammonites concerned:

1. They were swimming or floating forms.

2. Their attitude in life was exactly as postulated by Trueman (see page 51).

3. They could withdraw their bodies into their shells, as most gastropods do today.

Evidence of a more controversial kind comes from the famous trilobite of the Ordovician Utica shales of New York, *Triarthrus eatoni* (= *T. becki* auctt.). It is well known for its beautifully preserved appendages; but when Beecher (1894) described it, he noted that nearly all of the specimens were oriented with their convex dorsal sides downward, which could have resulted simply from settling of the body in quiet water. This is particularly likely since the projecting appendages gave the exoskeleton a dishlike form, convex upward in life, which would turn over as the animal sank. This is directly opposed to the effect likely to be produced in more disturbed waters, where convex shells tend to come to rest the other way up. An alternative explanation for the "upside-down" arrangement of *Triarthrus* was that the creature normally lived in this way, and a comparison was made with various living arthropods —for example, the young king crab *Limulus*—which float or swim in an "upside-down" position. A third suggestion, by Walcott (1881), was that the trilobites turned over after death due to gas in the viscera.

Sometimes the attitude of the fossil may give an indication of the mode of death, as is the case of the nine skeletons of the Pleistocene peccary *Platygonus*, which were found in a Kansas loess, lying side by side and facing the same way, apparently with their backs to the dust storm which had buried and killed them.

The valves of pelecypods gape open after death because of the re-laxation of the muscles and the longer survival of the ligaments which hold the valves together dorsally. The degree of opening may be a measure of the rate of sedimentation (Plate 6A to D). In the lower Eocene Bognor rock of Sussex, all the specimens of *Glycimeris brevirostris* are gaping to the same degree. This uniform gape does not tell us any-thing directly about the life or death of the organism concerned, but it does suggest the quietness of the conditions of sedimentation. Similar ef-fects may be informative about older and extinct groups. It may also be noted in passing that whereas in pelecypods the valves nearly always come apart (unless very quickly buried), in brachiopods they tend to stay together, since muscular action is needed to open them. Thus the evidence provided by separated valves differs from group to group.

There are many other possible death orientations and immediate postmortem effects which differ in their nature from group to group, and paleoecologists must always be on the lookout for such phenomena. As a completely different kind of orientation observation, I may in con-clusion quote Tillyard (1924) on the preservation of a Permian insect from Kansas: "The separation of the bases of the left pair [of wings] suggests the action of water, so that the outspread condition of the wings in the fossil may have been brought about by the dead insect floating on water before being covered over."

LIFE ORIENTATIONS

Having considered the above two alternatives as possible pitfalls, we come now to what chiefly concerns us in this aspect of paleoecology— the living attitudes of our fossils. Every paleontologist must, at some time, have found fossils in attitudes which can be interpreted without doubt as the normal life position of the organism concerned. Even more often, he must have found evidence which is equivocal and open to subjective interpretation one way or the other. In the specimen of an Eocene worm "reef" shown in Plate 2, a high proportion, though not all, of the specimens of *Rotularia bognoriensis* are oriented with their proximal, i.e., attached, ends downward, and other evidence suggests that they can hardly have been disturbed since they died.

Obviously life orientations are far more likely to occur in some groups of fossils than others. We will never find a fossil bird in position of life, but we will very commonly find burrowing pelecypods and tree roots as they were when alive. In any case, what is found may have a considerable bearing both on the mode of life of the organism concerned and on the conditions of deposition of the beds which contain it.

Under the first heading there is the example of *Lingula*, which seems to have lived in a vertical burrow, as it does today, since early Paleozoic times. Under the second heading we may compare the fossil trees of Yellowstone National Park in Wyoming with those of the Petrified Forest National Monument in Arizona. The former were buried in their living position by showers of volcanic ash during Miocene times. The latter are never found vertical as in life, but were carried as logs on rivers to lie horizontally in water-laid sediment far from where they grew, like the masses of driftwood seen near the mouth of the Mississippi today. Similarly, in Britain we may compare the tufa-covered stumps of trees in position in the Purbeckian "fossil forest" at Lulworth Cove in Dorset with the drifted logs of the "pine raft" in the lowermost Cretaceous of the Isle of Wight. E. D. McKee (personal communication, 1963), has told of palm trees being swept from a Pacific atoll during hurricanes and coming to rest in considerable depths of water in an upright position because of their heavy, stone-laden roots, so that even trees in position of life may not be completely beyond question.

Corals and stromatoporoids are particularly popular in studies of life orientations, and again innumerable examples are available. In my geological travels I have seen examples in the Silurian of the United States, the Devonian of Germany, the Carboniferous of Britain, the Triassic of Austria, the Jurassic of France (Plate 3, *top*), and the Cretaceous of Hungary, among many other horizons and localities. Often the orientation of such fossils reveals the mode of life of a whole community. In the Niagaran (Middle Silurian) limestones of northern Illinois, stromatoporoids and other colonial organisms in life position indicate a reef environment for other groups of associated fossils (Figure 5.5).

A statistical approach is especially desirable here, for such observations and interpretations can easily become highly selective and subjective. As an example of the simplest kind of quantitative approach, I may quote the observations by Misses Crosfield and Johnston (1914) on the English Wenlock (Middle Silurian) reefs, though I have never been able

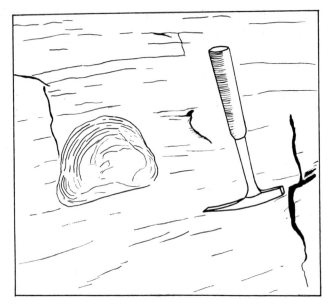

Figure 5.5 Stromatoporoid colony in position of life in a Niagaran (Middle Silurian) limestone at Thornton Quarry, near Chicago, Illinois. (Drawn from a photograph taken by the author.)

to confirm these figures from personal inspection. They gave the figures shown in Table 5.1 for the corals and stromatoporoids at four different

TABLE 5.1 *Orientation of corals and stromatoporoids in Wenlock limestone.* (*From Crosfield and Johnston, 1914*)

Locality	Reef			Interreef		
	Upright	Over-turned	Per cent upright	Upright	Over-turned	Per cent upright
1	35	5	87.5	4	36	10
2	38	2	95	12	28	30
3	39	1	97.5	3	16	7.5
4	37	3	92.5	7	33	17.5

localities, contrasting the reef, or "ballstone," percentages with those for the interreef "measures." It will be seen that in the reef facies, between 87.5 and 97.5 per cent of the organisms preserved were in position of growth, compared with only 7.5 to 30 per cent in the interreef facies. It may be objected that not enough observations were made to obtain significant results in every case, but paleontologists have to take their evidence where they can get it.

A more serious objection, even when the subjectivity of such ob-servations has been reduced by counting, is that the same effect could be brought about by mechanical means. It may be argued that a hemi-spherical body such as that shown in Figure 5.5 would tend to come to rest in this position on a current-swept floor simply because it is the position of greatest stability. Clearly we need to consider other evidence as well, such as the nature of the enclosing sediments.

While discussing the orientation of fossils within reefs, it may be pointed out that the reefs themselves may be oriented in a significant way. An interesting example of this is provided by the Danian (Paleo-cene?) bryozoan reefs of Denmark. Rosenkrantz and Rasmussen (1960) noted that they tend to be asymmetrical and to overlap each other in a general southerly direction.

Turning now to such forms as the burrowing pelecypods, in which the orientation is not so obvious, it is notoriously easy to get a false gen-eral impression that the shells in a particular bed tend to be oriented one way or another, though a simple count is usually sufficient to prove a really significant arrangement of this kind.

Thus I have observed that in the lower Eocene London clay of Alum Bay in the Isle of Wight, 92 per cent (46 out of 50) of the speci-mens of *Pholadomya margaritacea* were in presumed position of life, being inclined at a slight angle from the vertical with the posterior end uppermost. On the other hand, only about 60 per cent of the same num-ber of *Sinodia suborbicularis* in the lower Oligocene "*Venus*" bed of nearby Colwell Bay were found in position of life.

Even such orientations may be mechanical in origin under unusual circumstances. On the coast of north Somerset near Burnham on Sea, I have seen mud flats dried and cracked at low tide, with the cracks packed with pelecypod valves which had been washed in and trapped in a vertical position.

Pelecypods preserved in a vertical position are not necessarily burrow-ing forms, for many (like "*Venus*") live only partly buried in the sedi-ment. This was apparently the case with the abundant "*Megalodons*" of the Alpine Trias. These are commonly found on limestone bedding planes, where they are almost always seen in cross section, having the form of a cloven hoof. The shells are very difficult to extract, but Zapfe (1957) has shown how the various shapes observed in cross section relate to the shell as a whole (Figure 5.6). This indicates a constant orientation of the shell which must have lived with just its anterior end slightly buried in the limy mud.

Even forms which merely rest on the sea floor, or are anchored to it in some way, may be preserved in their living position in special circumstances. Sardeson (1924) described a specimen of *Cyrtodonta megambonum* from the Decorah shales in Minneapolis which had been buried while standing "upside down" on its sharpest edge (Figure 5.7).

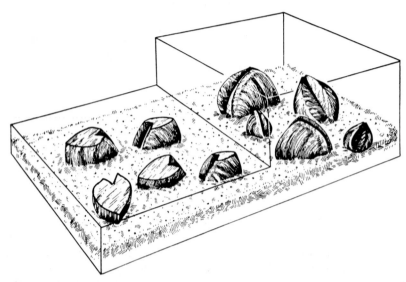

FIGURE 5.6 Block diagram showing the pelecypod *Conchodus infraliasicus* in presumed position of life (*right*) and as commonly seen in cross section on bedding planes (*left*); Upper Triassic Dachsteinkalk, Austrian Alps. (From Zapfe, 1957; by courtesy of the author.)

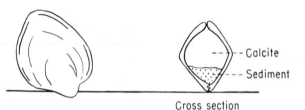

Cross section

FIGURE 5.7 An Ordovician pelecypod, *Cyrtodonta megambonum*, from the Decorah shales of Minneapolis, Minnesota, in presumed position of life—resting on its sharpest edge. (Redrawn from Sardeson, 1924.)

Sardeson presumed that this was the natural position for the animal and that it had been buried slowly while anchored to the sea floor.

Similar observations were recorded in a later paper by Sardeson (1929) on brachiopods. In this he noted that certain brachiopods, such as *Dinorthis deflecta*, were commonly found in the Ordovician Platteville limestone of Minnesota in an upright position with their cardinal areas pressed to the former sea floor (Figure 5.8). On the other hand, biconvex brachiopods, such as *Rhynchotrema minnesotensis*, were commonly found in the same stratum without a preferred orientation and were therefore thought to have been attached to floating vegetation.

Several writers have assumed derivation from elsewhere for pedunculate forms found in argillaceous strata, because of the preconceived idea that they could not have attached themselves to a soft sea floor. Thus Craig (1956) made this assumption even when he found eight out of thirteen specimens of *Camarotoechia pleurodon* in a vertical position with their beaks downward. He suggested that they might have floated into this position because of the accumulation of the gases of decay in the anterior part of the shell. It may be argued in return that at least one living pedunculate brachiopod, *Chlidonophora*, can attach itself to

Figure 5.8   Ordovician brachiopods from the Platteville limestone of Minnesota, in presumed position of life—with their cardinal areas pressed to the sea floor. **A,** *Dinorthis deflecta;* **B,** *Orthis tricenaria;* **C,** *Rafinesquina minnesotensis.* (After Sardeson, 1929.)

soft sediments by means of a branching pedicle, and it may well be that other genera could do so in the past. Alternatively, such forms may simply have fallen from floating seaweed with their heavier ends downward, as I have suggested elsewhere (Ager, 1962).

Another orientation study on brachiopods in soft sediment was that of Fenton and Fenton (1932b) on *Atrypa* in the Devonian of Iowa. This genus sometimes develops a remarkable broad fringe around the commissure which may have functioned like a snowshoe to prevent sinking in soft mud. The Fentons suggested that certain species changed their orientation with growth (Figure 5.9) to achieve maturity and stability lying on their flat ventral valves. They also showed that symbiotic associates living on the brachiopods could give evidence of the orientation of the shell in life.

Unusual Orientations

Tucked away in the vast literature of paleoecology, there are innumerable observations of fossil orientations of many strange kinds, sometimes showing great ingenuity on the part of the observer. To show

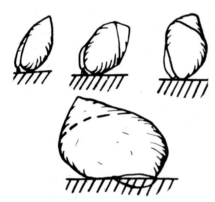

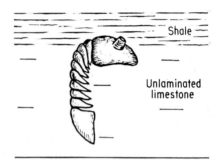

FIGURE 5.9 Supposed changes in orientation with growth in the Devonian brachiopod *Atrypa*. The shell has its dorsal valve underneath in youth and then, with increasing globosity, slowly overturns to rest on the ventral valve with its wide flange. (Redrawn from Fenton and Fenton, 1932*b*.)

FIGURE 5.10 Supposed life orientation of the Upper Ordovician trilobite *"Nileus" vigilans* in the Maquoketa shales near Elgin, Iowa. (As determined by Finch, 1904; reconstructed from various sources.)

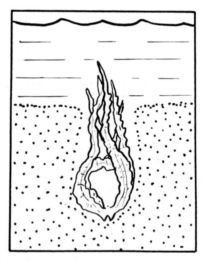

FIGURE 5.11 Supposed life orientation of the early ophiuroid *Taeniaster* in the Ordovician of Quebec. (After Billings, 1958.)

the range of observations which can be and have been made, just a few of the more unusual ones will be quoted.

Finch (1904) found a group of fifteen specimens of the trilobite *"Nileus" vigilans* in the Upper Ordovician Maquoketa shales near Elgin, Iowa. The prevailing position was as shown in Figure 5.10, with the head shields horizontal and just protruding above the surface of a bed and the rest of the skeleton vertical in the sediment. Finch suggested that they dug themselves backward into the mud while waiting for prey.

Billings (1858) figured the early ophiuroid *Taeniaster* from the Ordovician of Quebec, with its bulbous body concealed in a burrow and its long arms apparently reaching up to the surface to search for food particles (Figure 5.11). It may be noted in passing that among the starfish, probably more ophiuroids than asteroids are known as fossils simply because of the burrowing habits of the former.

An orientation of a completely different kind was recorded recently by Jefferies (1960). He described young individuals of the pelecypod *Lima lineata* from the German Triassic which were concentrated in the lunules of adult specimens. Of the 39 young Jefferies observed in this position, 29 of them had their lunules pressed to the floor of the adult lunule. Following from the deduction of Seilacher (1954) that this species lived with its anterodorsal margin close to the sea floor, Jefferies concluded that the young were photonegative in habit with a tendency to enter crannies.

FIGURE 5.12 *Scaphites warreni* with attached *Discinisca* from the lower Turonian (Cretaceous) of the Four Corners area of New Mexico. (Specimen kindly made available by the finder, Mr. J. W. Soderman.)

My final example comes from the calcareous algae, certain of which are commonly found as hemispherical masses like the corals and stromatoporoids. Nordeng (1959) studied the orientation of the main axes of the club-shaped alga *Collenia* in the upper Precambrian of Michigan. He found that these axes tended to be inclined in a particular direction, presumably toward the contemporary sun, and thence he estimated that the equator at that time passed through the point 27° N, 20° W; he claimed supporting evidence from other localities. Such observations could presumably be made on similar algal bodies at other stratigraphic horizons and in other parts of the world, but one would have to be sure that the inclination was caused solely by phototropism and not at all by currents or any other factor. Also there is the major structural problem of correcting for any later tectonic movements.

Orientations Deduced from Other Evidence

Quite apart from the evidence provided by the actual position of a fossil in the rock, it is sometimes possible to make deductions about life orientations from other lines of evidence. Deductions of this kind which have already been discussed are those of Trueman (1940) on the buoyancy of ammonites and those of Rothpletz (1909) on the marks made by ammonites on landing. Figure 5.12 shows a specimen of the partly uncoiled ammonite *Scaphites*, with an inarticulate brachiopod attached in exactly the position one would expect, given the postulated life orientation of the ammonite. This position would hardly be in keeping with a crawling habit or with attachment after the death of the host. Seilacher (1954, 1960) showed how the presumably negatively geotropic growth of symbiotic epizoans could be used to determine the orientation of a host fossil in life.

In a similar way, I have argued (Ager, 1961*b*), from the general absence of epizoans from the cardinal areas of a Devonian spiriferid, that this part of the shell was, in life, closely pressed to the sea floor (Figure 5.3*B*). This is supported by the finding in the field of occasional specimens oriented in this way (Plate 7*B*).

SIX

Organic associates

CONTEMPORARY ASSOCIATIONS

It is said that one can judge a man by the company he keeps, and this is certainly true of fossils. In a way, this is again uniformitarianism; but instead of trying to apply our uniformitarianism directly to the fossil concerned (which may not be possible), we are applying it by way of the fossil's associates. This may give us the advantage of several complementary lines of approach.

Very often the associates of an organism are directly involved in its life through a symbiotic or antagonistic relationship. These relationships are not the concern of this chapter (but will be dealt with in Chapter 15). I am here concerned solely with what can be learned about the habits and habitat of a particular fossil from the other fossils which are found in the same bed.

If we are studying fossil X, which belongs to an extinct group, we may observe that it is frequently associated with fossils A, B, and C but never with D, E, and F. If the living equivalents of A, B, and C are all marine creatures, whereas the living equivalents of D, E, and F are all fresh-water forms, then it is logical to suppose that X also lived in the sea. For reasons of this kind, few paleontologists have ever doubted that the extinct graptolites were marine creatures.

Of a similar nature have been the endless arguments about the habitat of the earliest chordates. The observations relating to the

Agnatha remain ambiguous, but there seems little doubt that the first fishes with jaws lived in fresh water.

The above examples only provide evidence of the general nature of the organism's habitat, but other associations may also provide circumstantial evidence of the habits of the organism concerned. Laughbaum (1960) provided a neat example of this from the Lower Cretaceous Denton formation of northern Texas. He started with the uniformitarian assumption that a dominance of arenaceous forms in a foraminiferal assemblage indicates deposition under conditions of slightly reduced salinity. He also deduced from general geological evidence that the sea floor sloped down to the south and southeast. He then noted that the oyster *Gryphaea washitaensis* (which is otherwise present in all beds regardless of lithology) is not found with foraminiferal assemblages dominated by arenaceous forms. Then Laughbaum recorded that *Ostrea* (*Arctostrea*) *carinata* only occurs farther north than *G. washitaensis* and is almost exclusively restricted to limestones and marls. Unlike the *Gryphaea*, it is rare in shales but does occur with abundant arenaceous forams. *Ostrea* (*Lopha*) *quadriplicata* occurs in the same types of sediments as *O. carinata*, but also in shales, and generally does not occur as far south as that species. At certain northern localities, *O. quadriplicata* is the only oyster present. From all this, the following deductions can be made:

1. *Gryphaea washitaensis* could not tolerate reduced salinities.

2. *Ostrea carinata* could tolerate reduced salinities, but was sensitive to turbidity.

3. *Ostrea carinata* was probably restricted to shallower depths than *G. washitaensis*.

4. *Ostrea quadriplicata* could tolerate reduced salinity and turbid water but could not live in such deep water as either of the other species. This is expressed diagrammatically in Table 15.2 (see page 258).

Ruedemann (1934) made an association study of much broader scope. He recorded the rare fossils that are sometimes found associated with graptolites in what he termed "pure graptolitic shales." These included sponges, brachiopods, annelids, mollusks, and crustaceans, and Ruedemann showed that they correspond closely with the present-day fauna which is found attached to the floating *Sargassum* in the Sargasso Sea and the Gulf of Mexico. All the organisms, including the graptolites, were interpreted as epiplanktonic. Nearly all of them are small forms with thin chitinous shells. They are widely distributed in the black graptolitic shales, but are absent from contemporaneous shelf-sea deposits. They are sometimes associated with carbonaceous fragments which are interpreted as "seaweed," but they are never associated with benthonic pelecypods, bryozoa, or corals.

Comparable association observations in a completely different setting were those of Coleman (1957) in the Permian of Western Australia. He noted frequent associations of productoids with certain other brachiopods, various bryozoans, and the bizarre crinoid *Calceolispongia*. The productoids and the crinoids appear to have lived in dense and mutually exclusive (though adjacent) colonies, although certain productoids attached themselves to the crinoid stems during early life. Some of the large productoids in turn acted as hosts to the parasitic worm *Conchotrema* and to other brachiopods. Equally important but negative observations made by Coleman were that close associations of the brachiopods with pelecypods and gastropods are comparatively rare but, when the latter two groups are found, pectinids and bellerophontids are the most common. It may be noted that, presumably, both of these were free-swimming forms which did not compete directly with the brachiopods on the sea floor.

The mention of densely packed colonies serves to remind us that significant, and yet commonly overlooked, associates of a particular fossil are other members of the same species. Allowing for the possibilities of concentration by physical agencies, one can sometimes determine if a species was solitary or gregarious in habit. I have noted that the degree of gregariousness may even vary within a genus. Most species of the Lower Jurassic rhynchonellid *Gibbirhynchia* are notably gregarious, occurring in lenses, or "nests," each of a single species in all its age groups; but one species, *G. tiltonensis*, only occurs as scattered individuals (Ager, 1954). This was confirmed by Hallam (1955), who went on to make quantitative studies which seem to prove the colonial nature of some of the contemporary "nests" (1962). Rózycki (1948) distinguished three ecological groups of Upper Jurassic rhynchonellids in the Krakow-Czestochowa chain of Poland. The first was a group found associated with reefs; the second was a group which occurs, with other brachiopods, in layers above the reefs; the third was a group which occurs only as isolated individuals. I have observed somewhat similar distributions in the Middle and Upper Jurassic of the southern French Jura. One of Rózycki's most interesting observations was that similar species of different genera succeeded one another in particular ecological niches and associations.

So far my examples have been of fossil associations which have a fairly obvious paleoecological significance. But the great majority of observed fossil associations do not have this. They are merely the normal life associations of a particular environment, like the daisy, dandelion, and clover association of my lawns. As such they are commonly overlooked.

Trigonia and its allies, for example, seem to have had a restricted range of associates in the Mesozoic. A *Trigonia* association which is familiar to every British paleontologist is that of the "roach" in the Portland stone of the Upper Jurassic. *Trigonia gibbosa is* found there in great numbers with the turreted gastropod *Aptyxiella portlandica;* usually both are seen only as internal and external molds. These two fossils are known to geologists by the quarrymen's names of "horses' heads" and "Portland screws" respectively, and the "roach" is seen all over Britain as a rough building stone in canals, railway embankments, and the like. An almost exactly similar association and preservation is seen in an ornamental building stone all over the United States. This is the Lower Cretaceous shelly Cedar Park limestone of Texas, which is also packed with molds of *Trigonia* and a turreted gastropod. Though separated in time and space, the association is virtually identical.

Another common association is that of certain gastropods and nautiloids in lower Paleozoic rocks. This is seen, for instance, in the Beekmantown limestone of eastern Canada and in the equivalent upper Durness limestone of Scotland. Foerste (1936) observed of the lower Paleozoic faunas that where cephalopods are abundant, mobile gastropods are also likely to be abundant but sedentary brachiopods, corals, and bryozoa will probably not be found in quantity. Flower (1942a) went further and remarked: "In the early Paleozoic, cephalopods occur commonly with abundant gastropods and trilobites, but brachiopods, bryozoa, and pelecypods are either altogether absent or very rare." On the other hand, Miller and Furnish (1937), working on the Upper Ordovician of the northwestern United States, noted the same nautiloid-gastropod association, but this time with corals.

A fascinating, straightforward, and yet seldom-attempted study in fossiliferous rocks is the simple recording of the different fossil groups, bed by bed in tabular form, followed by analysis of these tables for significant associations. This is comparable to S. S. Buckman's method of "faunal analysis" (e.g., 1920); but by his reasoning, if A and B never occur together they must be of different ages, whereas here it is suggested that they probably lived in different habitats. Care has to be taken to eliminate derived fossils, or at least to make allowances for them in interpreting the results.

A more scientific approach to the same problem was demonstrated by R. G. Johnson (1962a). In a study of sixty-three species of Pennsylvanian invertebrates in 152 collections from western Illinois, he set out to recognize significant associations, using the chi-square test. The following is an example of a test of the independence of distribution of two brachiopods:

	Chonetes granulifer		
	Present	Absent	Total
Marginifera splendens			
Present	25	12	37
Absent	14	101	115
Total	39	113	152

If the two brachiopods were distributed independently, they would be expected to occur together ten times only. The hypothesis of independence was rejected at the .005 level of significance, so a positive bond of association is established.

As a result of this analysis, Johnson was able to recognize six main groups of species, falling into three associations: (1) a *Chonetina* association, perhaps living offshore on a firm substratum, (2) an *Orbiculoidea* association, perhaps living on a soft substratum in shallow water, and (3) a gastropod association, perhaps living at intermediate depths on a soft substratum with abundant plant debris.

ASSOCIATIONS WITHIN THE INDIVIDUAL

Association work of a different kind is that of the many paleontologists who have to deal with organisms which commonly scatter into many separate parts on death. Paleobotanists are particularly adept at studies of this kind. They are constantly seeking to prove or disprove that root A belonged to stem B and to compound leaf C. This is a morphological matter rather than an ecological one, but obviously the very first thing to do when studying a fossil association is to put together those parts which could have belonged to the same organism. The same problem, in a more difficult form, confronts the conodont workers, who are dealing with parts of an organism which is virtually unknown. A statistical approach may usefully be employed to estimate the likelihood that the varied morphological types in an association belonged to the same animal.

A simple example of this was Müller's demonstration (1959) that the horseshoe-shaped conodont *Westergaardodina* in the Upper Cambrian and Lower Ordovician is always associated with a ball-shaped structure which is assumed to have rested on top of it in life (Figure 6.1). The association is proved by the coincidence of proportional sizes; i.e., large "horseshoes" are associated with large "balls" and small with small. This kind of work is also useful paleoecologically in that it may give an indication of the degree of approach to a living community in a fossil assemblage.

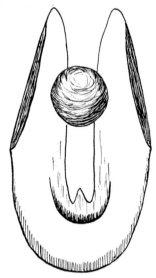

Figure 6.1   Association of the horseshoe-shaped conodont *Westergaardodina* and a ball-shaped structure, shown in the position it is thought to have occupied in life; lower Paleozoic, western Germany. (After Müller, 1959.)

SEASONAL ASSOCIATIONS

There remains a special type of association study which, to my knowledge, can only be illustrated by a unique series of examples. This is the use of fossil associations on single bedding planes as proof of the simultaneity of particular seasonal phenomena among the animals and plants of a past community. The examples are in that classic of paleoecology, Heer's *Die Urwelt der Schweiz* (1865, 1876).

Writing of the famous Miocene fossils of the finely laminated Oeningen beds near Lake Constance in Switzerland, Heer said:

On a slab from Oeningen side by side with the ripe delicately formed fruits of the *Podogonia*, winged ants are seen [Figure 6.2]. . . . The species . . . are most nearly allied to the large wood ant. . . . The winged individuals of the latter swarm between the beginning and the middle of the summer. . . . The winged ants lying beside the fruits of the *Podogonia* therefore supply evidence that these trees ripened their fruits in the summer . . . the season of flowering must have occurred very early in the spring; and in favour of this view we have a leafless poplar-twig which lies beside an equally bare twig of *Podogonia*. From this we learn further that in the *Podogonia* the flowers appeared before the leaves, in accordance with the well-known rule in very early-flowering trees and shrubs. At the end of March, however, they were in leaf; for we find a leaf with some willow-flowers on the same slab.

Thus Heer was able to deduce facets of the mode of life of the extinct plant *"Podogonia."*

When he considered only living plants, he was able to show that the seasonal features represented in the Oeningen beds were unlike those persisting in Switzerland at the present day but rather like those of latitudes much farther south—as in Madeira. Thus on a slab from the Schrotzburg, near Oeningen, he found flowers of the camphor tree (*Cinnamomum polymorphum*) lying close to the male flowers of the

FIGURE 6.2 Association of a flowering branch of *Podogonia knorri* with the male winged ant *"Formica lignitum,"* from the Miocene Oeningen beds of Lake Constance, Switzerland. (After Heer, 1865.)

willow (*Salix varians*) and near leaves of the plane, the liquidambar, and the maple. Therefore the first two had flowered at the same time, and planes had already unfolded their leaves. This state of affairs no longer prevails in Switzerland or anywhere in the temperate zone, where there is always a gap between the final fall of willow flowers and the appearance of leaves on the plane. In Madeira, however, the two phases overlap at about the end of March and also coincide with the flowering of the camphor trees. Similarly, poplar and plane flowers coincide in the Oeningen beds and in present-day Madeira, but are more than a month apart in present-day Switzerland.

The possible limitations in these arguments are obvious, but there are several different approaches involved in Heer's work, and this remarkably original line of reasoning is unique in paleoecology.

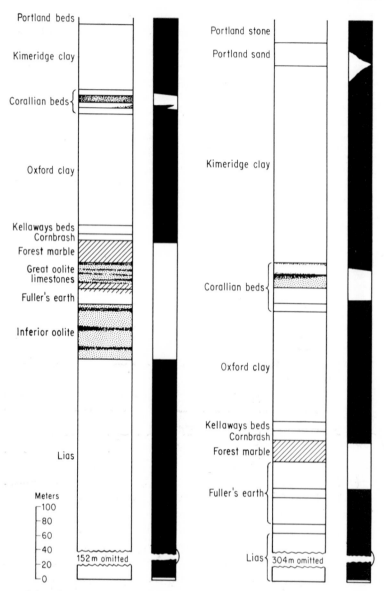

FIGURE 6.3 The Jurassic succession in Britain, showing the mutual exclusiveness of ammonite-bearing formations (black) and coral-bearing formations (stippled). (From Arkell, 1933; by courtesy of Oxford University Press.)

NEGATIVE EVIDENCE

This is a field of study where negative results may also be very instructive. For instance, Arkell (1933) pointed out that in Jurassic rocks, ammonites are almost never found with autochthonous corals. This is demonstrated for the British Jurassic succession in Figure 6.3. It was confirmed in the Texas Cretaceous by G. Scott (1940). Similarly, Müller (1959) has stated that conodonts are never found with fusulinids. Again,

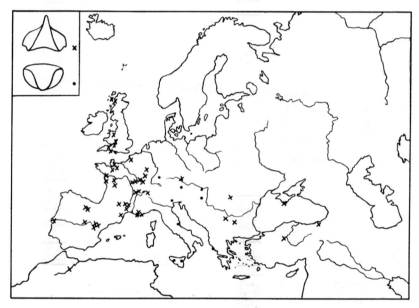

FIGURE 6.4 Mutually exclusive distribution of sharply uniplicate rhynchonellids (crosses) and sulcate forms (dots) in the European Pliensbachian (Lower Jurassic).

Elliott (1950) noted the rarity of brachiopods on post-Paleozoic coral reefs, which he suggested might be caused by the vulnerability of the very localized brachiopod larvae to the carnivorous coral polyps.

In my own work on Mesozoic brachiopods, I have noted several mutually exclusive distributions. Figure 6.4 shows how the sharply uniplicate *Homoeorhynchia* is rarely if ever found with sulcate rhynchonellids or terebratulids in the European Pliensbachian (Lower Jurassic).

Among the vertebrates, negative evidence of the same kind disproved the suggestion that the Permian reptile *Sphenacodon* was the female equivalent of the well-known *Dimetrodon*. Romer and Price (1940)

pointed out that the two genera are never found together, but were in fact separated in life by several hundred kilometers and a broad sea. This hardly suggests a successful marriage.

Finally, in the plant kingdom, Rezak (1959) noted an inverse relationship between two calcareous algae in the Permian of Saudi Arabia. Core samples from a deep well showed that where *Gymnocodium* was abundant in the lower part of the section, *Epimastopora* was absent or rare, whereas higher up, the roles were reversed. Rezak interpreted this as reflecting a decreasing depth of water through time and compared it with depth zonation among living algae.

PSEUDOASSOCIATIONS

The problems of derived fossils in paleoecology are immense. It is virtually impossible in many cases to prove that all the fossils found in one bed are of the same age and from the same environment. Sometimes we tend to ignore the possibility of derivation, and sometimes we tend to use it too freely to explain awkward members of an assemblage.

Micropaleontologists are particularly aware of these problems, since minute organisms are so easily reworked and redeposited with sediment. Eva Hanzlíková (1953) used the term *pseudoassociations* for assemblages of indigenous and derived forams in the Carpathian Mountains of Czechoslovakia. She found that Paleogene faunas there often contain a strong admixture of Upper Cretaceous forms, which she noted were particularly abundant in red clays.

G. F. Elliott (1956a) has drawn attention to the fact that it is not always possible to depend on the criterion of mechanical wear, for transport of brachiopods may occur without their showing any signs of abrasion, size grading, or parallel orientation, and even postmortem concentrations of shells of one species are possible by purely mechanical processes. In exceptional circumstances, the criterion of mechanical wear can be completely misleading, because the younger fossils may be more worn than the older ones. This may occur through the reworking of thick fossiliferous beds, producing a condensed deposit in which the later fossils have suffered more wear than the hardly disturbed specimens at the bottom of the section (Figure 6.5).

Too often we tend to think of derived fossils as rare phenomena, whereas if we consider present-day evidence, we find that in particular areas they are very common indeed. This is especially true where the sea is eroding unconsolidated fossiliferous sediments, as must have happened over and over again in the stratigraphical record. Most paleontologists know coast lines with tumbling cliffs of Tertiary sediments and fossils mixed with recent shells along the strandline. Crouch (1954) reported that nearly half the samples he took off Long Beach, California, contained fossil as well as Recent forams, some of them as old as Miocene. The same is true for older consolidated strata—such as the Chalk, or even Paleozoic limestones—so long as the fossils are easily separable from their matrix. Usually the difference in preservation is sufficient to distinguish the fossil from the modern organism without difficulty, but this would not be so when both had been buried together for millions

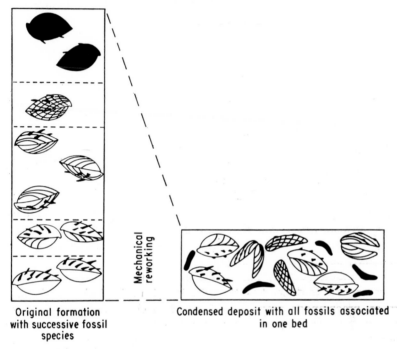

Original formation
with successive fossil
species

Condensed deposit with all fossils associated
in one bed

FIGURE 6.5 Idealized sections showing how the reworking of a fossiliferous succession to produce a condensed deposit may result in the younger fossils suffering more wear than the older.

of years. The allied problem of specimens carried after death from their living environments is discussed elsewhere.

Another, less obvious way in which we may get a misleading association of small fossils is in the excreta of larger animals. It has been suggested that some of the associations of conodonts, which have been interpreted as constituting a single animal, may in fact be the remains of several different conodont-bearing animals which were eaten by the same predator and passed out together in its excreta. W. S. Bucher (1929) suggested this explanation for an association of conodonts with sponge spicules in the Mississippian of Ohio, and other excretory assemblages were described by E. P. Du Bois (1943). H. W. Scott (1942) rejected such explanations, however, for assemblages which consisted of perfectly balanced sets of different conodont types. Such explanations are even more doubtful when the same constituents, in the same numbers, are found in widely separated associations, as in the cases quoted by F. H. T. Rhodes (1952).

SEVEN

Evidence of activity

APART from obvious fossils in the sense of the actual remains of animals and plants, we can also learn a great deal about their past life from various signs of their activity which we may find in the rocks. Some paleontologists like to distinguish between the former, which they call *body fossils* (*Körperfossilien*), and the latter, which they call *trace fossils* (*Spurenfossilien*). The latter have been studied in great detail by a series of Germans and Austrians, notably Fuchs (1895), Richter (1931, 1936, 1941), Krejci-Graf (1932), Abel (1935), and most recently by Seilacher (1953, 1958, 1962). It has been argued that these are not ecological matters at all, but aspects of ethology, in the sense of the study of habits. However, this is little more than a semantic quibble and need not concern us here.

The study has become almost a science on its own (ichnology, or palichnology), and it is sometimes so elevated in importance as to be the main paleoecological subject. These phenomena are, of course, extremely important as direct evidence of an organism's actions during life; but many of them are extremely rare, and they hardly ever give us precise evidence of the nature of the organism which made them.

Seilacher (1953) distinguished five main groups of trace fossils as follows:

Ruhespuren, or *resting traces:* the marks made by animals at rest in one place

Kriechspuren, or *crawling traces:* the marks made by animals moving across soft sediment

105

Weidespuren, or *browsing traces:* the marks made by animals feeding
on the surface

Fressbauten, or *feeding structures:* the burrows, etc., made by animals moving through sediment while feeding

Wohnbauten, or *dwelling structures:* the burrows, etc., made by animals for habitation

Seilacher later prepared what he called *Spurenspektren* (e.g., 1958),
on which he plotted the relative abundance of the different kinds of
trace fossils in particular types of sediment. He showed, for instance,
that flysch deposits have an exceptionally high proportion of *Weidespuren*, whereas epicontinental deposits tend to have few of these but
a large proportion of *Fressbauten*. These spurenspektren (or trace spec-
tra) are simple pie diagrams based on the abundance of taxa and not
on the abundance of individuals.

For the present purpose we will subdivide trace fossils and other
evidence of organic activity into the following categories:

1. Tracks and trails
2. Burrows and borings
3. Eggs and excrement
4. Other evidence

This is an artificial subdivision, proposed for convenience and to avoid
unnecessary terminology. The categories will be considered in turn.

TRACKS AND TRAILS

Generally we can say that the former signify vertebrates and the
latter signify invertebrates.

Tracks

This term is used here in the popular sense for the marks made by
quadrupedal or bipedal animals walking over soft sediment. Any number
of examples are known, most made by Paleozoic and Mesozoic reptiles and
amphibians, but it is not often possible to attribute the tracks to particular animals. Seilacher (1953) used the terms *ichnogenus* and *ichno-
species* for named trace fossils, and emphasized that a trace fossil need
not correspond with a "body" genus or species in the Linnaean sense. A
famous ichnogenus for a track is *Cheirotherium* from the Trias of western
Europe, which has caused considerable discussion since it was first described in 1835. The prints are large and handlike, but the "thumbs"
point outward. This caused Charles Lyell to interpret them as the tracks
of a froglike animal which crossed its legs as it walked! However, they
are now known to belong to dinosaurs—possibly to *Plateosaurus*, which
is discussed later in another connection (see page 174).

Ellenberger and Ellenberger have recently described a slab from the Upper Trias of Basutoland (1960) on which there are no fewer than eight different lines of footprints, belonging to at least five different kinds of animals.

In a number of cases, tracks have been used to determine the exact gait of particular tetrapods (Figure 7.1), and of course they provide indisputable evidence that the animals concerned actually lived in the area where the tracks are found. Isolated finds provide fascinating glimpses of precise moments in the past, as when a dinosaur, walking in the rain, stepped into a pool of water. Perhaps most intriguing of all are the ground-sloth tracks found in the courtyard of the prison at Car-

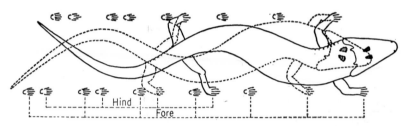

FIGURE 7.1 The fishlike mode of locomotion of the Carboniferous amphibian *Eogyrinus*, as deduced from its footprints. (From D. M. S. Watson, 1951; by courtesy of the author and Yale University Press.)

son City, Nevada, which Mark Twain attributed to the erratic course of a drunken man!

It should be borne in mind that not only the feet but also the tail may make preservable impressions, and at least one example is known of the impression of the rump of a dinosaur as it sat down. Presumably this would come within Seilacher's category of resting traces. In the modern intertidal sediments of the Wash in eastern England, I have seen the groove actually being made by a seal dragging its body across the surface. Also, my colleague Dr. Graham Evans has drawn my attention to such other potential trace fossils as the scratches made by crabs' claws, the swish marks made by birds' tails, and the peck marks by their beaks. All of these would be difficult *problematica* in the stratigraphical record.

Trails

This term is taken to mean the marks left by crawling organisms in soft sediments. Such marks are very common in the stratified rocks, but only very rarely can they be referred to the animal which made them, and even the phylum responsible is sometimes a matter of dispute. For instance, the markings called *"Arthraria,"* which are known from Cambrian to Devonian rocks, were attributed by Fenton and Fenton (1934*a*) to two separate organisms, an annelid and a gastropod. Conversely, we know that related living organisms may leave very different trails.

Caster showed in a series of papers (e.g., 1944) that many supposed vertebrate tracks were, in fact, trails made by the king crab *Limulus* and its allies. The best possible proof of the nature of the organism which made these markings was produced by Walther (1904), who described trails from the Solenhofen stone of Bavaria actually leading to fossil king crabs. Flower (1942*a*) also described nautiloid shells at the end of trails in the Ordovician of Kentucky.

Unlike the tracks of vertebrates, trails cannot usually be expected to demonstrate the mode of progression of the animal concerned; but Ringueberg (1886) did claim that certain trails from the Medina group of New York were produced by a jumping trilobite, and Vokes and Brown (1944) suggested that trails in the Cretaceous of Montana may have been made by a bouncing dibranchiate cephalopod! More seriously, Seilacher (personal communication, 1962) has made detailed studies of trilobite trails and concluded that they rarely jumped, they sometimes walked straight forward, or, more commonly, they walked slightly obliquely dragging one set of legs behind them to rake the mud surface for food.

Certain trails and other organic markings seem to be characteristic of particular environments. The most famous of these is perhaps the whole assemblage of markings found commonly in the Alpine flysch and often thought to represent abyssal conditions, e.g., by Seilacher (1958). A selection of Seilacher's typical trace fossils from the flysch is shown in Figure 7.2. Henbest (1960) has discovered very similar trails and burrows in what were certainly shallow, well-aerated water sediments in the Pennsylvanian of Arkansas.

An interesting excursion into experimental science was made by McKee (1947), in studying possible modern analogues of the tracks and trails of the Permian Coconino sandstone of northern Arizona. He constructed a long, narrow trough in which various animals were persuaded to move from a darkened to a sunlit section across a ridge of sand comparable to that of the formation studied. An intriguing feature of the Coconino footprints is that they almost always run uphill on the steeply inclined bedding planes of this dune sandstone. It was found that several species of lizards, large millepedes, scorpions, and wood lice all left marks comparable to the fossil marks, but that the modern animals' marks were only similarly preserved (with sharp outlines) in loose, dry sand. It was also observed that sliding and slumping tended to obliterate downhill tracks on steep slopes (28°) like those on the lee sides of dunes. I have noticed the same effect in the footprints of waders on beaches and coastal sand dunes. So the implausible idiosyncrasy of the Permian animals in always walking uphill is explained (as are so many things in paleontology) as a matter of preservation.

FIGURE 7.2 Trace fossils from Cretaceous and Tertiary flysch deposits. A, *Taphrhelminthopsis;* B, *Helminthopsis;* C, *Helminthoida;* D, *Polykampton;* E, *Palaeodictyon;* F, *Muensteria;* G, *Medusina;* H, *Taenidium;* I, *Gyrophyllites.* (After Seilacher, 1958; by courtesy of the author.)

The great center for research on the "paleontology of the present" has always been the Senckenberg am Meer Institute at Wilhelmshaven (see page 35). In this tradition W. Häntzchel has there recorded many observations of modern fossilizable phenomena (e.g., 1956), including numerous descriptions of modern trails which are very useful in interpreting trace fossils. He has also drawn attention to other relevant factors, such as the way in which the traces made by a particular animal may differ according to the type and condition of the sediment in which they are found (Häntzschel, 1955).

The Russians have been doing a great deal of work in this field, notably with their research ship *Vitiaz,* and have put on record many interesting observations on present-day sea life. A notable Russian photograph which has received a great deal of publicity shows the trail of an unknown animal on the floor of one of the deepest parts of the Pacific (Vyalov and Zenkevich, 1961). This is reproduced in the frontispiece through the kindness of Academician Vyalov.

BURROWS AND BORINGS

The distinction drawn here is between burrows in soft sediments and borings in solid rock or in other organisms. Both may be for either habitation or feeding.

Burrows

These are the most common of all trace fossils; in fact, they are probably more common than most geologists realize. When studied closely enough, a large proportion of shallow-water sediments show signs of *bioturbation,* or disturbance by burrowing organisms. An even greater proportion of deposits probably were disturbed in this way but preserve no record of it simply because of the uniformity of the sediment.

When such burrows are seen, they are usually attributed to "worms" (in the broadest sense), but it must be realized that many of them were made by organisms such as mollusks, arthropods, and echinoderms. It must also be realized how very abundant burrowing organisms are in present-day shallow-water sediments. Virtually all the permanent macrofauna of intertidal beaches burrow to some extent.

Though it is not always possible to be certain about the function of a particular structure, we may distinguish between the burrows made by organisms for habitation—such as those of *Lingula*—and the burrows made by animals passing through soft sediment as their normal way of life—such as those of the common earthworm. These are the *Wohnbauten* and *Fressbauten,* respectively, of Seilacher (1953). In the first category we have such common fossils as the U-shaped tubes usually called *Arenicolites,* from their resemblance to the burrows of the common lugworm *Arenicola.* Figure 7.3 shows a selection of fossil burrows of this kind.

Many habitation burrows are lined in various ways, often with shell fragments, like the one described by Hallam (1960b). Some of their inhabitants—like living forms—can be shown to have been highly selective in the fragments used. Bather (1911) described English Cretaceous worms of which some used only fish debris to line their burrows, others used plant fragments, and at least one used only echinoderm ossicles. The various sorts of material never seem to have been mixed together. These habits were later confirmed in Swedish specimens by Grönwall (1912).

Modern habitation burrows often have various patterns in the sediment around their apertures, produced by the feeding action of the

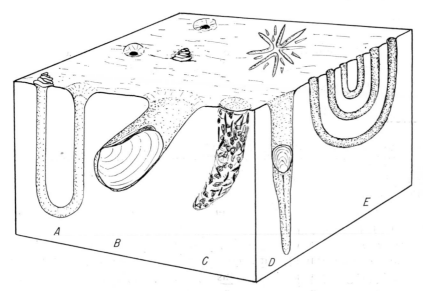

Figure 7.3 Fossil burrows. (From various sources.) **A,** *Arenicolites;* **B,** *Edmondia;* **C,** *Terebella;* **D,** *Lingula;* **E,** *Corophioides.*

organism—for example, the stellate pattern made by the pelecypod *Scrobicularia.* These belong to Seilacher's *Weidespuren* category. Many trace fossils have been attributed to this form of activity.

Habitation excavations of a different type are the structures in lower Paleozoic rocks which have been called *Cruziana.* Abel (1935) showed that these were the resting burrows, or "nests" of trilobites. Fenton and Fenton (1937) attributed such structures in Lower Cambrian sediments to the work of mesonacid trilobites (Figure 7.4), and Caster (1957) reported the finding of several *Calymene* specimens *in situ* in similar structures in the Ordovician of the Cincinnati area. Crabs can easily be watched making similar excavations in modern mud flats.

Although we tend to think of fossil burrows as the work of marine organisms, there are also records of land forms. Perhaps the most remarkable burrows ever described were in continental sediments. These were the "devil's corkscrews" found in the Miocene of Nebraska and latinized by Barbour (1894) as *Daimonelix*. These are large, vertical, spiral structures, often 2 m long, each of which terminates in an equally long straight tunnel (Figure 7.5). They are nowadays thought to be the

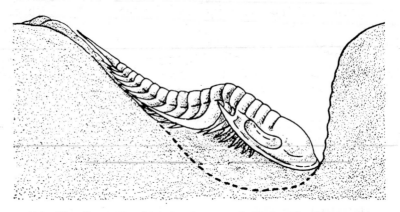

FIGURE 7.4 *Olenellus* restored as in the act of digging the burrow known as *Cruziana jenningsi*. The broken line shows the final depth of the burrow. (From Fenton and Fenton, 1937; by courtesy of *American Midland Naturalist*.)

FIGURE 7.5 *Daimonelix*, the burrow attributed to an early beaver from the Miocene of Nebraska. (From a photograph in Barbour, 1894.)

PLATE 4 **Organic activity in hard and soft sea floors.**
Top, bored and oyster-encrusted surface, Bajocian (Middle Jurassic), near Chelten-
ham, Gloucestershire, England. ×¾. *Bottom,* bioturbated sandstone with bedding
destroyed by burrowing organisms, lower Eocene, Alum Bay, Isle of Wight, England. ×½.

work of an early beaver, *Steneofiber,* the remains of which were found in the basal section of one burrow, though some confusion was caused by the finding also of parts of the skeleton of a much larger carnivore in another burrow. This had apparently occupied a beaver burrow and then been drowned in a sudden flood.

Confirmatory evidence of the nature of these structures was provided by Wood and Wood (1933) who described similar spirals from the Pleistocene of Rock Creek, Texas, containing the remains of a prairie dog, a rabbit, and an insectivore.

D. J. C. Laming (personal communication) also found some remarkable land burrows, in Permo-Triassic red beds in south Devon, England. These were up to 17 cm across and could be traced for up to 2 m through the beds, both along and across the bedding.

This brings us to the second category, burrows made by various organisms as they pushed or ate their way through soft sediment; for Laming's burrows are obviously of this type.

Usually burrows are only noticeable if there are sharp variations in the nature of the sediment, so that the sediment filling the burrows contrasts with that around. Such structures are common in rocks of all ages, but often show up in thin sections only, or when treated by the observer, or under special conditions of weathering. The bioturbation in Plate 4, *bottom,* is only visible as shown when the rock is smoothed and wetted. A very comparable example from the Paleozoic was figured by Kuenen (1961).

A supposed feeding burrow of a remarkably regular type is *Chondrites,* which is common in Paleozoic and early Mesozoic rocks. This was the subject of a detailed study by Scott Simpson (1957). The structure descends through the rock and branches out in all directions along a particular bedding plane (Figure 7.6). Simpson suggested that *Chondrites* fed from a fixed point on the surface and explored a layer of food-bearing sediment to the maximum extent possible in the primary branches of the burrow. It constantly worked backward from these extreme points, exploring the sediment sideways as it did so. Through some process not yet understood, the animal was always able to terminate one branch of its burrow just before meeting an earlier branch. No living organism is known to feed in this way. Plate 5 shows a similar type of feeding burrow from the Cretaceous, though without the lateral passages.

Though they are not burrows in the usual sense of the word, we may also include here the root traces of plants, which often look remarkably like the burrows of animals, and are probably often mistaken for them. They are seen, for example, in the famous Eocene colored sands of

Alum Bay in the Isle of Wight. They exist only where the plant remains themselves have disappeared and therefore tell us nothing about the ecology of a particular organism, though they do tell us something about the environment.

Borings

This term is here restricted to holes made by organisms in hard rocks and shells, either for protection or as parasites in search of food. Borings in already-lithified sediments are likely to be preserved but are also likely to be restricted to particular horizons. They are especially common

FIGURE 7.6 Reconstruction of the *Chondrites* system of burrows. (From Scott Simpson, 1957; by courtesy of the author and the Geological Society of London.)

where a hard rock surface was exposed on the sea floor for a time before being covered by transgressive marine deposits. Familiar examples in the British succession exist below the transgressive Upper Bajocian strata (Middle Jurassic) in the Cotswolds and Mendips, and below the transgressive Eocene in the London basin (Figure 7.7 and Plate 4, *top*).

A different kind of boring activity by organisms in a transgressive sea was recorded by Rioult (1958). He described and figured the etched surfaces of Paleozoic sandstones and quartzites immediately below unconformable Jurassic sediments in the May-sur-Orne syncline in northwest France. These very old and hard rocks are often covered with "pockmarks"; Rioult suggested these might have been produced by the action of simple algae living in the tidal zone and forming the food of the abundant herbivorous gastropods which are found in pockets at this level.

Borings in shells are very common and can be attributed to many different groups of animals, including gastropods, sponges, "worms," and arthropods. As with burrows, it is often difficult to distinguish between borings for habitation and those for feeding. A typical severely bored shell from the Eocene is shown in Plate 6F. This can be blamed

PLATE 5   Fossil feeding burrows.
Radiating burrows, presumably made by a wormlike creature exploring a particular horizon from one point on the surface; Aptian (Lower Cretaceous), near Shanklin, Isle of Wight, England. ×⅓.

on one of the best-known boring organisms, the monaxonid sponge *Cliona*, which is known in rocks of all ages from Silurian to Cenozoic. Thomas (1911) described some in Devonian brachiopod shells from Iowa which showed that the sponge bored for protection and not for food. Fenton and Fenton (1932*a*) described the same phenomena from the same area and showed how the position of the borings in the shells gave evidence of the orientation of the hosts during life. As previously mentioned, this is one of the lines of evidence which supported the

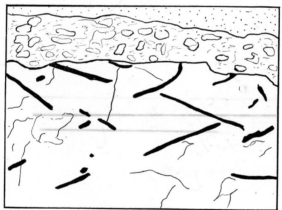

FIGURE 7.7 Borings in rocky sea floors below transgressive deposits. *Top*, in Middle Bajocian limestone below transgressive Upper Bajocian (Middle Jurassic), Cotswolds, England. *Bottom*, in Upper Cretaceous Chalk below transgressive lower Eocene gravels, Harefield, west of London. (Drawn from photographs.)

hypothesis that the large *Atrypa* shells from this area lay on their flat ventral valves during adult life (see page 89).

Joysey (1959) has recently described a single specimen of the echinoid *Echinocorys* from the English Chalk which contains in its test

PLATE 6   Life and death of fossil pelecypods.

A–D, different stages in the gaping of pelecypod valves after death. A, *Sinodia suborbicularis* with color bands, Lower Oligocene, Colwell Bay, Isle of Wight. B, *Anodonta cygnea,* Pleistocene (last interglacial), Erith, Kent. C, *Glycimeris brevirostris,* lower Eocene, Bognor Regis, Sussex. D, *Cardinia listeri,* Lower Jurassic, Frodingham, Lincolnshire.

E, *Gryphaea dilatata,* Upper Jurassic, near Weymouth, Dorset. Valves closed; serpulid worms on the left valve and oyster spats on the right.

F, *Ostrea bellovacina,* lower Eocene, Charlton, Kent. Valves closed; many borings made by parasitic sponges.

All ×⅔ approximately.

118

borings made by many different organisms. He attributed them to cirripedes, phoronids, and echiuroids, and possibly also to a pelecypod, a polychaete, other "worms," and sponges.

Apart from borings in shells, there are many records of borings in fossil wood. One of the best-known examples is in the London clay (lower Eocene) of Sheppey in the Thames estuary, where there occur great masses of driftwood bored through and through by the "shipworm" *Teredo* and still containing the shells of that mollusk (see page 193). Further examples of borings will be discussed in Chapter 15.

EGGS AND EXCREMENT

Although eggs and other reproductive structures differ importantly from the other matters discussed in this chapter, they are evidence of activity of a special kind and are not body fossils as generally understood. They are also often confused with fecal pellets; hence the strange juxtaposition in the heading above.

Clearly there is no problem about the famous *Proceratops* eggs from the Cretaceous of Mongolia, described in detail by van Straelen (1925, 1928), which throw much light on the habits of that dinosaur. There is no doubt about the bird's egg from Miocene tuffaceous marls in Fiji, described by Ladd (1934), which still had its original speckled color pattern. There is even less doubt about the giant *Aepyornis* eggs of Madagascar (one of which hatched so alarmingly for the collector in H. G. Wells's short story). But the tiny eggs of invertebrates are much more debatable.

Two good examples of minute reproductive bodies come from Ordovician rocks in the British Isles. Gertrude Elles (1940) described a variety of structures found associated with graptolites and known by the general name of *graptogonophores*. She showed these to be almost certainly reproductive in character. The most interesting of them are the *saccoids* (Figure 7.8), which are direct outgrowths of the thecae and which are often associated with vast numbers of siculae, i.e., the initial stages of new colonies. Alan Wood (1946) described structures from the Lower Ordovician of north Wales which he interpreted as sponge embryos comparable to modern forms.

Fossil excreta are probably extremely abundant in the rocks, but are not often recognized and do not tell us much about the mode of life of the producing organism. Excreta undoubtedly form a major constituent of many of the "pellet limestones" now being distinguished by sedimentologists.

Common in the older rocks is the ovoid body known as *Tomaculum*, which has been variously regarded as seaweed vesicles, egg cases of various groups, and fecal pellets. Richter and Richter (1939) produced several reasons for regarding it as the fecal pellets of trilobites.

For modern comparisons there are a useful series of papers by H. B. Moore describing the fecal pellets of various living groups. These are listed and summarized in Moore's contribution (1939, 1955) to the symposium on Recent marine sediments organized by the American Association of Petroleum Geologists.

The term *coprolite* is usually restricted to the excreta of vertebrates. Coprolites are large enough to be readily recognized, and often provide

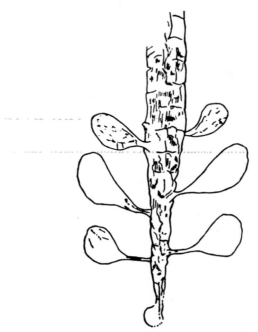

Figure 7.8 The Ordovician graptolite *Diplograptus*, with graptogonophores of saccoid type. (From G. L. Elles, 1940; by courtesy of *Geological Magazine*.)

much ecological information in that they tell us what the animal (if it is identified) actually ate. For this reason it is thought that the Mesozoic ichthyosaurs included belemnites in their diet. Similarly Wetmore (1943) described a coprolite from the Miocene of Maryland, which he attributed to a large fish or crocodile and which showed numerous impressions of feathers, implying a bird-eating habit.

Many coprolites show distinctive markings—grooves and ridges—which enable them to be attributed with more confidence to particular creatures. Matley (1939) described a number of coprolites from the Maleri beds of India, which he was able to identify as belonging to the lungfish *Ceratodus*.

We may also include under this heading such objects as worm casts, which are produced by the worm's extrusion of digested sediment in the process of burrowing through it. Shrock (1935) described very abundant worm casts from the Mississippian Salem limestone of Indiana. He observed that much of the limestone "must have passed through the bodies of worms at one time or another."

Not all such castings are necessarily the work of worms. Fenton and Fenton (1934*b*) reexamined the castings known as *Lumbricaria* in the Upper Jurassic Solenhofen stone of Bavaria, and concluded that they more closely resembled the castings produced by the holothurian *Leptosynapta inhaerens*, which lives in intertidal flats around Puget Sound (and elsewhere) at the present day.

OTHER EVIDENCE

There are many other isolated observations which can only be included here. These range from the Cretaceous wasp nest from Utah described by Brown (1941) to the bones gnawed by hyenas in the Pleistocene cave earth of Kent's Cavern in Devon.

Most of these finds serve merely to confirm the hypothesis that animals in the past had habits similar to those of living forms. Thus we know that certain pelecypods have secreted pearls at least since the beginning of Mesozoic times; and during the same period, certain reptiles and birds have used gastroliths, or stomach stones, to aid their digestion.[1] A final "inorganic fossil" may be included: the stone axe made by early man, which provides the chief record of his activities during the greater part of his history.

I may point out, in passing to a chapter on associated sediments, that the most obvious record of organic activity in the stratigraphical column is the sediments themselves, even though all trace of organisms may be lost. This is particularly significant in Precambrian rocks, where deposits such as limestones, ironstones, and graphite schists have been attributed to organic activity. In the case of carbonaceous material, considerable support for an organic origin has been forthcoming in recent

[1] Frizzell and Exline (1958) and Frizzell and Horton (1961) described fossil crustacean gastroliths from the Eocene of Texas and Louisiana, though these are concretionary and probably served a different function from those of the vertebrates. Very similar concretions are known in present-day lobsters and crayfish.

years through the study of isotope ratios, particularly the ratio C^{12}/C^{13}. There has been much dispute over the nature of the evidence, but the Finnish geologist K. Rankama (1954) has been the chief protagonist of the approach and has summarized the evidence. He placed the lower limit of the above ratio in biogenic carbon at 90.5, and concluded that —in the absence of contradictory evidence—carbon in shales, slates, and schists is biogenic if its isotope ratio comes above that limit.

EIGHT

Associated sediments

The study of the sediments in which the fossils occur is perhaps the most obvious approach in paleoecology. Clearly this is almost the only way to study the environments in which the organisms lived, and many papers on paleoecology concentrate almost entirely on this aspect of the subject, e.g., R. C. Moore's survey, "Modern Methods in Paleoecology" (1957). However, I do not feel that discussion of the sediments themselves has a place in a textbook on paleoecology. The sedimentologist is just as much concerned with environments as the paleoecologist, but no worthwhile treatment of his side of the subject is possible here.

What I do want to consider here are studies in which the faunas and floras have been directly related in some way to the sediments which contain them, as in the example shown in Plate 1 (page 17). Although this is an obvious approach, surprisingly little has been done about it except in a superficial way. There are vague general statements, such as "Ammonites are most common in clays," but there are very few detailed correlated studies on fossils and sediments. This results from the inevitable specialization of research; paleontologists are usually unwilling or unable to do the sedimentology, and sedimentologists are always unwilling to tackle the paleontology. Though I cannot speak for the disinclination of most general geologists toward paleontological matters, every paleontologist is only too aware that the vast detail of paleon-

123

tological research is such as to exclude the possibility of worthwhile studies on the sediments in which the fossils occur.

I frequently hear pleas for a paleontologist to study the fossils associated with a particularly intriguing sedimentary-facies change, or for a sedimentologist to seek an explanation in the rocks for some anomalous fossil distribution. Unfortunately, such invitations usually mean that the second specialist (who probably has his own commitments anyway) is called upon merely to provide a service for the first specialist, and not surprisingly, he is usually unwilling to cooperate.

Alternatively, if the paleontological and sedimentary studies of a particular problem are done at different times, as is commonly the case, then the older study almost invariably becomes out of date or is otherwise inadequate or oriented in a different way, so that the two studies cannot be properly correlated.

Usually the observations which can be useful are in the form of asides buried deeply in great thicknesses of morphological paleontology, and for this reason the literature is almost incapable of synthesis. Even if this were not so, such comments are often of doubtful validity, being founded on limited observations and on insufficient consideration of other factors. To say that a certain fossil "occurs most commonly in limestones" may mean that its optimum environment was a limestone-depositing sea, but could mean one or more other things instead. It could mean that the author looked at more limestones than shales or that there was more limestone exposed in his area; it could mean that the fossil concerned was better preserved in limestones or more obvious to the collector. It could mean a hundred other things besides, and even then the observation is inadequate, for it tells us nothing at all about the sediment except that it is made of calcium carbonate and could be anything from a shallow-water calcarenite or lagoonal pisolite to a deep-water calcilutite.

Bearing in mind all these difficulties, the relationship of fossils to their enclosing sediments may be considered under three headings: (1) composition of sediments, (2) texture of sediments, and (3) sedimentation structures. Again, these divisions are rather artificial but are convenient for the present purpose.

COMPOSITION OF SEDIMENTS

The majority of paleoecological studies in which the sediments are considered treat them only in a very general way—as limestones, shales, and so on. In a study of this kind of agnostid trilobites, Howell and Resser (1933) made the following observations on sedimentary preferences:

Of 216 species,
28 were found in sandstones,
of which 5 were found *only* in sandstones;
137 were found in limestones,
of which 61 were found *only* in limestones;
and 145 were found in shales,
of which 81 were found *only* in shales.

They also noted that more occurred in black shales and slates than in blue or green shales and slates. Similar observations have been made for other trilobites. It has also been observed that species occurring in shales tend to have a thinner exoskeleton than those in limestones but the reverse is not necessarily true.

Comparable observations on another group were those of Mojsisovics (1882, 1899) on Triassic ammonites in the Alps and Himalayas. He noted a coincidence of smooth forms with limestone deposits having a low clay content and of ornamented forms with muddier sediments. Diener (1895) drew the same distinction in comparing the Middle Triassic ammonites of the limestone crags of Chitichun in India with those of the main Himalayan region.

Negative evidence is also often useful in this connection. Guillaume (1927) commented on the remarkable independence of facies displayed by the pelecypod *Posidonia ornati* (= *Posidonomya alpina*) in the Middle Jurassic of France. It occurs abundantly in argillaceous sediments but is equally common in limestones of all kinds, in sandstones, and in ferruginous sediments. All this suggests the ubiquity of a pelagic organism, and R. P. S. Jefferies (personal communication) has confirmation, from other lines of evidence, of a free-swimming mode of life in *Posidonia*.

It is to be expected that some types of fossils are far more likely than others to show a constant relationship with the type of sediment in which they occur. Obviously, benthonic animals, which are intimately associated with the bottom sediments, are more likely to be controlled by them than are pelagic forms. This is probably the main reason why pelagic forms, such as ammonoids, are so much more widespread geographically and therefore so much more useful stratigraphically. This tendency for pelagic forms to be more independent of sedimentary facies is often obscured by other factors. The graptolites, which are generally thought to have been planktonic or epiplanktonic, are nevertheless most characteristic of a restricted sedimentary facies of dark slates and shales. This is probably a reflection, not of the habitat of the graptolites, but of the environment in which their remains are likely to have been preserved in large numbers. In the shallower waters of more varied sedimentation, both the fragility of the graptolite skeletons and the activities of scavengers are likely to have operated against the fossilization of their remains. In quieter waters, the rate of sedimentation is likely to have been the deciding factor. It should always be remembered that the abundance of any fossil species is a reflection partly of its original abundance and partly of the rate at which the sediments accumulated. Often the second factor is far more important than the first.

C. Collinson has observed (personal communication) that Mississippian conodonts in the type sections of western Illinois are remarkably independent of sedimentary facies. They occur in all kinds of sediment, and their frequency can be attributed only to the rate of deposition.

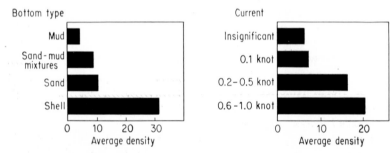

Figure 8.1 Relationship of the average density of individuals of *Mercenaria mercenaria*, the bottom type, and the current in Chincoteague Bay, Maryland. (After H. W. Wells, 1957.)

This evidence may be used also as an argument for a pelagic mode of life for the mysterious conodonts.

Benthonic organisms are therefore our most promising field of research here, and several studies on modern benthos suggest possible lines of approach. A few of these follow.

H. W. Wells (1957) produced clear evidence of a close correlation of bottom sediment type with the abundance of the quahog, *Mercenaria mercenaria*, in Chincoteague Bay, Maryland (Figure 8.1). He showed that the abundance of this pelecypod decreases progressively in the passage from a shelly bottom to sand, to sandy mud, to mud. This decrease also corresponds with decreasing current strength, and the two factors are, no doubt, closely connected.

A similar study was made of the mollusks living on the sea floor around the Rhone delta by van Straaten (1960). He showed that bottom texture and sediment supply are two of the main factors determining mollusk distribution. The abundance of specimens on different types of bottom is shown in Figure 8.2.

Sorgenfrei (1958) pointed out that certain modern mollusks, such as *Ostrea edulis* and species of the genera *Solen, Patella,* and *Acmaea,* are "rather fastidious in selecting their substratum, but most molluscs will apparently settle in rather different environments, and at a wide range of depths." He went on to emphasize, however, that each species will probably thrive best in particular circumstances. Here, as so often in paleoecology, it is more important to note the abundant majority rather than the isolated occurrence.

The above are all examples of sedimentary features related to distributions of particular species and genera. We may also consider the way in which the form of a particular species differs in different sediments.

The burrowing gaper clam, *Schizothaerus nuttali* of the West Coast of North America has been mentioned by MacGinitie and MacGinitie (1949) as varying in this way. It is said that in pure sand it has a large smooth shell, in sandy clay it is somewhat smaller and more rounded, and in pure clay it is smaller still and even more rounded.

Similarly Purchon (1939) found that the common cockle, *Cardium edule* (which was noted by Sorgenfrei as a species tolerant of different bottom conditions), has a more lightly built and more symmetrical shell, with fewer ribs, in estuarine muds than in shallow marine wave-beaten sand.

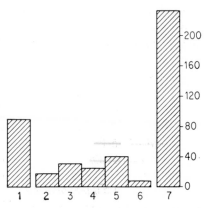

FIGURE 8.2 Average number of mollusks (larger than 2.5 mm) for main types of bottom lithology in the Rhone delta. Left to right: 1, rock and gravel; 2, sand; 3, slightly pelitic sand; 4, pelitic sand; 5, sandy and silty pelite; 6, pelite; 7, coquina. (From van Straaten, 1960; by courtesy of *Geologie en Mijnbouw.*)

The Russian zoologist Sokolova (1959) showed that there is a close relationship between the nature of the sea-floor sediment and the nature of the bottom fauna in deep ocean trenches. This arises through the feeding habits of the organisms. In a study of the bottom fauna of the Kuril-Kamchatka trench and the Bering Sea, she found that about 55 per cent of the deep-sea benthos are deposit feeders and about 25 per cent are suspension feeders. Their distribution therefore depends largely on the amount of organic matter on the bottom and in the water close to it. In areas of rapid sedimentation, deposit feeders predominate;

where the rate of sedimentation is low but the concentration of suspended matter is high, the suspension feeders are more important; where both sedimentation and suspended matter are low, the bottom fauna in general is sparse.

Turning now to fossil benthos, we have the interesting studies by the Australian paleontologist D. Hill on Lower Carboniferous rugose corals. She showed (1938) that it is possible to distinguish three main sedimentary facies associated with particular coral assemblages.

Facies 1 consists of alternations of dark, calcareous shales and thin-bedded, black, argillaceous limestones. This facies is characterized by a coral fauna of small solitary forms without dissepiments, comparable to the ahermatypic types today which live in cold, dark or murky seas.

Facies 2 consists of almost pure limestones with little land-derived material. It has a fauna of compound rugose corals, with dissepiments, like modern hermatypic types.

Facies 3 consists of light-colored massive or thin-bedded limestones with little arenaceous, argillaceous, or organic material. Its corals are of an intermediate type, mostly large solitary forms with dissepiments.

A more specific study on corals and their sediments was that by Chernyshev (1930). He showed that three different variants of the Devonian coral *Calceola sandalina*, which had been thought to be of stratigraphical value, were in fact characteristic of three different sedimentary facies in the Salair Range of the U.S.S.R.

One of the few papers which have really combined detailed paleontological and sedimentological studies is one by R. M. C. Eagar (1953) on nonmarine pelecypods in a thin band of the British Upper Carboniferous "Coal Measures." He showed that there was a close correlation between lateral changes in the faunas and changes in the petrology and chemical composition of the containing sediments. His general conclusion was that dominantly elongate shells occur in fine-grained highly carbonaceous shales, but that these pass laterally into a fauna of relatively short forms in shaly mudstones with more detritus and less carbonaceous material. His observations were clearly and convincingly demonstrated by means of pictographs (Figure 8.3). He suggested that the band as a whole represents brackish conditions, but that there was a transition toward more marine conditions in the shaly mudstone facies. This is supported by changes in the clay-mineral content, since there is a progressive increase in the proportion of illite in the same direction. In the same way, Broadhurst (1959) demonstrated a correlation between shell size in similar nonmarine pelecypods and the nature of the containing sediments. He produced evidence of a direct relationship between fossil size and the sediment content of organic carbon and detrital quartz, and evidence of an inverse relationship between size and the content of macroscopic pyrite.

One reason that such studies are regrettably rare among the students of macrofossils is the unfortunate tendency of specialists to study them as specimens in museum trays, quite divorced from their matrix. The

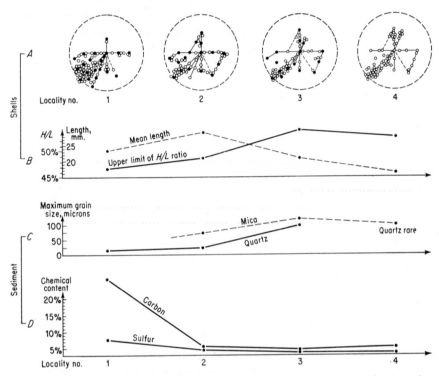

FIGURE 8.3 Relationship between changes in the range of variation of nonmarine pelecypods and changes in the lithology of the containing sediment, traced laterally in the Upper Carboniferous "Coal Measures" of the north of England. The top row represents the variation of four populations in pictographs. (From Eagar, 1953; by courtesy of the author and the Liverpool and Manchester Geological Society.)

micropaleontologist is always more intimately associated with the sediment in which his fossils occur and is usually more aware of this relationship. Eva Hanzlíková has demonstrated this very clearly in her series of papers on the foraminifera of late Mesozoic and Paleogene rocks in the Carpathian Mountains of Czechoslovakia (e.g., 1953, 1956, 1959). She found that the foram faunas are very sensitive facies indicators in these rocks, and often change abruptly with changes in sediment type.

For example, in the lower and middle Eocene rocks of a borehole near Těšín Český, Hanzlíková (1953) found that grayish-green marls invariably had a fauna of agglutinating forms dominated by *Trochamminoides subcoronatus*, whereas red marls had faunas dominated by *Haplophragmoides suborbicularis* and *Recurvoides* spp. A simultaneous alternation of both sediments and faunas was repeated three times in this borehole.

Lalicker (1948) noted a comparable relationship in the foram *Heterostegina texana*, which characterizes a zone in the Oligocene Anahuac formation of Texas. Where the top of the zone is a sandstone (Figure 8.4*A*), there are normal-sized variants of the species; but where the top of the zone is a shale (Figure 8.4*B*), specimens are very small

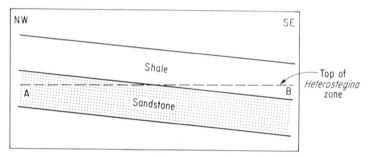

FIGURE 8.4 Relationship between the top of the *Heterostegina* zone and diachronous sediments in the Oligocene Anahuac formation in Texas. At *A*, specimens of *Heterostegina texana* are normal in size; at *B*, they appear to be stunted. (After Lalicker, 1948.)

and apparently stunted. Clearly one must guard against mechanical sorting in such cases.

With modern advances in many fields of sedimentary petrology and geochemistry, all sorts of exciting possibilities open up in paleoecology. Very little has been done so far, for example, in the way of relating faunal content to trace elements. Boron, for instance, is a possible indicator of salinity. Trace-element studies, clay mineralogy, and isotope ratios are just beginning to be applied in this work.

Imbrie (1955) made one of the very few studies of this kind on the Permian Florena shale of Kansas. His aim was to produce quantitative data on the fossils and to relate these to lithological data. Apart from the ostracods, which were counted, fossil abundance was calculated in terms of weight and so only provided a relative measure of the various major groups present. Imbrie's general conclusions were that the faunas were dominantly current drifted and that there was little if any statistical relationship between the insoluble residues of the sediment and the abundance of any particular group. He did find, however, a close relationship between the strontium/calcium ratio in the carbonate portion of the shale and the abundance of certain groups, notably the Bryozoa and Echinoidea (Figure 8.5). He suggested, following

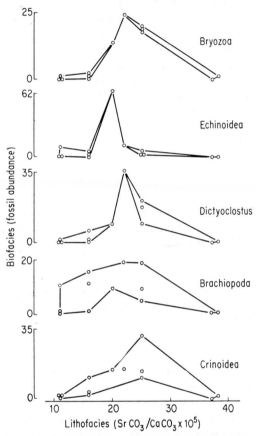

FIGURE 8.5 Abundance of selected groups of fossils plotted against strontium-calcium ratios in thirteen samples from one locality in the Florena shale. The fossil abundance is plotted as

$$\frac{\text{weight of fossil group in sample} \times 100}{\text{weight of fossil group in thirteen samples}}$$

The lines represent the scatter peripheries. (From Imbrie, 1955; by courtesy of the American Association of Petroleum Geologists.)

Turekian (1955), that both the ratio and the fossil abundances reflect the salinity of the Florena sea.

These and other modern methods of high potential value will be discussed further in Chapter 13.

Paleoecological Preconceptions

Unfortunately, a number of paleoecological preconceptions have grown up about the nature of the sediments in which certain fossils may be found. Thus I have seen abundant and obviously indigenous examples of the coral *Halysites* in a good Silurian graywacke at Dolayba in western Turkey, though my previous experience and prejudices led me to expect it only in limestones.

One of the most popular of these preconceptions is about crinoids. The idea has grown up that crinoids could only live in a clear sea and therefore could only be autochthonous in pure limestones. In my opinion this is demonstrably untrue. An example of where this preconception has affected a paleoecological interpretation is provided by the famous bioherms of the Mississippian Borden group, east of Bloomington, Indiana. Here there are lenses of crinoid remains which were interpreted as bioherms by Stockdale (1931). He assumed that the crinoids "demanded the presence of clear waters covering restricted patches." He therefore deduced that the lenses represented the living communities of growing crinoids and that the intervening shales represented occasional invasions by a muddy sea, which smothered the growing bioherms. In the field I found that the lenses are entirely composed of isolated and comminuted ossicles, whereas in the intervening shales there are lengths of unbroken crinoid stems, and in nearby shales there are more complete crinoids—with calices and holdfasts—together with an associated fauna, e.g., the symbiotic gastropod *Platyceras*. The inescapable conclusion seems to be that these crinoids, at least, lived in muddy seas, and the limestone lenses are merely mechanical accumulations of drifted crinoid debris. Confirmation of this observation has been obtained from several other localities and horizons. Echinoderm debris is particularly liable to be concentrated in this way. It has unique hydrodynamic properties due to the intricate canal system that penetrates every plate, giving it a lower density than comparable solid-shell material. This was pointed out by Sorby (1908), though this observation appears to have been overlooked by most geologists.

Another paleoecological preconception, mentioned earlier, is that pedunculate brachiopods could not live on a soft sea floor, and the occurrence of such fossils in clays and shales has usually been explained as derivation from elsewhere. This also does not necessarily follow. It has been known for a long time that certain modern brachiopods have finely branching pedicles by which they can anchor themselves in soft sediments. Muir-Wood (1959) figured a specimen of the terebratuloid *Chlidonophora* from the Indian Ocean, attached by such a pedicle in soft *Globigerina* ooze. Rudwick (1961b) quoted several other modern instances of brachiopods living on soft sediments or on the stems of seaweed. On the basis of purely fossil evidence, I suggested (Ager, 1962) the further possibility that many brachiopods—notably, small thin-shelled rhynchonelloids—may have attached themselves to floating weed. This would explain the common occurrence of isolated rhynchonelloids, such as *Leiorhynchus* in the Texas Permian, in shaly sediments otherwise lacking in benthonic organisms.

TEXTURE OF SEDIMENTS

In many cases it seems to be not the chemical nature of the sediments so much as their grain size which acts as a controlling factor on bottom-living forms. Thus the modern pelecypod *Mya arenaria*—as its name implies—requires somewhat sandy conditions. Swan (1952) showed, by careful experiments in natural conditions, that this species grows on the average about twice as fast in sand as in a compact mud-gravel-shell mixture.

Lamont (1934) suggested a direct relationship between the sharpness of the costation of brachiopods and the grain size of the sediment in lower Paleozoic rocks of Girvan on the west coast of Scotland. He noted that strong ribbing was commonest in shells which lived in sand, while those living in mud tended to have a finer ornament. This he interpreted as an adaptation for greater stability on the sea floor, though it may also be connected with H. Schmidt's suggestion (1937) that the function of the costation was to form a sieve to exclude sediment grains from the feeding streams.

Unfortunately the matter is probably not as simple as this, and these ideas do not fit in with my own observations in the Mesozoic, where many different types of ornament are found associated in what seem to be natural assemblages. Perhaps the most that can be said at the moment is that in the average coarse shallow-water sediments (such as bio-clastic calcarenites) brachiopod ornament tends to be either very strong or very smooth, whereas in the finer-grained rocks, fine costae or capillae are more common.

Lamont went on to suggest that brachiopods which lived on muddy sea bottoms tend to be flattened, with wide hinge lines. This he related to the fact that muddy bottoms are often poor in oxygen, so that there is a need for the brachiopod mantle to extend over as large an area as possible for the maximum oxygen absorption. I have found (Ager, 1960) that in the Alpine region of the European Mesozoic, at least three different brachiopod families independently produced forms with widely expanded anterior margins. Three typical examples are shown in Figure 8.6. There is also the remarkable series of perforate forms which are the extreme versions of deeply indented shells (see inset of Figure 10.5). These features may also be connected with the need for oxygen absorption on a sea floor of calcareous mud in the geosynclinal Tethys.

FIGURE 8.6 Brachiopods from three different families in the Lower Jurassic of Greece and Switzerland, showing similar expansion of their anterior margins. Left to right: 1, the terebratulid *"Terebratula" helenae;* 2, the rhynchonellid *Prionorhynchia hagaviensis;* 3, the zeilleriid *Zeilleria hierlatzica.* (After Renz, 1932, and others.)

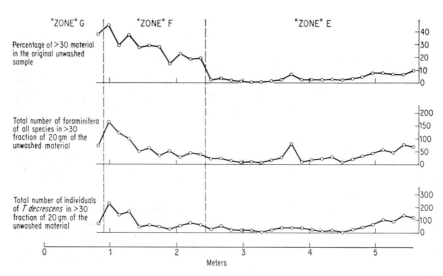

FIGURE 8.7 Relationship between foram abundance and sediment grain size in the upper Pliocene Coralline crag of Suffolk, England. (From Carter, 1951; by courtesy of *Geological Magazine.*)

To return once more to the question of grain size and brachiopods, Coleman (1957) noted that productoids in the Permian of Western Australia are restricted, almost invariably, to very fine-grained micaceous sandstones. One species, however—the large, robust *Taeniothaerus teicherti*—occurs commonly in coarser sandstones and grits with well-rounded pebbles and shell fragments; the characters of the brachio-pod and the sediments both suggest close-inshore conditions.

One important consideration in studying the relationship between fossils and sediments must be that the fossils are themselves part of the sediment and may behave like it. This is particularly relevant in the case of microfossils, which may be of the same size and weight range as some of the sedimentary grains in the vicinity. D. J. Carter (1951) showed this clearly in a study of the foraminifera of the Coralline crag (upper Pliocene) of Sutton in Suffolk, England. In this deposit he found that the forams were sorted with the sediment, so that there was a remarkable correspondence in relative abundance between the sediment of a particular grain size and forams of the same size (Figure 8.7). It has often been said that forams would not stand long trans-portation on the sea bottom, but Miss M. Illing (1950) has observed that many of the foraminifera of the Recent deposits on the Bahama Banks have been much sorted and transported for some distance, but are still beautifully preserved.

SEDIMENTATION STRUCTURES

Besides studying fossils in relation to the composition of the sedi-ments containing them, we can study them in relation to the structures shown by those sediments. The massive unbedded limestone of a reef, compared with the bedded limestone of the interreef facies, is an obvious case.

In the sandy basement bed of the London clay (lower Eocene) at Harefield in Middlesex, I noticed a close correspondence between the nature of the bedding and whether or not the burrowing pelecypods are in position of life.

Similarly, in a quantitative study on a modern beach in Somerset, I noted a marked contrast in the abundance of pelecypods on smooth and ripple-marked surfaces. From a large number of observations, the average concentrations per square meter at the top of the beach were as follows:

	Whole valves	*Fragments* *> 4 sq mm*
Smooth sand flats	5.25	15.75
Ripple-marked surfaces	0	2.5

It is commonly observable in the fossil record that whole shelly fossils are rare on ripple-marked surfaces.

Seilacher has found (personal communication, 1962) that there is a close correlation between certain types of sedimentation structures and certain types of trace fossils. With turbidite structures there occur *grazing patterns* in the form of meanders, spirals, and branching and reticulate patterns, whereas with oscillation ripple marks the trace-fossil association is dominated by arthropod tracks and burrows and by *resting marks*. Other types of trace fossil, such as *Chondrites* (Figure 7.6), seem to be independent of facies and are found with both kinds of sedimentation structures.

However, there is a danger of cyclic reasoning in relating organisms to sedimentary structures, since the former commonly modify the latter. One might in this way allege that burrowing organisms are most common in poorly bedded sediments. Dapples (1942) usefully summarized the effect of macroorganisms on nearshore marine sediments, showing how creatures as varied as holothurians and lobsters modify the sediments by destruction of bedding, mixing of grain sizes, trituration and solution, addition of fecal debris, initiation of cementation, bleaching or coloration, and destruction of organic material.

NINE

Lateral variation

THERE are great paleoecological potentialities in the study of how a fossil species varies laterally in contemporaneous strata. This may relate directly to changes in the sediment, as discussed in the last chapter, but variations are often observed where there is no apparent change in sedimentary type, and these are considered here. Once again we must remember that many environmental factors leave no geological record at all, or at least none clear enough to explain the observed fossil variations.

Such variations are commonly overlooked by paleontologists, or hidden by taxonomic splitting, or explained as evolutionary changes. It is therefore necessary to refer more than ever in this chapter to present-day examples, and to consider whether these phenomena may not also be preserved in the rocks.

SIZE VARIATIONS

With the felling of most of Britain's forests during the Middle Ages, the red deer were forced out onto the open, inhospitable moors, such as those of the Scottish Highlands (still paradoxically known as "deer forests"). As a result, the Scottish red deer is now much smaller than the same species in its natural woodland habitat elsewhere in Europe.[1]

A somewhat comparable fossil example is the North American bison, which in Pleistocene times ranged from Atlantic to Pacific and as far north as Alaska. It then occupied a great range of environments and showed a correspondingly great range of sizes, including giant forms

[1] It is commonly regarded as a separate variety—*Cervus elaphus scoticus.*

137

with a 3-m spread of horns, compared with which the modern survivors are almost diminutive examples. But vertebrate fossils are rarely abundant enough for statistically acceptable quantitative studies, so that invertebrate examples are more suitable for our purpose.

If one collects shells on the beaches of Sweden or on the island of Bornholm in the Baltic, one immediately notices that the best-known species, such as the common cockles and mussels, are noticeably smaller than their equivalents in the North Sea or the English Channel (Figures 9.1 and 9.2). This is simply a reflection of the much lower salinity of

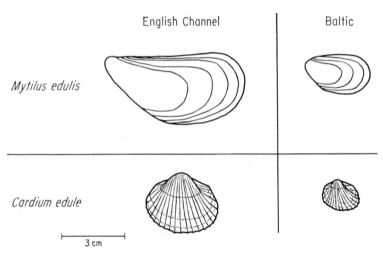

FIGURE 9.1 *Mytilus edulis* and *Cardium edule:* average-size adult specimens from (*left*) the south coast of England and (*right*) the southeast coast of Sweden. (Selected from collections made by the author.)

the Baltic, and until modern geochemical techniques have been perfected, it will not be detectable in sediments. Lateral changes in another species of mussel—*Mytilus californianus*—were discussed by MacGinitie and MacGinitie (1949). They mention three localities for this species. At Newport Bay in southern California it reaches 18 cm in length, at Pacific Grove in northern California it reaches 23 cm, and at Tillamook Rock in northern Oregon it reaches 35 cm. In other words, there seems to be a progressive increase in length northward.

The tendency among living species to attain a larger size in colder regions is known as the Bergmann principle, and it applies particularly to warm-blooded animals. This principle, however, tends to operate in the opposite direction for cold-blooded animals, though there are many exceptions, of which *M. californianus* is one.

Thus the occurrence of abundant, unusually large invertebrate fossils has often been taken as evidence of past high temperatures. Arkell (1956*a*) commented: "At the present day the largest forms of arthropods, snails and all shells . . . are found in equatorial or tropical regions. By analogy it is difficult not to believe that the immense Portlandian ammonites lived in much warmer water than anything possible in similar latitudes at the present day."

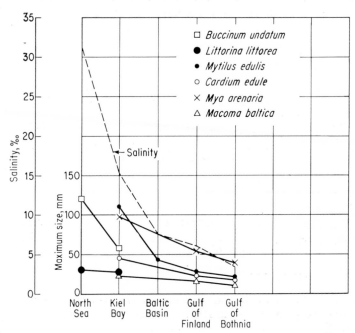

FIGURE 9.2 Maximum sizes of six common mollussan species at different localities in the North Sea and the Baltic. (From Sorgenfrei, 1958, after Brandt, 1897; by courtesy of the former.)

The crux of the matter lies in the expectation that the maximum size of a species should occur in the optimal part of its range, i.e., in the area most favorable to its development.

There are numerous studies in paleontology in which size variations have been correlated (in a very general way) with geographical distribution, for example, among the rudist pelecypods of the Cretaceous (see page 153). It is logical then to argue that the place where a particular fossil species reaches its best development is where the environment was most suitable for its development, and this place is likely to be particularly instructive about the autecology of the fossil species concerned.

Once more I must emphasize that many different factors may contribute to the optimum conditions for any species. It is never just a matter of temperature or salinity or depth as seems to be implied by some writers. The other factors just may not be obvious at first sight, even when studied with living material. Thus Matteson (1955) showed that when certain fresh-water pelecypods live in the headwaters of streams, specimens of medium weight are more successful than heavier ones because the former are less liable to be buried during periods of flood. In order for it to live on a very soft substratum, the density of the pelecypod's body must be equivalent to, or less than, that of the sediment. Matteson also found that the size of the stream is important.

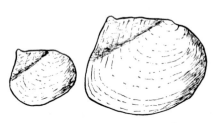

FIGURE 9.3   Variation in the fresh-water pelecypod *Lasmigona complanata*. (After Matteson, 1955.)

Figure 9.3 shows the difference in size of two specimens of *Lasmigona complanata* which have about the same number of growth lines; the smaller shell came from a smaller stream in which the planktonic food supply was low. These forms also tend to be compressed in headwaters and more obese downstream. All these features may well be discernible in fossil forms such as the abundant *Unio* and *Neomiodon* shells in the Lower Cretaceous Wealden deposits of the south of England, and might well repay the labor of a quantitative study.

This brings us naturally to the subject of environmentally induced "dwarfing." This is a popular concept in paleontology, yet it is surprisingly difficult to find indisputable examples in the fossil record. In a symposium on the subject organized by the Society of Economic Paleontologists and Mineralogists, hardly a single good example could be produced by the distinguished group of paleontologists present. Thus H. W. Scott (1948) could not find a single acceptable case among the fossil crustacea and trilobites.

What are often called "stunted" or "dwarfed" fossils are nothing of the sort, but just naturally small species. The dwarf birch, for example —*Betula nana*—which figures so largely in the literature of the Pleistocene and the modern arctic, is only a dwarf in the sense that it is a small species of the genus compared with the common birch, *B. alba*. Whereas the former only exceptionally reaches 6 m in height, the latter reaches 16 m in favorable locations in the south of England, and some of the American species reach 23 or 25 m. But these are different species, and there is no question of a retardation of growth to account for *B. nana* not reaching the same size as the others.

Similarly Kummel (1948) described a fossil association from the Upper Triassic of Peru in which the ammonites were "dwarfed" but the associated bottom fauna of crinoids, pelecypods, gastropods, brachiopods, bryozoa, and sponges was "normal." This is the opposite of what one would expect, and Kummel concluded that the ammonites were not really dwarfed at all, but belonged to naturally small stocks which had evolved independently though along the same lines as their larger relations elsewhere.

The terms "dwarf" and "dwarfed" are really quite unsatisfactory in this connection, since they seem to imply a genetic control. It is advisable to restrict these words to teratological specimens (monstrosities), which are also known as fossils but which are apparently independent of environmental control. Two other words which are commonly used for "dwarfed" faunas are "depauperate" and "diminutive," but the first should be rejected on the grounds of obscurity and unfamiliarity, and the second means nothing more than small.

It is therefore clearly better to use "stunted" to indicate retardation of growth as a result of environmental factors, and within the range of normal variation in size we may accept this adjective as a descriptive term for forms which are unusually small because of unfavorable conditions. The Baltic cockles and mussels serve to illustrate this. We may expect to find such associations as fossils, but we must be extremely careful not to say a fossil is stunted, without a great deal of complementary evidence of normal-sized forms elsewhere.

As Cloud pointed out (1948), there are three ways in which associations of small specimens may come about.

1. True stunting: due to physiological retardation of growth by various factors. In fossil assemblages we would expect a natural association of various age groups, but the adults would not have reached the average adult size.

2. Concentrations of immature specimens: due to environmental factors producing subnormal life-spans or exceptionally high infant mortality. In other words, we may have a natural association of forms which are small because they died young.

3. Concentrations of mechanically sorted small specimens: due to simple segregation by moving water or other agency which left the big ones in one place and the small ones somewhere else.

Both (1) and (2) are clearly ecological matters, but (3) is a sedimentation phenomenon and so a process we have to steer clear of as paleoecologists. Often, true stunting in fossils can be blamed on particular sedimentary environments (generally unusual ones such as iron-rich waters), but this takes us back once more to the previous chapter.

Shimer (1908) discussed the causes of stunting in a much-quoted paper, with many examples. The most commonly suggested causes are (1) changes in chemical composition of a water environment, (2) introduction of impurities, (3) changes in temperature, (4) changes in height or depth, and (5) overcrowding. Examples of all of these may be found among fossils, though some of them would be a little strained.

Some paleontologists use the term "gigantism" when members of a species reach an extraordinarily large size. As with "dwarf," "giant" and "gigantism" are unsatisfactory terms implying monstrosities, but in the environmentally induced sense, gigantism is probably a very rare phenomenon comparable to stunting. Bearing in mind the possibility of isolated monstrosities, it is more logical to regard associations of unusually large forms as representing the species realizing its potentialities under optimum conditions, unless it can be shown to be a special race or geographical subspecies. The other members of that species, including the "average" forms, are then more or less stunted or, more accurately, have not realized their potentialities to varying degrees.

In a few groups only—for example, in the Foraminifera—true environmentally induced gigantism may occur, because of individuals continuing to grow under unfavorable circumstances without reaching the sexual maturity at which growth usually ceases.

SHAPE VARIATIONS

Shape variations are even more liable than size variations to be concealed in the fossil record by taxonomic splitting.

In the well-known Middle Devonian coral beds of Skaneateles Lake, New York, J. W. Wells (1937) found that the rugose coral *Heliophyllum halli* included at least eleven other nominal species and subspecies which have been founded on shape variations by various workers. Every specialist knows similar examples from his own group. Thus Buckman (1907) founded eighteen new species on slight variants of the Lower Jurassic terebratuloid *Cincta numismalis,* all from the same horizon and locality.

When the variants all come from a single locality, there is probably not much environment-induced variation, except such as may have resulted from an individual's unfavorable position in a crowded community, its attack by parasites, or another comparable event. When the variants come from the same horizon but widely separated localities, the chances of ecological variation are immense.

One of the few ecological studies which have been made on modern brachiopods was that of H. M. Du Bois (1916) on the terebratuloid *Terebratalia obsoleta.* He found that specimens from different environments varied considerably in external form, from round and smooth to wide *Spirifer*-like forms. The shorter, rounder shells occur in the roughest water, and Du Bois thought that abnormalities were produced by the bruising of the mantle margin by buffeting in the water.

Among fossil brachiopods, we have the quantitative study by McKerrow (1953) of various species in the Fuller's earth rock of the Bathonian (Middle Jurassic) in the west of England. He found that

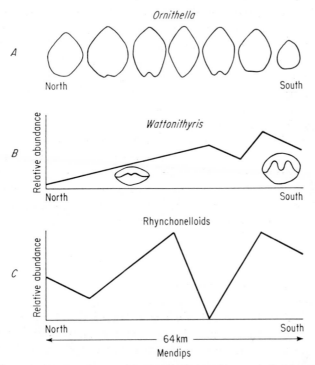

FIGURE 9.4 Lateral variation in shape and abundance of brachiopods in the Fuller's earth rock of the Bathonian (Middle Jurassic) in western England, when traced over the positive line of the Mendips. *A,* changes in the outline of *Ornithella* (There is much variation at each locality, and the shapes of the anterior margin have been exaggerated.); *B,* changes in the relative abundance and in the anterior commissure of *Wattonithyris; C,* changes in the relative abundance of the rhynchonelloids. (From McKerrow, 1953; by courtesy of the author and the Geological Society of London.)

when this bed is traced across the "positive" line of the Mendip Hills, various shape changes occur in certain of the terebratuloids (Figure 9.4) which probably reflect regional changes in environment.

Hayasaka (1960) discussed shape and size variations in modern and fossil oysters. He showed that exceptionally large oysters in the Japanese Pleistocene—*Ostrea* (*Crassostrea*) *gigas*—lived on oyster banks and that forms scattered separately on a soft muddy bottom were always smaller and had more rounded outlines. A feature of particularly crowded oyster banks is the development of abnormally elongate forms which grow upward for food and water. The example of this cited by Hayasaka was the well-known *Crassostrea virginica.* In the English Jurassic we have a much older example, *O. hebridica* var. *elongata,* in the oyster banks of the Bathonian on the Dorset coast (Figure 9.5).

In a few cases, differences in ornament have been observed in a species when collected at different localities. Resser (1939) noted that

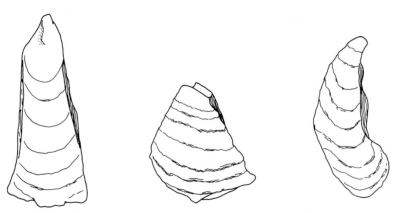

FIGURE 9.5 Variants of *Ostrea hebridica* in the Bathonian (Middle Jurassic). *Center:* "normal" form, as found all over the British Isles. *Left* and *right:* var. *elongata,* as found in an oyster bank near Herbury on the Dorset coast. (Drawn from specimens in the author's collection.)

various trilobites in the Middle Cambrian of the Wasatch Mountains in Idaho and Utah are all highly ornamented with strong tubercles, whereas the same species in a neighboring region have the ornament much less developed. Usually, however, such phenomena must have been concealed by the profusion of names.

Variation of a special kind within a species is the tendency known as Allen's rule; in this the body extremities tend to be smaller in the arctic and larger in the tropics. This is seen in the length of ears of foxes and in the length of the arms and legs of *Homo sapiens,* which tend to be much longer in relation to body length in a Negro than in an Eskimo. This is probably connected with the need for more transpiration in a warmer climate.

An interesting example of lateral variation in shape within plant species is provided by the development of *dripping points.* These long attenuated tips are found in some forms in areas of heavy rainfall and are presumably connected with the runoff of the excess moisture. Berry (1914) noted that dripping points are well developed on fig leaves from the Upper Cretaceous of South Carolina (Figure 9.6) but are absent in the same species farther north.

On a smaller scale, ecologically significant changes may occur through slight differences in the immediate environment. Thus the growth of corals or sponges may be considerably affected by the roughness and the shallowness of the water. In rough water, corals tend to form encrusting masses or short thick branches; in gentler water, they grow more gracefully, branching and extending upward. Shallow-water corals (if the water is not too rough) tend to form short wide branches or thin

FIGURE 9.6 Leaf of *Ficus crassipes* from the Upper Cretaceous of Rocky Point, South Carolina, showing well-developed dripping point. (After Berry, 1914.)

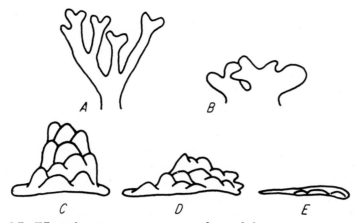

FIGURE 9.7 Effect of water movements on coral growth form.
Top: Porites, porites, Florida. **A,** in quiet water; **B,** in shallow rough water.
Bottom: Diploria clivosa, Florida. **A,** in quiet water; **B,** in rough water; **C,** in shallow, very rough water. (After Vaughan and Wells, 1943.)

plates, transverse to the current direction, while in deeper water columnar structures are produced (Figure 9.7).

Comparable observations have been made on fossil corals. Frentzen (1932) described two Upper Jurassic coral assemblages from near Nattheim in southern Germany. At one locality he recorded a rough-water association of massive, nodular, and encrusting corals, with a few fasciculate forms and a few large solitary individuals. At the second locality he recorded a calm-water association of foliate, laminar, and branching corals. He also noted differences in the associated fauna.

A similar type of lateral variation has been described in living gastropods by H. B. Moore (1934). He found that the common limpet, *Patella vulgata,* differs in shape according to its position on the beach (Figure 9.8) and that an individual will change its growth form if moved from one place to another.

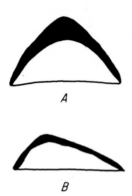

The crowding together of individuals in a dense colony may also produce shape variations. Zapfe (1937) demonstrated lateral shape variations related to crowding in the pelecypod genus *Hippurites* in the Austrian Cretaceous. Forms which grew closely packed together are tall and thin because of the struggle for upward growth, whereas those which lived separately are thick-shelled and broad. Similarly, spiriferoid brachiopods which lived closely packed together in colonies commonly developed asymmetrically (Ager and Riggs, 1963).

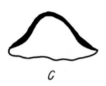

FIGURE 9.8 Vertical sections of limpets (*Patella vulgata*). A, from high water level; B, from low water level; C, after transfer from an exposed rock surface to a pool. (After H. B. Moore, 1934.)

OTHER FORMS OF LATERAL VARIATION

Many curious lateral differences in living animals and plants have not been explained in terms of environment, but should be borne in mind as possible pitfalls in paleoecological studies. Thus there are the the so-called "ring species," such as the five "species" of gulls which in distribution encircle the arctic; each member grades into its neighbors except at the two ends of the ring in Britain, where we have the Lesser Black-backed Gull and the Herring Gull living as virtually distinct species (de Beer, 1958).

We also have such problems as the species of *Patella* described by Fischer-Piette (1935), which appear to be three distinct and mutually exclusive species in one area but which pass laterally into a single interbreeding species elsewhere. I have suggested (Ager, 1956*b*, 1961*c*) that certain Lower Jurassic zeilleriid brachiopods may represent the same phenomenon, and Arkell (1956*b*) described a similar state of affairs in Jurassic ammonites.

These are evolutionary, rather than ecological, matters; but they are also potential causes of confusion.

TEN

Geographical distribution of single taxonomic groups

I N my visits to geology departments in various parts of the world, I have always been struck by the contrasts in their collections of common local fossils which their students are expected to know. In London we would have our familiar *Micraster* from the Chalk and our *Didymograptus* from Abereiddy Bay. In Grenoble, France, one finds numbers of the remarkable local brachiopod *Pygope* and the curiously flattened belemnite *Duvalia*. In Illinois, every student knows, or should know, the twisted axes of the bryozoan *Archimedes* and the corallike brachiopod *Prorichthofenia*. So it is that wherever one goes, one finds locally abundant and well-preserved fossils which are completely unknown to students elsewhere except as figures in textbooks. At the same time one discovers that some of the best-known fossils of one's own country have not been heard of by the local paleontologists. Under the unique University of London system of external degrees, a very familiar English Liassic ammonite was included in an examination for Hong Kong, and

147

a plea came back from the local teacher for it to be replaced by the better-known local fossil *Hongkongites hongkongensis!*

On the other hand, one finds that some fossils are known almost universally. *Halysites* is as well known in Istanbul as in Illinois, in Lund as in London. This illustrates what is, to me, one of the most fascinating aspects of paleoecology.

We may study the geographical distribution of fossils on any scale. The world-wide distribution of a form may not appear at first sight to be an ecological subject, but it may have a direct relationship with such ecologically significant matters as climatic zonation and ocean currents. As one increases the scale of the map, distributions come more and more into contact with problems of local environment. At one extreme there are studies of the world distribution of rudistid pelecypods (Dacqué, 1915); on an intermediate scale there are studies of continent-wide distributions of Cambrian trilobites (Lochman-Balk and Wilson, 1958); and at the opposite extreme there are studies of the distribution of various fossils across a Permian reef belt in Texas (Newell et al., 1953) or a Cretaceous sandbank in southern England (W. E. Smith, 1961). I find it impossible to draw a line and say, "This is paleoecology, and this is not." All distributions are ecological matters and will be regarded as such here.

The study of the geographical distribution of fossils is, in a way, a much more scientific business than suppositions about the mode of life of individuals. We can be fairly sure whether a particular form has ever been found in a particular area, at least if it is at all common. Its absence may, of course, be for other than ecological reasons—erosion, nonpreservation, scavengers, and so on—but these possibilities can be allowed for. Thus, apart from the well-known but local *Kingena wacoensis*, there are remarkably few brachiopods in the North American Cretaceous, compared with contemporary rocks in Europe. This cannot be entirely explained by nonecological factors, and the variety of sedimentary facies available makes it unlikely that unfavorable local environments are the key to the problem, so it seems that major factors of geographical distribution must be responsible. Such fossil distributions may be compared with the present distribution of the Amphineura, which are very common in the North Pacific but sparse in the North Atlantic.

Much of the argument in distribution studies arises from the postulation of barriers—but what is meant by the term "barrier"? This is usually thought of as a great topographical ridge cutting across a seaway in a dramatic fashion and forming an impassable obstruction to marine organisms. But clearly, barriers may be of many different types, so that the term should be used in a broad sense, that is, for anything which obstructs the spread of organisms. Rivers may be effective barriers, as are the Niger and Volta Rivers in west Africa (Booth, 1958). The Grand Canyon is an effective barrier, not because of its depth or the

Colorado River at its bottom, but because of the climatic zones organisms would have to cross to get from one side to the other. Similarly in marine environments, an ocean current or abrupt change in salinity may be as effective a barrier as an isthmus.

What is more, within the vast resources of geological time, a barrier may open and close many times like a gate. Again like a gate, a barrier may be highly selective in what it stops and what it lets through. A five-bar gate that will stop a cow will not necessarily stop a horse; a mouse may escape through a hole in the baseboard that will stop a cat.

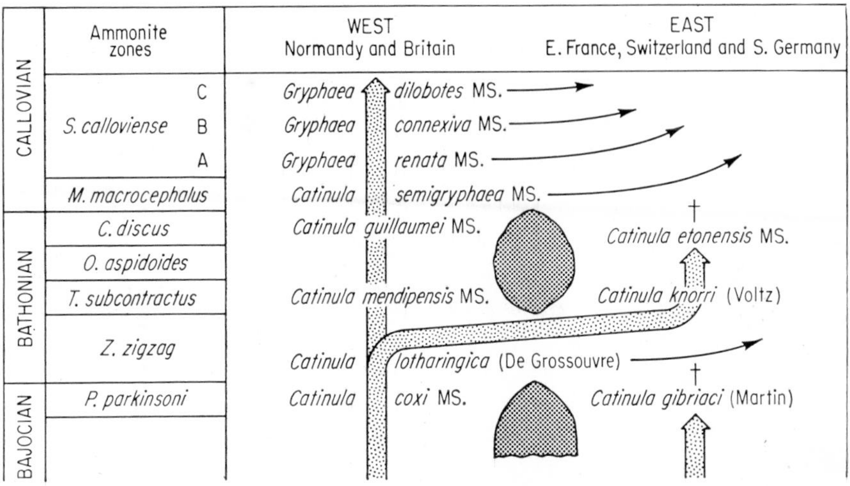

	Ammonite zones		WEST Normandy and Britain	EAST E. France, Switzerland and S. Germany
CALLOVIAN		C	*Gryphaea* ← *dilobotes* MS. ——→	
	S. calloviense	B	*Gryphaea* *connexiva* MS. ——	
		A	*Gryphaea* *renata* MS. ——	
	M. macrocephalus		*Catinula* *semigryphaea* MS. ——	
BATHONIAN	*C. discus*		*Catinula guillaumei* MS.	*Catinula etonensis* MS.
	O. aspidoides			
	T. subcontractus		*Catinula mendipensis* MS.	*Catinula knorri* (Voltz)
	Z. zigzag		*Catinula* *lotharingica* (De Grossouvre) ——	
BAJOCIAN	*P. parkinsoni*		*Catinula* *coxi* MS.	*Catinula gibriaci* (Martin)

FIGURE 10.1 Geographical barriers and speciation in Jurassic oysters. Broad arrows indicate phylogeny, crosshatched areas represent geographical barriers, and narrow arrows indicate directions of subsequent migration. (From Sylvester-Bradley, 1959; by courtesy of the author and the Linnean Society of London.)

G. G. Simpson (1940, 1953) distinguished three main sorts of paths of faunal and floral interchange: *corridors, filters,* and *sweepstake routes.* A corridor is a route along which the spread of animals and plants is probable; it is without effective barriers of any importance. A filter is a route with a "semibarrier" which allows the passage of some elements but not others. A sweepstake route is a route with an effective barrier which regularly prevents the passage of organisms but is occasionally crossed by some. Examples of the last are seen in Figure 11.5.

In his fine study of the ecology of Saipan in the Mariana Islands, Cloud (1959) placed the oceanic barriers of the Pacific in the filter and sweepstake categories of Simpson, and emphasized the widespread distribution of many of the species. He deplored the tendency (which is even more apparent in paleontology than in neontology) of regarding great geographical separation alone as a sufficient basis for taxonomic separation.

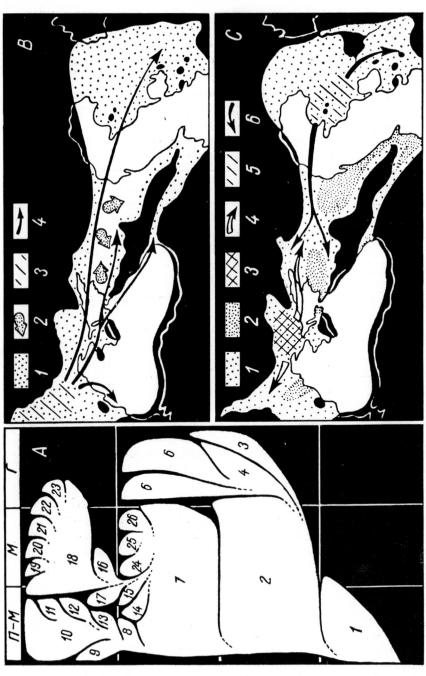

Figure 10.2. Evolution and distribution of certain Miocene Mactridae in southern Russia. (From Gekker, 1957, after Kolesnikov, 1949). A, phylogeny of twenty-six species of *Mactra* through the Samatian. Left, nearshore species; center, shallow-water species; right, deep-water species.

One further important matter arises from this. If we accept standard evolutionary theories barriers of some kind must always have been essential in the process of splitting up a species into geographical subspecies and thence into new species. The classic example of this is the mountain-living Birds of Paradise in New Guinea, which are separated into five species by deep valleys which they cannot cross. After the original separation of the parent stock, interbreeding must have ceased and the isolated populations evolved independently.

Fossil examples of this process must be sought if we are to demonstrate and fully understand the mechanics of evolution, but few have as yet been claimed. Termier and Termier (1948) maintained that they could relate speciation in the brachiopod genus *"Halorella"*[1] in the Devonian of Morocco to geographical isolation, and Sylvester-Bradley (1959) gave an example from the much-studied Jurassic oysters (Figure 10.1). Perhaps the best example available is that quoted by Gekker (1957) from the work of Kolesnikov (1949) on the evolution of species of the pelecypod *Mactra* in southern Russia (Figure 10.2).

LIMITATIONS

A great problem in fossil-distribution studies is whether or not the remains could have traveled far after death. This is very relevant in the large-scale, detailed studies, where only a few kilometers are involved, but the possibility of postmortem transport is probably overrated in more general studies. This is particularly so if we take into consideration just the prolific occurrences of a particular fossil and not the places where it only occurs as a great rarity, though even such rare occurrences may be useful as evidence of a sea connection or an ocean current. Thus the ten thousand gastropods in a bed are more significant ecologically than the one ammonite, though stratigraphically the situation might be the other way about.

The question of the drifting of dead organisms is very closely related to the nature of the remains. McGinity (1955) described shells of the cephalopod *Spirula spirula*, commonly thrown up on Florida beaches, which had apparently floated on sea currents for a considerable time,

[1] This is almost certainly not the true *Halorella*, which is restricted to the Alpine Trias.

B, distribution up to the beginning of middle Sarmatian times. 1, *M. eichwaldi* (species 2); 2, intrusion of *Mactra* into zone of deeper water; 3, initial area of *M. fabreana* (species 7); 4, dispersal routes of this species.
C, distribution in middle Sarmatian times. 1, *M. fabreana;* 2, deep-water *Mactras;* 3, initial development of *M. subvitaliana* (species 15); 4, dispersal routes of this species; 5, initial development of *M. pallasi* (species 8); 6, dispersal routes of this species.

being encrusted with colonies of goose barnacles. These shells are extremely light, with many gas-filled chambers, and so are suited to floating in this way. Similarly the living *Nautilus* is restricted to the southwest Pacific, but its shells are found as far north as Japan (Stenzel, 1948; Kobayashi, 1954).

The beaches of Jan Mayen—the remote arctic island between Iceland and Spitsbergen—are thickly strewn with logs which apparently came down the rivers of Siberia and floated hundreds of kilometers to the west. Clearly we must be very careful when dealing with fossils which could have floated a long way after death, but with most sedentary groups this problem does not arise.

Macquarie Island lies in one of the remotest parts of the South Pacific (54° S, 157° E), and was covered by a thick ice sheet in the Pleistocene. Yet thirty-five species of plants have reached the island since the glaciation (Taylor, 1954). The majority of these species have large seeds and must have been brought to the island by birds.[2] If all these species can have been transported to a small, inhospitable island in the course of a few thousand years, the problem of spreading the meager *Glossopteris* flora from continent to continent during millions of years does not seem to be so serious, though it must be remembered that there were no birds in the late Paleozoic to provide the transportation.

Though the land colonization of remote islands is more obviously problematical, the provenance of shallow-water organisms also requires explanation. Crisp and Southward (1953) commented: "A critical distance must exist, related to the current system and the duration of the free-swimming stages, beyond which the rate of settlement of the larvae is normally insufficient to reach the minimal population density within the life-time of an individual." This point was considered by Knox (1954) in a discussion of the origin of the shallow-water fauna of Chatham Island, which lies about 900 km east of New Zealand. Paleontological evidence shows that this island must have been repopulated from New Zealand after the Pliocene, and Knox drew attention to the selective nature of this colonization. Many of the commoner species of New Zealand shores are completely absent. He concluded that the velocity and direction of the ocean currents were appropriate for transporting the free-swimming larvae of many species, and he thought that many others may have been carried on drifting seaweed.

Turning to a fossil example, Flower (1942a) described exotic species of nautiloids in the Ordovician of Kentucky which occur in a vertical position, suggesting that their shells floated in with gas in their posterior chambers. They resemble species otherwise only known far to the north, and may have drifted long distances after death. But it seems unjusti-

[2] Seeds have actually been seen adhering to the feet of albatrosses.

fiable to postulate long-distance drifting when the faunas concerned are abundant and varied.

Apart from these difficulties, it is clearly impossible for one man to study thoroughly the distribution of any forms over more than a small area. It took me three seasons' field work thus to study the geographical distribution of brachiopods in one thin zone of the British Jurassic, and it proved a physical (and financial) impossibility to work in the same way over the whole of Europe. So we are forced to utilize the work of others, and many errors are likely to creep in. In practice the main thing is knowing the reliability of the data. There are, in fact, four kinds of available data, of progressively decreasing reliability:

1. Specimens collected personally.

2. Specimens examined personally in museums or private collections —the reliability varying according to the standards of collection and curation.

3. Published figures—sometimes more reliable than (2) if we ignore what the author calls them and if the figures are good enough and the species distinctive enough for confident identification.

4. Published or unpublished records without figures—usually of no reliability at all, and therefore of no use except perhaps as an indication of where it might be worth looking.

In this sort of study, one tends to get rather cynical and distrust every identification except one's own. This is not to say that one's own identifications are necessarily more correct than the next man's; but at least they are all made by the same person, so that the total amount of subjectivity is reduced. My *Atrypa reticularis* is not necessarily the true *Atrypa reticularis,* but all the specimens which I call by this name are more likely to be of the same species than are all the specimens so named by several different people. It is a useful rule, when studying other people's collections, to make one's own identification before reading the curator's label.

DISTRIBUTION OF MAJOR GROUPS

If all the members of a particular major group have similar ecological limitations, the study of the geographical distribution of their fossils may be very illuminating.

One of the most interesting extinct fossil groups which may be studied in this way is the rudistid pelecypods, the aberrant group which appeared and flourished in late Mesozoic times but disappeared completely at the end of that era. Dacqué (1915) drew attention to their restricted, low-latitude distribution. In Europe, for example, they are very abundant in the south, but in northern countries such as England

and Sweden they occur only as rare, local specimens, which were regarded by Dacqué as stunted. The idea of an equatorial belt of rudistid
faunas received startling support from Hamilton's discovery (1956) of
rudistids dredged from Cape Johnson guyot, halfway between Honolulu
and Bikini. This record has been added to Dacqué's data on Figure 10.3.

One of the exciting papers in this field is that by Stehli (1957) on
possible Permian climatic zonation as indicated by the geographical distribution of certain marine invertebrates. He plotted the world-wide
distribution of various families of brachiopods and fusulinids and
noted also the outcrops of marine Permian strata which had not yielded

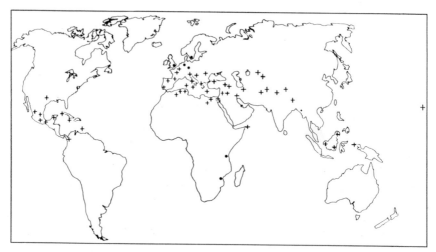

Figure 10.3 **Distribution of rudistid pelecypods in the Cretaceous. The dots indicate stunted forms.** (Information largely from Dacqué, 1915.)

examples of each family concerned (Figure 10.4). This plotting of negative as well as positive evidence is very valuable in such studies.

The main point emerging from these plots was the definition of a
line at about 55° N which marked the northern limit of most of the
forms. The evidence from the Southern Hemisphere is very incomplete,
partly because of the lack of outcrops and partly because of the lack of
detailed studies; but there are similar anomalies at the present day.
Coral reefs, for instance, are absent over large areas, e.g., on the west
coast of the Americas, because of cold currents.

Stehli drew attention to the fact that the sharpest break in marine
faunas at the present day comes between the subtropical and the temperate zones (Ekman, 1953). This break can be seen in almost all major
invertebrate groups and in the vertebrates and plants. It corresponds
roughly with the 15°C winter isotherm; and Stehli suggested that it

might be connected with the fundamental properties of water, and so, presumably, of protoplasm.

There are several temperatures at which sharp changes occur in the chemical properties of water, but the only one within the normal range of temperature of sea water is 15°C. The solubility of about two hundred substances in water changes perceptibly at this temperature (Drost-Hansen and Neill, 1955), and it may therefore be a controlling factor in the distribution of faunas (though nothing like an absolute break is implied). On the basis of all this, Stehli suggested that the

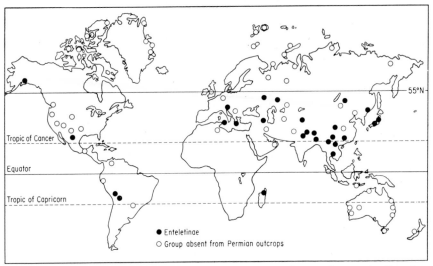

FIGURE 10.4 Distribution of the brachiopod subfamily Enteletinae in Permian rocks. (From Stehli, 1957; by courtesy of *American Journal of Science.*)

15°C winter isotherm in Permian times corresponded roughly with the 55° N latitude.

This "magic figure" of 55° N, we find, fits very well with other faunal distributions in the past. For example, it fits with the northern limit of the Cretaceous rudistids, discussed earlier, and is roughly the margin of the "Eu-American" flora of Pennsylvanian times. Jurassic corals reach as far north as the Queen Charlotte Islands, i.e., to about 53° N (Arkell, 1956a). Triassic corals extend to about 61° N (J. P. Smith, 1927). All these distributions suggest a climatic zonation parallel to the present equator and so do not support hypotheses of polar wandering. This will be further discussed later.

An interesting corollary of Stehli's hypothesis comes from a consideration of the next critical temperature in sea water. This is 30°C (Drost-Hansen and Neill, 1955). The highest temperatures known in the open sea today are about 35°C,[3] but these are very exceptional, and no winter isotherms reach anything like that figure. Typical winter lows are about 22°C in the Atlantic, about 24°C in the Red Sea, and about 27°C in parts of the Pacific. If in Permian and later times the 15°C winter isotherm was as far north as 55° N, then there may have been an equatorial belt in which the temperatures regularly exceeded 30°C. Nowhere in the seas of today does high temperature tend to restrict marine life—just the reverse—but it may be that in the past there was a "hypertropical" belt with a distinctive fauna of its own. The disappearance of this belt with the deterioration of the climate since the beginning of the Tertiary may account for the extinction of groups such as the rudists and the nummulites, which reached their optimum development in the equatorial region. It was suggested by Cailleux (1951) that the absence of Paleozoic reef corals from the tropics (Figure 10.7) may be explained by their not being able to tolerate the high temperatures there, and J. W. Wells (1957a) quoted 36°C as the maximum endurable temperature for reef corals. R. G. Evans (1948) determined the lethal temperatures for eleven species of mollusks. For all of these he found that the safety limit was high, with no possibility of heat death in nature at the present day, but in every case the temperature at which spontaneous movement ceased was just above 30°C. Similarly Gunter (1957) put the thermal death point for most marine animals at between 30 and 35°C.

However, negative evidence in fossil distributions can be very misleading, and we must also consider in every case whether there are rocks of the right age and facies exposed in the areas concerned. The absence of Paleozoic corals from the tropics may be simply due to there being no suitable rocks preserved there. Both the supposedly boreal belemnites and the supposedly equatorial rudists are notably absent from the west African Cretaceous.

An important distinction to remember, when relating certain fossil distributions to past climates, is the difference between macro- and microclimates. Strictly local circumstances may favor a particular species but give no indication at all of the general conditions. In studying Pleistocene beetle faunas, G. R. Coope (1962) found that species that live in dung or heaps of rotting vegetation are widespread in distribution and do not reflect the macroclimate of the localities in which they are found. On the other hand, ground beetles, being more exposed to the macroclimate, are very good indicators of its nature.

DISTRIBUTION OF SMALLER GROUPS

Coming down the taxonomic scale, there are many famous distributional studies at the level of genera. One of the most famous is that of

[3] Temperatures in excess of 40°C have been recorded in the Gulf of Mexico.

Lower Cambrian trilobites such as *Olenellus* and *Callavia* and their relations. It has long been well known that *Olenellus* and its allies occur in the Lower Cambrian of northwest Scotland, Greenland, and western Newfoundland and down through the Appalachian region of North America (Stubblefield, 1939). *Callavia* on the other hand, is found with its relations in the Welsh borderland of England, in southern Scandinavia and Poland, in eastern Newfoundland, and along the seaboard of Nova Scotia and New England. Although apparently contemporaries, the two genera are never found together, and it has long been supposed that there was a barrier between them. This distribution has also been used as evidence for the drifting apart of Europe and North America.

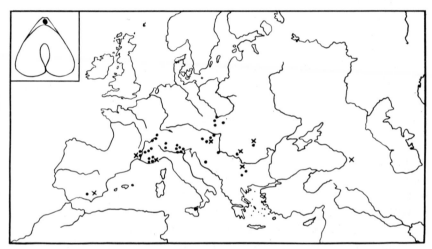

FIGURE 10.5 Distribution of the perforate terebratulid *Pygope* and its allies in the Late Jurassic and Early Cretaceous rocks of Europe. Dots, Jurassic; crosses, Cretaceous.

Lochman-Balk and Wilson (1958) have put forward an entirely different explanation of this and other anomalous trilobite distributions in the Cambrian. They postulate three biofacies belts around the Cambrian continents. These may be termed cratonic, miogeosynclinal, and eugeosynclinal environments, or in common parlance, shallow-shelf, intermediate, and open-ocean environments. *Olenellus* is regarded as a shallow-shelf or intermediate form and *Callavia* as an open-ocean form.

In my own work I have studied the distribution of many different genera of Mesozoic brachiopods. Figure 10.5 shows the distinctive spread of *Pygope* and its allies in the highest Jurassic and Lower Cretaceous of Europe. These are common in the Alpine region but become very rare around it, as in Yugoslavia, and farther afield are completely absent except for a single specimen found by D. T. Donovan in East Greenland. It is anomalies of this kind which make these studies particularly fascinating.

A study of a different kind was that by G. Scott (1940) on the distribution of various ammonite genera in the Upper Cretaceous of Texas. Being pelagic forms, these might not be expected to show such clear boundaries, but going southeast from north Texas into Mexico, Scott claimed to distinguish six facies:

Facies 1. Littoral zone: no ammonites, which presumably could not stand the extremes of temperature, the turbulent water, or the reduction in salinity. Reefs were similarly lacking in ammonites.

Facies 2. Offshore mud flats: ammonites still absent or very rare.

Facies 3. Infralittoral zone (epineritic zone of Scott): only thin, involute, and lightly ornamented ("tenuous") ammonites, such as *Engonoceras* and *Oxytropidoceras*, associated with large numbers of echinoids, pelecypods, and gastropods.

Facies 4. Circalittoral zone (infraneritic zone of Scott): a very great variety of ammonites, notably heavily ornamented, and uncoiled forms.

Facies 5. Upper part of the bathyal zone (epibathyal of Scott): smooth ammonites, such as *Desmoceras*, with ovate to subquadrate cross sections.

Facies 6. Lower or main part of the bathyal zone (infrabathyal of Scott): smooth, obese ammonites with thin shells, such as *Lytoceras* and *Phylloceras*. This zone is found not in Texas but in the supposed depths of the Cretaceous geosyncline in Mexico. This fits in with the classic observations of Haug, in the Alps, that the basic stocks of *Phylloceras* and *Lytoceras* dominated in this facies.

Scott's Texas study illustrates the way in which diverse lines of evidence may be used in paleoecology, for though it is included here, it might have been considered equally well in at least four other chapters.

Again descending the taxonomic scale, the distribution of a single species is controlled by many factors, any one of which is sufficient to restrain its expansion. (See discussion of Leibig's law of the minimum, page 10.) Every species may be thought of as constantly pressing against its boundaries and being restrained by the environment. The moment conditions change in a favorable way, the population will spread rapidly until it reaches another ecological barrier.

Fossil species are such an extremely subjective matter that few of the recorded geographical distributions can be regarded as completely reliable. At one extreme there are "species" such as *Atrypa reticularis* and *Stringocephalus burtini* which are recorded (in most cases probably quite wrongly) all over the world. At the other extreme there are examples of species which are known only at one horizon and one locality.

Many of these only have separate validity in the minds of their authors, but a few are indisputable. Thus there is the little problematical fishlike creature *Palaeospondylus gunni*, which has a family and order all to itself and which is only known from a single band in a single quarry in the Middle Devonian of northeast Scotland. It has no known ancestors, relations, or descendants.

INTERPRETATION OF PRESENT DISTRIBUTIONS

Every natural modern distribution of a plant or animal must be the direct result of the geological history of that species, and clearly we can learn a great deal from the study of such distributions.

Some have argued that there is a direct connection between the areal extent of a species and its geological age. This is the *age-and-area hypothesis* of J. C. Willis (1922), which, as originally postulated, simply said that the older a species was, the wider would be its distribution. Wrigley (1945) applied this to fossils in his studies of Tertiary gastropods. He stated that generally speaking, this was true for species of the Turridae, and that small genera with few species extended through less time and space than large genera with many species.

Others, e.g., Rosa (1931), have argued, on the contrary, that forms with wide continuous distributions are new successful species, whereas the really old species are those with wide discontinuous distributions, which occur today in widely separated localities as relicts.

Such discontinuous distributions have been explained in several different ways, with and without the assistance of paleontological evidence. The evidence indicates in many cases, that the present occurrences may be the last surviving pockets of a former more extensive distribution. In other cases, where such evidence is lacking, land bridges from continent to continent have been postulated or the Wegener hypothesis of continental drift has been invoked. Some interesting cases were discussed by Mayr (1951).

The outstanding example of a discontinuous distribution at the present day is the redwoods. *Sequoia*, or *Sequoiadendron*, occurs only as two species in California, and *Metasequoia* was found only in 1945 in a small area in Szechwan, central China. All sorts of imaginative land bridges and continental driftings might be postulated were it not for the evidence of the fossil redwoods which spread right round the Northern Hemisphere.

The same is true of *Araucaria*—the monkey puzzle—and its allies which in Mesozoic times was widespread in Europe, Asia, and North America, but now is restricted to very scattered areas in the Southern

Hemisphere (Figure 10.6). The extreme case is *Ginkgo,* formerly very widespread but surviving to today only as a single species, through preservation in Chinese and Japanese temple gardens.

An invertebrate example of a discontinuous distribution has been provided by Muir-Wood (1959)—the brachiopods *Dyscolia* and *Dallithyris,* which occur on both sides of the Atlantic and in the Indian Ocean, but there is no paleontological evidence to suggest how they crossed the deep ocean. These observations are taken as evidence of a former shallow-water connection across the Atlantic or of continental drift.

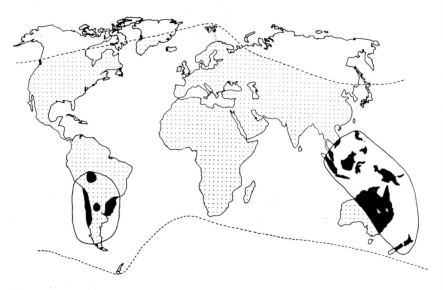

FIGURE 10.6 General limits of distribution of *Araucaria* and its allies in the Mesozoic (stippled) and at the present day (black).

Distributions never remain constant; they are always changing and adjusting themselves to the changing circumstances of the physical world. Just as uplift and erosion and climatic changes never stop operating, the biogeographical changes which are related to them go on and on. Man has, of course, considerably speeded up the rate of change, and every year it becomes more difficult to determine "natural" distributions. In some cases the interference has been direct and obvious; thus I have heard it said that at the present day there are more lions per square mile in England than in Africa! In other cases the interference has been more insidious; it has been said, for instance, that the distribution of the edible snail *Helix pomatia* around the world can be related to the distribution of French consulates. Apparently French sailors commonly carried barrels of living snails in their vessels to relieve their monotonous diet, and must often have made presents of them to fellow countrymen in remote parts of the world. The recipients no doubt ate the larger specimens and set the smaller ones free in their gardens to provide a continuing source of home comforts, often with disastrous results for the local vegetation.[4]

Even more indirect have been the effects of man via cultivation, civil engineering, domestic animals, and the transmission of diseases. Great efforts are now being made to counteract these effects by way of national parks and protection laws. Such efforts are very praiseworthy and very useful to biologists, but ultimately they are not very logical, since the organic world must change; species must extinguish other species as they always have done, and *Homo sapiens* is just one more species in the paleoecological record making its mark on its neighbors. although somewhat more destructive than most.

DISTRIBUTION OF MORPHOLOGICAL TYPES

We may study not only the distribution of a species or larger group but also the distribution of particular morphological features, regardless of the taxa to which they belong.

Reference was made in Chapter 9 to two rules of faunal distribution relating the size of animals and their parts to temperature. Two other rules may be applicable here. Jordan's rule states that fish tend to have more vertebrae at lower temperatures. G. L. Clarke (1954) quoted the case of cod hatched off Newfoundland at temperatures between 4 and 8°C having fifty-six vertebrae and those hatched off Nantucket at 10 to 11°C having only fifty-four vertebrae. Gloger's rule states the tendency in mammals, birds, and insects for species to be more melanic in warm, humid climates. This is obviously true in *Homo sapiens,* but there are many exceptions, e.g., the fulmars—*Fulmarus glacialis glacialis*—which include an increasing proportion of dark variants as one goes north in the North Atlantic. This rule is hardly applicable among fossils, but the others may be. Thus we have the contention (Dunbar, 1924) that the large size of the insects in Upper Carboniferous deposits in the Northern Hemisphere implies a warm climate. There are endless possibilities in studying fossils in this way, but very little has yet been done.

In a long series of papers, Ting Ying Ma (e.g., 1937, 1954, 1957) plotted the world distribution of growth features in fossil corals, working on the principle that seasonal effects are only appreciable outside

[4] It has even been suggested that the arrival of *H. pomatia* in Saint Helena can be attributed to Napoleon's enforced stay on that island.

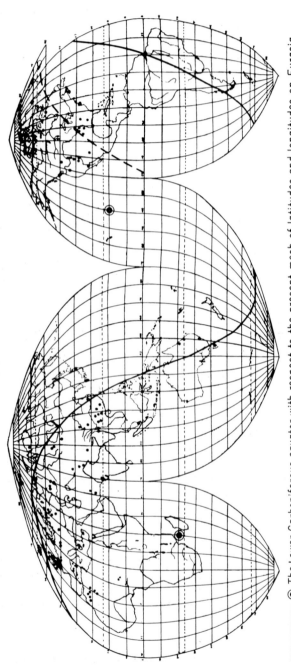

⊙ The Lower Carboniferous equator with respect to the present mesh of latitudes and longitudes on Eurasia and the corresponding poles.

– – – The Lower Carboniferous equator with respect to the present mesh of latitudes and longitudes on North America.

• Localities of fossil corals.

Figure 10.7 Distribution of Lower Carboniferous corals in relation to supposed contemporary equator. The broken line through North America indicates the position of the equator as deduced from coral growth; the solid line through South America represents the continuation of the Eastern Hemisphere equator when plotted as a great circle. (From Ma, 1954; by courtesy of the author.)

the tropics and that corals with regularly arranged dissepiments (not grouped in rings) are likely to have lived near the equator.[5] From large numbers of observations, Ma deduced a supposed equator for most of the geological systems. His map for the Lower Carboniferous is shown in Figure 10.7. He further maintained that, since his equators did not form great circles, it was necessary to postulate a drifting apart of the New and the Old World.

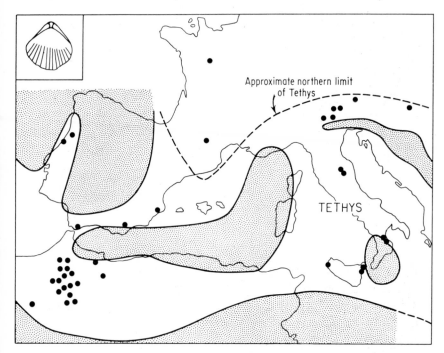

FIGURE 10.8 Distribution of costate terebratuloids in certain Lower Jurassic rocks of Europe and North Africa. (Data chiefly from Dubar, 1942; paleogeography after Wills, 1951.)

Returning, as usual, to the Mesozoic brachiopods, we have an example on a different scale in the work of Dubar (1942) on the distribution of costate terebratuloids in the Jurassic. He was able to show that, regardless of the genus and, in fact, the family involved, costation occurs on these usually smooth brachiopods within quite sharply defined geographical limits. Dubar was interested chiefly in Morocco, where there is a great concentration of these morphological types, but if his records are plotted on a paleogeographical map (Figure 10.8), they are found

[5] The same arguments have been used about the absence of seasonal rings in Pennsylvanian trees in the Northern Hemisphere.

to correspond almost exactly with the limits of the geosynclinal Tethys.

The examples quoted so far have related morphological types to major features of climate or paleogeography. However, the approach being discussed here is capable of use on a much more detailed level. Thus the swamp, or bald, cypress, which has often been recorded as a

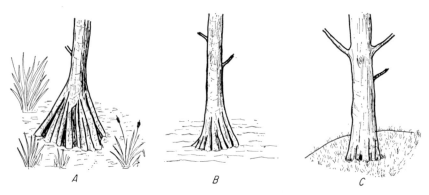

FIGURE 10.9 Pneumatophores, or "knees," in the swamp cypress, *Taxodium distichum*. A, in a permanent swamp in Louisiana; B, in a pool in Kew Gardens, London; C, on dry land in Illinois. (Drawn from photographs taken by the author.)

fossil in Cenozoic sediments, varies considerably in form. It is well known for its remarkable pneumatophores, or "knees," which are enlargements at the base of the trunk due to excessive cambial growth in the presence of abundant water and oxygen. They are best developed in a permanent swampy situation at the water-air junction; they are generally absent in deep water, on dry land, and where there is only brief flooding (Figure 10.9). The observation of such features in fossils would be instructive not only about the habitat of the fossil concerned but also about that of its associates.

ELEVEN

Changes in habitat and habit

Omnia mutantur—all things change. The only constant in geological history is the state of change, and this is as true in paleoecology as in every other part of the subject. The processes may have remained the same—erosion, evaporation, evolution, and the rest—but the products have always been slightly different from their predecessors.

From the paleoecological point of view, organisms may change their habitats or their habits, but the former kind of change is usually much easier to detect than the latter.

CHANGES IN HABITAT

In this context, habitat is taken to mean simply the *place* where an organism lives. The study of changes in this habitat, or migration, is probably the most important aspect of paleoecology for the stratigrapher, since every change in the fossils of a succession must be due either to evolution (and therefore potentially useful stratigraphically) or to migration (and therefore potentially misleading stratigraphically). Figure 11.1 is taken from a previous discussion of this problem (Ager, 1956b), and serves to illustrate the essence of the problem with the minimum of words.

Until we have an extremely exact method of absolute dating, the problems of fossil migration will be almost insoluble. At present we have to measure one ruler against another. We have to accept the graptolites or the ammonites as arbiters in order to deduce the migrations of the trilobites or the brachiopods. Paleontologists have often maintained that migration is so rapid, compared with sedimentation that it would not show up at all in the rocks. S. S. Buckman was the great protagonist of this dictum. For example, he wrote (1922): "The rate of Ammonite migration to that of deposition was like the flight of an aeroplane to the progress of bricklaying." This is all very well if we think of a new species evolving suddenly in one place and then spreading (instantaneously, from the geological point of view) throughout a universal, uniform, and continuous environment. It is not logical, however, to accept diachrony in sediments but to deny it in fossils, as did Buckman. As long as a particular environment persisted in a given area, the organisms not suited to that environment must have been excluded. Any

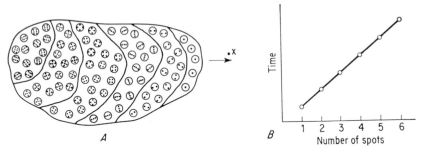

FIGURE 11.1   **How apparent changes in fossil characters with time, studied in one small area, may be due to migration, not evolution.** *A,* map of the distribution of a hypothetical species, ranging from forms with one spot to forms with six. The arrow indicates direction of migration past locality X. *B,* plot of specimens collected from successive horizons at X, showing an apparent evolutionary trend from forms with one spot to forms with six. (Redrawn from Ager, 1956*b.*)

succession of varying sediments with varying faunas and floras demonstrates the fact that recognizable migration took place, and the argument becomes merely one of degree.

In this regard, some paleontologists distinguish between free-moving forms such as the ammonites and sedentary forms such as the corals. But it seems doubtful that the brevity of the free-swimming life of any organism would have delayed its spread to an extent commonly appreciable in the rocks. Thorson (1946, 1950) has written at length on the larval ecology of modern benthonic animals, and his work is a mine of information about this all-important stage in any migratory process.

One case in which the duration and activity of the free-swimming larval stage may possibly be reflected in the fossil record was discussed by Arkell (1935). He suggested that the lack of variety in the coral faunas of the British "Corallian" (Upper Jurassic) may have been due to the fact that only certain species were able to migrate into and colonize the area in the short time available between two muddy-sea episodes. However, it is quite apparent that even the most sedentary of creatures, with the briefest of opportunities for migration during a single lifetime, can spread at a remarkable rate.

As in evolution, it is opportunity rather than potential ability that has probably always been the controlling factor in migration. Interference by man has provided several illustrations of this principle, a good one being the arrival and spread of the American slipper limpet, *Crepidula fornicata*, in southern Britain. This is a sessile animal which was introduced accidentally with a cargo of oysters into the Thames estuary in about 1890 (Figure 11.2). It had reached the Solent, behind the Isle of Wight, by 1915, and very soon became the commonest shell

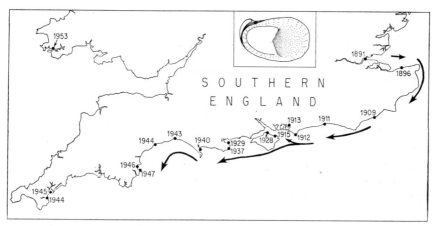

FIGURE 11.2 The spread of *Crepidula fornicata* in southern Britain. The isolated records at Falmouth and Milford Haven probably represent independent introductions. (Compiled by Miss Mary E. Pugh from numerous sources.)

on the south coast of England. Similar rapid spreads of this American species are known to have occurred in other parts of Europe.

There is a possibility that further accidental introductions occurred at various places, e.g. at Milford Haven and Falmouth (Figure 11.2). Assuming, however, a simple spread from a single starting place, the British rate works out at about 320 km in twenty-five years, or 13 km a year. At that rate, *C. fornicata* could go right round the world in about three thousand years, which is no time at all geologically speaking, but it would have to have the right sort of coastal waters all the way. In practice, it would be repeatedly delayed, awaiting the opportunity for further migration, and this might make its movements discernible in the stratigraphical record. We may, in fact, consider how long *C. fornicata* had to await the opportunity provided by man to cross the Atlantic. Although other species are known in Europe as late as the Miocene, *C. fornicata* appears to have been restricted to the Atlantic and Gulf Coasts of North America from the Miocene until the last century.[1]

It may therefore be said that this gastropod was restricted to the west side of the North Atlantic for perhaps 20 million years before the opportunity arrived for it to cross to the highly suitable European environments. The opportunity which came was artificial, and it is impossible to estimate how much longer it would have had to wait under natural circumstances.

In this example, the opportunity required was that of transport to an already-favorable environment. Alternatively there is the situation in which the means of transport are available but the favorable environment is lacking. If this then suddenly becomes available, migration takes place very quickly indeed. Arkell (1956*a*) has recorded an example of this in Egypt. Lake Birket Qârûn in Faiyûm was fed by the Nile and had a normal Nile fresh-water fauna for tens of thousands of years, as proved by associated paleolithic implements. In 1907 the lake was partly drained to provide more agricultural land; its salinity increased, and it suddenly became suitable for marine organisms. By 1927 the dominant mollusks were *Cardium edule* and *Scrobicularia cottardi*—both fully marine forms—and these were abundant enough to have formed a shell bank for miles along the lakeshore. These pelecypods must have come from saline lakes near Alexandria across more than a hundred miles of desert, and they are thought to have been carried in the mud on the legs of the ducks and flamingos which have always visited both lakes.

This last example is more in keeping with what may be expected in paleoecology than the preceding one, since increasing salinities are commonplace in the stratigraphical record but rapid ocean transport is not. Nevertheless, we must remember that birds cannot be postulated as a means of transport before they evolved in the Jurassic. Trueman (1947) used this point in discussing the spread of nonmarine pelecypods in the Upper Carboniferous. He suggested that the lack of such transport might explain the fact that the faunas of the intermontane "limnic" coal basins were more restricted than those of the marginal "paralic" basins.

Another common reason for the rapid spread of a particular species is the disappearance of its natural enemies. This may be the explanation of the "explosive" expansion of the armadillo into the southern United States in the last hundred years. Apparently no armadillos lived in the United States before the middle of the last century. They crossed the Rio Grande in about 1854, and since then there has been a continuous advance, mainly toward the northeast (Figure 11.3). One movement toward the northwest, just into New Mexico, was followed by a retreat;

[1] There is another form, *C. onyx*, with the same stratigraphical range on the Pacific Coast, which may be conspecific.

and one isolated colony in north central Oklahoma has also disappeared. For the most part, however, the advance (perhaps assisted here and there by man, notably in Florida) has been steady in rate; and as yet there is no apparent slowing up (Buchanan, 1958). Other small animals such as the coatimundi and the road runner have been moving in the same direction, probably influenced directly or indirectly by the works of man.

Other expansions have no apparent cause, or at least none that has yet been found—for example, the recent westward spread in Europe of the collared dove (Figure 11.4).

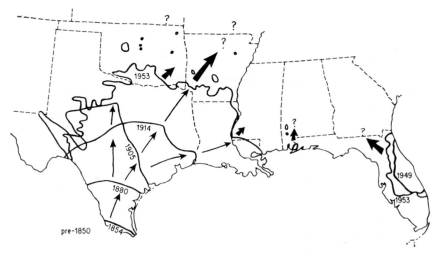

FIGURE 11.3 Spread of the armadillo *Dasypus novemcinctus mexicanus* in the southern United States. The circles indicate outlying colonies in 1953; the heavy arrows indicate the directions of spread since 1953. (Slightly simplified from Buchanan and Talmage, 1954; by courtesy of *Texas Journal of Science.*)

We normally think of migration as an animal activity, but many cases are also known of the rapid spread of land plants, once they are given the opportunity. The prickly pear cactus (*Opuntia*) was introduced into Australia like the rabbit and rapidly became as big a curse to agriculture. At one time it was estimated that the prickly pear was spreading at the rate of an acre a minute!

Fossil Migrations

Probably the best-documented studies of fossil migrations have been some of those on the larger Pleistocene mammals. The route and timetable of some members of the elephant family is known in detail. *Archidiskodon,* the southern mammoth, is believed to have started its long journey from the Vaal River area of South Africa in early Pliocene times

(Osborne, 1935, 1942). It spread through North Africa and then around the north side of the Mediterranean, via Roumania, Italy, and France, to England, which it reached by lower Pleistocene times. Another branch spread, perhaps via northeast Arabia, to India, which was reached by upper Pliocene times, and thence to the Bering Strait and across into North America by the early Pleistocene. Then it spread down the west side of this continent, and is found from Saskatchewan to Mexico, with an extension into Florida. Altogether it covered something like

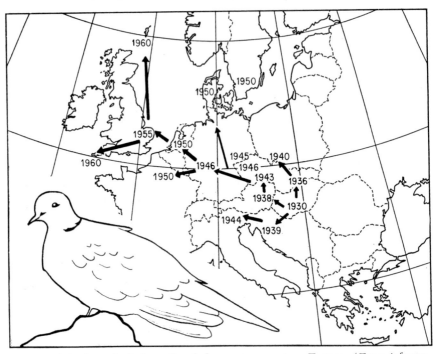

FIGURE 11.4 Spread of the collared dove across western Europe. (From information in *British Birds*.)

24,000 km in 3 million years. Some of the mastodons went even farther and moved into South America.

Elephants are large, obvious, and well-studied fossils, but among the invertebrates it is only in the most studied parts of the world and the most studied parts of the stratigraphical column that we may begin to attempt deductions about migrations. As yet, remarkably little has been done.

The *Pleuroceras spinatum* zone of the British Lower Jurassic has large and varied brachiopod faunas, but follows strata which are almost completely without brachiopods. By relating these faunas to those of other parts of Europe, I was able to suggest (Ager, 1956a) the direc-

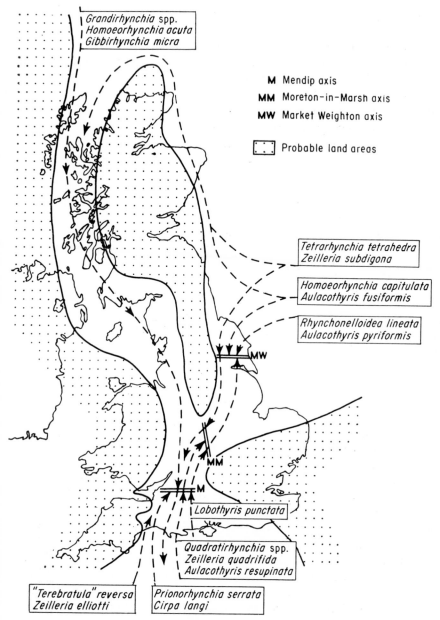

Grandirhynchia spp.
Homoeorhynchia acuta
Gibbirhynchia micra

M   Mendip axis
MM Moreton-in-Marsh axis
MW Market Weighton axis

[∴] Probable land areas

Tetrarhynchia tetrahedra
Zeilleria subdigona

Homoeorhynchia capitulata
Aulacothyris fusiformis

Rhynchonelloidea lineata
Aulacothyris pyriformis

Lobothyris punctata

Quadratirhynchia spp.
Zeilleria quadrifida
Aulacothyris resupinata

"Terebratula" reversa
Zeilleria elliotti

Prionorhynchia serrata
Cirpa langi

FIGURE 11.5   Probable directions of brachiopod migration into the British area during *spinatum* zone (Lower Jurassic) times. Only certain of the more abundant species are indicated. (From Ager, 1956a; by courtesy of the Geological Society of London.)

tions of brachiopod migrations into the British area during *spinatum* zone times (Figure 11.5). I deduced that there were three immigrant streams, one from Normandy and the south generally, one from north France and Germany, and one from the north (perhaps from Greenland).

Brachiopods seem to be particularly amenable to this sort of study. The Polish paleontologist G. Biernat (1957) has noted the occurrence of the large Cretaceous brachiopod *Peregrinella* as early as the Valanginian

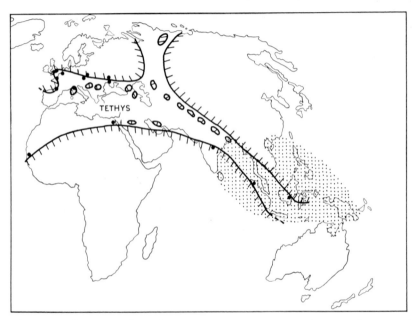

FIGURE 11.6 Supposed paleogeography of lower Eocene times, showing the distribution of the stemless palm *Nipa* by heavy dots. The stippled area represents the present limits of this genus. (Redrawn from Edwards, 1936, with additional records from Kuźniar, 1910, and Rásky, 1948.)

in California, whereas it only arrives suddenly in Europe in the upper Hauterivian. Similarly, in much later rocks, Elliott (1956b) was able to show that certain brachiopods, notably *Hemithyris psittacea*, migrated across the arctic from the Pacific to the Atlantic in Quaternary times.

Movements of animals and plants in Cenozoic strata can often be related to major climatic changes. The stemless palm *Nipa* lives along the seacoasts of the Indo-Malayan region at the present day. Because of its nearshore habitat and the large and distinctive nature of its fruits, *Nipa* is well represented in the fossil record as far back as the Eocene, when it was much more widespread. W. N. Edwards (1936) plotted its distribution in lower Eocene times (Figure 11.6) and showed that its northernmost limit just about corresponded with the famous occurrence in the London clay of Sheppey in the Thames estuary (Chapter 12). He suggested that it was distributed by means of the large floating fruits which were carried up and down the Tethys by currents. *Nipa* retreated southeastward to its present domicile as a result of climatic deterioration during the Tertiary. This seems to have been a restriction of a wide distribution rather than true migration; but several other Tertiary distributions, in various groups, fit into the same pattern of southeasterly retreat through Tertiary times.

The echinoid *Amphiope* had a circummediterranean distribution in the Eocene and Oligocene (Stefanini, 1924); it spread to Indonesia in

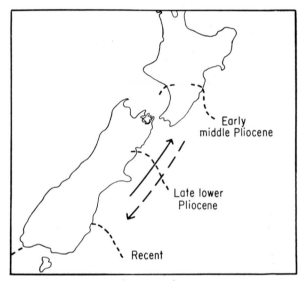

FIGURE 11.7 Changes in distribution of the *Chlamys delicatula*—*C. campbellica* lineage in the late Cenozoic of New Zealand. (After Fleming, 1944.)

the Miocene and is now entirely restricted to that region. The pelecypod *Trigonia* was ubiquitous in the Mesozoic; in the Tertiary it became restricted to a few species in eastern Asia and Australasia; at the present day it is known only around Australia. Perhaps the best example is provided by the gastropod *Gilbertina* and its relations, which, according to Rosenkrantz (personal communication, 1960), moved from Greenland progressively southeastward to New Zealand within the Paleogene.

All the above movements were probably due to climatic deterioration; and indeed, in the absence of major paleogeographical changes, faunal and floral migrations may provide a very delicate record of climatic changes in the past. C. A. Fleming has shown (1944) how the differences in mollusk distributions in New Zealand through Pliocene times reflect the climatic changes (Figure 11.7). He found, however, that in late Pliocene times, the inception of a current of subtropical water in the north stabilized the water temperatures in spite of the continued lowering of air temperatures which culminated in the Pleistocene glaciation on land. Thus the only marine mollusk which became extinct because of the climate was the intertidal pelecypod *Anadara trapezia*, and this may be blamed on its exposure to frost when the tide was out.

In all these examples of migration this enigma still remains: to be sure of our migration we must be sure of our correlation, and to be sure of our correlation we must be sure that there was no appreciable migration.

Marine Migrations and Currents

The New Zealand study just mentioned indicates the importance of currents in marine migrations, and a fascinating side issue in the study of fossil migrations is the elucidation of past current directions. Clearly currents must have a major effect on the distribution of marine forms, both pelagic and benthonic. D. M. Reid (1935) showed, for instance, how the distribution of the modern sea urchin *Echinus esculentus* is related to the North Atlantic Drift (Figure 11.8). Sewell (1940) discussed the relationship between the distribution of marine organisms and hydrographic conditions, and suggested possible current directions since mid-Tertiary times. Kobayashi (1954) demonstrated the persistence of ocean currents, using the evidence of occasional drifted nautiloids in the Japanese Tertiary. Similarly Fell (1953) emphasized the importance of currents in discussing the origin of the Cenozoic echinoderm faunas of Australasia. He showed how these shallow-water forms are restricted by deep-sea barriers unless a favorable current is present.

Alwyn Williams (personal communication, 1958) has even been able to relate brachiopod distributions in the lower Paleozoic of Europe and North America to the major current pattern in the North Atlantic of that time.

Seasonal Migrations

When we speak of fossil migrations, we naturally think of long-term and permanent changes and extensions in distribution and not of seasonal migrations which we could hardly expect to see fossilized. However, there is at least one record of a supposed seasonal migration. This is the remarkable picture of Upper Triassic dinosaur habits worked out by von Huene (1928) on the basis of fossils found near Trossingen in Württemberg. The local geography of the time was an upland area separated by a strip of arid desert from an inland sea. The theropod dinosaur *Plateosaurus* apparently lived mostly in the forested upland areas but in the annual dry season migrated across the desert to the plentiful fish-and-reptile diet of the inland sea. Von Huene noted that the length of the hind leg in a fairly small specimen was about 1.3 m, and from this he calculated a stride of about 1 m. Assuming a normal rate of about two strides a second, the rate was 120 m a minute, or 7.2 km an hour. The desert belt was at least 100 km wide, and von Huene suggested that the dinosaurs may have made the trip in two

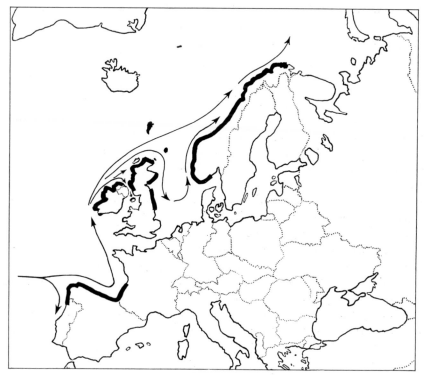

FIGURE 11.8 Shore distribution of the echinoid *Echinus esculentus* in relation to the North Atlantic Drift. (After D. M. Reid, 1935.)

days, perhaps traveling in the cool of the night. He further noted that the remains of *Plateosaurus* found in the loesslike deposits of the desert belt around Trossingen were invariably young or poorly developed individuals which perished on the march! W. E. Swinton (1934) raised the objection that von Huene was giving *Plateosaurus* mammallike attributes of herd behavior and sustained effort; and the whole theory is obviously highly subjective. We may concede, however, that the very different place in the world of the reptiles of the past went with habits and modes of behavior very different from those of today.

CHANGES IN HABIT

That changes in habit are even more difficult to determine in fossils than changes in habitat is a matter of which we must all be aware. Yet even within the few years of recorded natural history, indisputable changes in habit have been observed. A well-substantiated case is that of the small British bird the tree creeper—*Certhia familiaris britannica* —which within the last fifty years or so has acquired the habit of hollowing out a nest for itself in the soft bark of the giant redwood *Sequoiadendron giganteum*. These trees were only introduced to Britain from the Sierra Nevada of California about a hundred years ago, and have to be about forty years old before the bark is thick enough for the bird to use. In an even shorter time—in the thirty-odd years since the introduction of the milk bottle—tits have learned to remove the cardboard or metal caps for the food supply underneath.

Owing to current ecological fashion, the popular small birds are much better studied than most other groups, but examples of habit change are even known in such unpopular groups as the marine invertebrates. Thus Dexter (1947) described how the mollusk *Lacuna vincta* changed its habits on the coast near Cape Ann, Massachusetts. Its usual food, the eelgrass *Zostera marina*, disappeared completely from the area because of an epidemic, and the mollusk was forced to change to the brown alga *Laminaria digitata*.

Fossil examples of habit change within species are difficult to prove, but undoubtedly have occurred. G. R. Coope (personal communication, 1962) has found evidence in British Pleistocene beetle assemblages that several species appear to have changed their habits in the last few millennia. Species which are mutually exclusive in distribution today are found together in interglacial deposits. It may be argued that other explanations are possible, but the apparent change in habits of some species may be contrasted with the demonstrably constant habits of others. Thus a water beetle which lives on tadpoles and sticklebacks at the present day was found associated with stickleback and frog bones in a Pleistocene deposit (Coope et al., 1961).

Changes in the habits of genera are easier to demonstrate. Three of the commonest pelecypod genera in the shallow-water facies of the European Jurassic are *Trigonia*, *Astarte* and *Pholadomya*, all of which still live at the present day; but nowadays *Astarte* is boreal, *Trigonia* lives only in the warm water around Australia, and *Pholadomya* is abyssal (Arkell, 1956a). Woodring (1960) also drew attention to the apparent change in habits of *Astarte*. In early Eocene times this was associated with the palm *Nipa*, discussed above, and with a large variety of other now-tropical animals and plants; but today *Astarte*, with its distinctly northerly distribution, is separated by several thousand kilometers from *Nipa* and the others. Woodring called this an example of "paleoecologic dissonance" and suggested that this is more common than is generally supposed.

One of the most quoted examples of habit change through geological time is that of the Hexactinellida (Hyalospongea), or glass sponges. It is commonly stated, e.g., by Oakley (1937), that at the present day they only live in deep water, and down to the maximum depths known, and reach their greatest abundance between 1,000 and 10,000 m depth. They are certainly rare at less than 200 m, and the only place where they occur in shallower water is under thick ice in the antarctic, where the situation, in terms of temperature and light, is comparable to deep water. Yet all the evidence of this group in the Paleozoic, notably the wonderful Devonian faunas of New York State, points to shallow-water conditions.

This would seem to be an object lesson in the limitations of uniformitarianism applied to fossils. However, R. E. H. Reid (1958, 1962) has disputed the popular assumption about the depth habits of modern hexactinellid sponges. He wrote: "It does not . . . seem to be well known that Hexactinellids appear today to be as abundant at little more than 100 fathoms as at any greater depth . . . abundance [at that depth] is not anomalous by modern standards." We have, therefore, the alternative object lesson of the undesirability of drawing uniformitarian conclusions from an inadequate knowledge of modern forms.

There are other major groups which we can say, with fair confidence, changed their habits during geological time. The shallow seas of the Paleozoic were dominated by brachiopods in the ecological niches which are occupied by mollusks and other groups at the present day. Gekker (1957) suggested direct analogies between brachiopods such as *Gigantoproductus* of the Carboniferous and the oysters of the Mesozoic and Cenozoic; others such as *Irboskites*, he suggested, were comparable in habit with the modern barnacles. These are certainly not the habits of the majority of living brachiopods, and the group as a whole seems to have retreated into deeper water since the beginning of the Tertiary.

Changes in habit are often accompanied or followed by apparent morphological changes, as in the case of melanism in moths and butterflies which now live on the dark foliage of industrial areas. This was accepted for a while as a genuine evolutionary change in response to a changed environment, but Kettlewell (1957) has shown that it is probably a return of the rare darker variants to the dominant position they held in the past when there was a darker, coniferous vegetation. The process is the usual one of natural selection, effected in this case by predatory birds.

A comparable fossil example may be the change in coiling direction in the foram *Globorotalia truncatulinoides*, which has been observed in deep-sea cores going down into late Pleistocene deposits. Ericson et al., (1954) found that the coiling direction changed repeatedly. This was not an absolute change of the whole population, but a change in the proportion of dextral and sinistral forms (Figure 11.9). The map

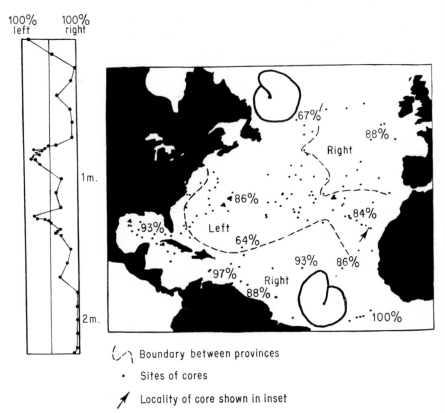

FIGURE 11.9 Coiling of *Globorotalia truncatulinoides* in the surface layer of cores from the North Atlantic. The column on the left shows the form of the coiling in a core penetrating Pleistocene sediments. (After Ericson, Wollin, and Wollin, 1954.)

shows the lateral variation at the present day, and it may be presumed that some undetermined environmental factor is involved.

Casey (in Eagar, 1952) has suggested a remarkable correlation between changes in habit and changes in anatomy in some Middle Jurassic pelecypod genera from Scotland. The record is one of change from fully marine to estuarine to fresh-water conditions, and Casey recognized three new genera in the later deposits: first, a fresh- or brackish-water adaptation of the marine pelecypod *Protomiodon;* secondly, another form like *Protomiodon,* except for a hinge indicating affinity with another marine form, *Hartwellia;* and thirdly, a modified version of the marine pelecypod *Corbicella.* In all three there was a tendency to strengthen the lateral teeth, as in fresh- or brackish-water genera such as *Corbicula.*

Similarly, Trueman (1940) was able to show experimentally that there was probably a change in habit—from swimming to crawling—in the well-documented ammonite lineage *Liparoceras-Androgynoceras.* The slender, evolute, lightly ornamented *Androgynoceras* was almost certainly a normal swimming form, whereas the globose, involute, tuberculate *Liparoceras* probably crawled on the sea floor. This seemed to be a rather sudden change in habit, which may help to explain the relatively few, though indisputable, intermediate forms between these two very different genera.

PART THREE

Paleosynecology

*T*HIS part of my book deals with what many would regard as
"true paleoecology," that is, with the study of the living
communities of the past, their relationships with their physical
and chemical environment, and their interrelationships among
themselves. Thus C. L. Fenton (1935) has written: "Paleoecology
. . . . is primarily concerned with the sociology of fossil organisms,
and any narrower concept will hamper its development and
usefulness."
I am therefore now concerned with the methods that can be used
in the study of whole assemblages of fossils, not just that of
isolated individuals. It is especially important from the start
to differentiate between an assemblage, used here for any
association of organisms whether living or dead, and a community,
which is essentially a living association of many different kinds
of animals and plants. This brings me naturally to the first of
our methods of study.

TWELVE

Comparison with living assemblages

M Y first method in paleosynecology—as in paleoautecology—is that of uniformitarianism and the interpretation of the past in the light of the present.

So much has been written about the misleading nature of the fossil record that every student should already be well aware of the difficulties inherent in the comparison of fossil and living assemblages. It is a useful, even essential exercise for every paleontologist to make a detailed study of some modern community, at all levels, and then to consider under what circumstances and in what form it might survive as a fossil association.

Many paleontologists like to talk about biocoenoses, or "life assemblages," and thanatocoenoses, or "death assemblages." The greater part of modern ecology concerns itself with living communities, and some prefer to call this subject "biocoenology." (There is, in fact, a Russian journal with that name.) Ladd (1959) has followed Hutchinson (1957) in suggesting that paleosynecology should therefore be called "paleobiocoenology." It could be equally well argued that the present subject should be called "thanatocoenology," since we are entirely concerned with "death assemblages" (in the broad sense). On the same principle, Morishima (1948) has suggested "paleothanatology" for the study of fossil assemblages.

But all these ugly words are inadequate, inaccurate, and ambiguous; and the underlying fact which cannot be emphasized too strongly is that no fossil assemblage is a biocoenose as understood by the ecologist, that is, a living community, though some may approach it a little closer than others (Plate 8). Thus Craig (1953) argued very reasonably that we should avoid ambiguous Latin and Greek terms and use the simple expressions "fossil community" for associations of fossils ecologically related among themselves and to their containing deposit, and "fossil assemblage" for associations of fossils without ecological implications. I agree wholeheartedly with this view, though it must be appreciated that it is very difficult to draw a line between the two.

The paleoecologist must never forget that he is studying not the living inhabitants of the village but only the bodies in the churchyard, and then only after many visits by grave robbers. Usually the fossil assemblage bears very little resemblance to the living community which it represents. In a few rare miracles of preservation there is an approach to it, but this can never be very close. Thus there were Walcott's famous discoveries in the Burgess shale of British Columbia, where a wonderful cross section of the soft-bodied life in a Middle Cambrian sea was beautifully preserved; and there was Mackie's accidental discovery of the Rhynie chert in eastern Scotland, in which a whole series of Middle Devonian plants were perfectly petrified together with the fungi growing within their tissues and the earliest known insects which lived among the vegetation. Such finds give great insight into the life of the past, but even the best fossil assemblage cannot but be a very poor reflection of the original living community.

Figure 12.1 shows diagrammatically all the things which may happen to a living community in the process of fossilization. The most nearly perfect (but quite unattainable) conditions are represented by the series on the left of the diagram, but even here there would be confusing anomalies in the resultant fossil assemblages. Thus the birds and the flies would be in the same bed as the mice and the worms; or, in a marine deposit, pelagic organisms from all levels of the sea would lie with the forms which lived on the bottom (Figure 2.1). In practice, the fossil assemblage is always much further removed from the living community, if only because of selective fossilization and the mixing together of successive generations.

Under stable conditions the latter problem may not seem to be important, but it will almost certainly completely distort any quantitative picture of the community. On the average, a snail which lives for two years will be twice as well represented as a fish which lives for four years.

To pursue my village-population metaphor, consider the organic population of the Roman city of Pompeii. There have been three fundamentally different assemblages connected with that unfortunate city. First there was the living population as it existed up to the 24th of August, A.D. 79. This living community, or biocoenose, must have consisted of old men and women, middle-aged men and women, young men and women, boys and girls, babies, horses, cattle, dogs, sheep, goats, birds, mice, lizards, fleas, cockroaches, trees, shrubs, vegetables, grass, and so

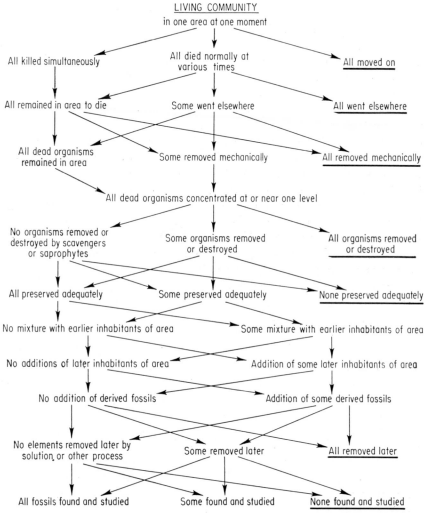

FIGURE 12.1   The various possible fates of a living community during the process of fossilization. Phrases underlined indicate complete exclusion of the community from the fossil record.

on and so on. Scores of species of animals and plants must have lived together in that hot southern city.

The second Pompeian assemblage is that of the necropolis just outside the Nicerian Gate, which, like the village churchyard, contains the remains of human beings who died in the ordinary way over a long period of time. This differs from the first population in a number of ways. In the burial assemblage there is only one species, *Homo sapiens;* none of its associated organisms are represented. What is more, this one species is represented in a very biased way. It must contain an overrepresentation of old people and, considering the high infant-mortality rate of those times, of babies also. Other age groups must be underrepresented. In other words, this is an assemblage that—just like the average fossil assemblage—was highly selective both in species and in age groups.

Finally, there is what I may call the catastrophic population of Pompeii—the organisms buried and preserved under the volcanic ash of the fatal eruption. In this assemblage, there are human individuals of all ages in more representative proportions (unless more young people escaped through being able to run faster). There are also other species of the community, such as dogs and beans. Yet the process of burial and fossilization was still highly selective, and many major groups, such as the insects, are not represented at all. The catastrophic population at Pompeii is therefore a little closer to the living population than is the cemetery assemblage, but still very inadequate.

In normal paleoecological studies there are even more difficulties, because of all the complications brought about by later geological events. Fossils may be transported from one place to another, they may be mechanically sorted or derived from older beds, and the remains of many generations will almost always be mixed together. Some paleoecologists, then—for example, Sartenaer (1959*b*)—use further terms to distinguish different stages in the obscuration of the biocoenose in the fossil record. Thus following on thanatocoenose there are taphocoenose (burial assemblage) and oryctocoenose (outcrop assemblage)—both terms proposed by Efremov (1940).

THE STATISTICAL STUDY OF FOSSIL
ASSEMBLAGES

C. B. Williams (1954) has shown how essential a statistical approach is in modern ecology for obtaining an accurate picture of a large and varied community; and statisticians are always only too willing to tell us how to design our experiments. But regrettably, all this is rarely possible in paleoecology. In the vast majority of fossiliferous deposits, we cannot sample adequately, we can only take what is there. The micropaleontologist is usually better off through the sheer abundance of his material, but the student of larger fossils must realize his limitations. Yet paleontologists themselves add to all their natural difficulties by their subjective and unscientific modes of collecting, and generally

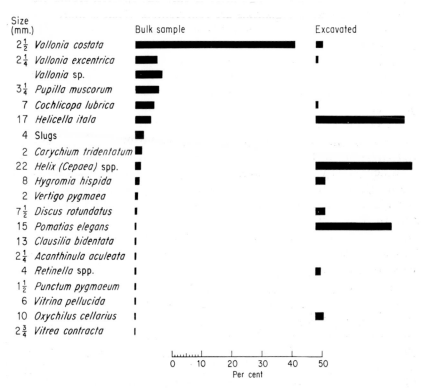

FIGURE 12.2 Comparative histograms for Quaternary mollusks obtained by bulk sampling and sieving (*left*) and by hand picking from the surface (*right*); Arreton Down, Isle of Wight. (Unpublished, reproduced by kind permission of the author, Mr. B. W. Sparks.)

speaking, do not seem to realize the huge subjective errors which come into these normal collecting methods. B. W. Sparks has demonstrated these in a startling way by comparing the results obtained from bulk samples with the results obtained by ordinary collecting by hand and eye (Figure 12.2). The comparison comes from a study of Quaternary non-marine mollusks on Arreton Down in the Isle of Wight. The species overrepresented in the hand-picked samples are, in every case, forms which are conspicuous by reason of size or color. Though paleontologists cannot often take bulk samples and extract *all* the fossils, they should obviously do so where possible.

The size of the bulk sample required for an adequate cross section of a fossil population depends on many factors, including the rate of sedimentation and the density of the original community. In theory, one should determine the minimum sample size independently for each bed, by taking a series of samples and observing at what level the percentages of each element in the population become asymptotic. In practice, this is rarely possible, and one develops a set of standards for each type of sediment.

Emiliani (1950) put forward the proposition that there is a direct relationship between a physical environment and the total variability of its dead population. He suggested that studies of the "total mean," "total standard deviation" and "total variability" of fossil assemblages might enable one to determine the physical character of the contemporary environment. The total variability of all the fossils present obviates any problems connected with age considerations. Under optimum conditions, this variability will be smallest, since the variability of each growth stage and the number of immature dead will be at a minimum. For the interpretation of past environments, a set of standards from modern "death assemblages" in different environments would be necessary. Emiliani illustrated his proposition with data derived from assemblages of small forams. Clearly the results obtained from more complex assemblages would be more difficult to interpret.

Boucot (1953) was concerned with the more strictly paleoecological problem of distinguishing between "life assemblages" and "death assemblages" of fossils. He endeavored to do this by a statistical examination of each species present. His first method was the simple size-frequency distribution curve, as illustrated in Figure 12.3. With a single generation of fertilized eggs one would expect a distribution as in curve A, this being the normal survivorship curve for a single population. From the paleontological point of view, this might be modified according to the stage in development at which a fossilizable shell or skeleton starts to form. It is also modified by the lower limit of practical measurement. With the appearance of more larvae having the same mortality rate, the asymmetry would be exaggerated, as in curve B. With varying mortality rates, right-skewed curves would be produced with variable curvature, as C. The predicted size-frequency curve for any one species in a true fossil community would therefore be of the form shown in curve E.

If only one age group were present (an almost impossible circumstance under natural conditions), a bell-shaped curve like D might be produced. This type of curve might also be expected if any kind of mechanical sorting, selective predation, solution, or the like had occurred. It should be noted, however, that transported assemblages of small shells may strongly simulate the right-skewed size-frequency distributions of living communities. Another complication is that seasonal spawning may produce multiple peaks.

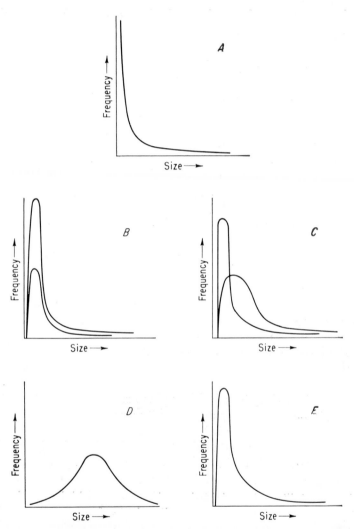

FIGURE 12.3 Size-frequency distribution curves for various types of population. A, normal survivorship curve; B, mortality curves for different initial population densities with uniform mortality rates; C, mortality curves for populations with different mortality rates; D, bell-shaped normal distribution curve; E, predicted curve for a "life assemblage." (From Boucot, 1953; by courtesy of *American Journal of Science*.)

A further factor which Boucot considered, in distinguishing fossil "life assemblages" among bivalve mollusks, was the ratio of articulated to disarticulated shells. He also suggested studying the ratios of opposite valves when they occur in the same deposit. If the right valves show a mode very different from the left valves, then obviously this cannot be a "life assemblage."

Boucot's final method was that of population densities on individual bedding planes. This is largely a function of the rate of sedimentation,

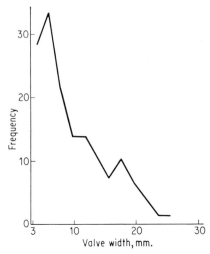

Valve width, mm.

FIGURE 12.4   Size-frequency distribution of *Globithyris callida* (number of specimens per 10-cm cube) in a supposed true fossil community from the Lower Devonian of Maine. (From Boucot, 1953; by courtesy of *American Journal of Science*.)

but may indicate if a given bedding plane represents one generation or many. The subject of density and diversity among fossil assemblages will be discussed later (Chapter 14).

Boucot applied these principles to a study of six fossil assemblages in the Lower Devonian of northern Maine. For five out of the six he obtained bell-shaped curves and concluded that these were "death assemblages." For one assemblage he obtained right-skewed curves, concave upward in the expected form (Figure 12.4). This he accepted as a true fossil community. Clearly, in a full paleoecological study the same approach would be necessary for every species present before one could say that one had anything like a true biocoenose.

In a further development of this line of study, Boucot et al. (1958) utilized the ratio between articulated and disarticulated shells in brachiopods and pelecypods as a measure of their degree of transportation. They suggested that by contouring the proportion of disarticulated shells, it should theoretically be possible to locate the source area from which the shells came.

Eagar (1960) has used three ratios of this sort in studies of Upper Carboniferous nonmarine pelecypod faunas: (1) a *closure ratio*, between closed and open bivalves; (2) an *articulation ratio* between articulated

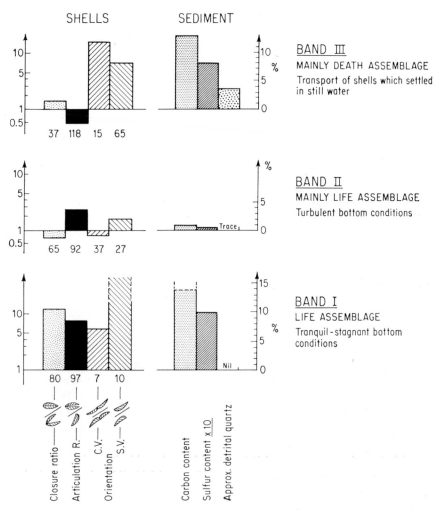

FIGURE 12.5 Histograms showing the closure, articulation, and orientation ratios for the pelecypods in three bands above the Flockton thin coal (Upper Carboniferous) near Barnsley, Yorkshire, Also shown are carbon, sulfur, and detrital-quartz content. (From Eagar, 1960; by kind permission of the author.)

and disarticulated shells, and (3) an *orientation ratio* between valves (or whole open shells) that are concave upward and those which are concave downward. To simplify, it may be said that all these ratios would be high under quiet conditions and low under turbulent conditions. These are illustrated in Figure 12.5.

Reference has already been made to Veevers's work (1959) on *Schizophoria* from the Devonian of Western Australia. The shelly faunas he was studying from limestone bands had been completely silicified, and it was therefore possible to extract literally all the fossils by solution of the rock in dilute acid. He then applied Boucot's criteria and found that species such as S. *stainbrooki* gave a curve of the "life assemblage" type (Figure 3.12). Veever's collections were, in fact, bulk samples such as are usually only possible from rocks of much later age.

R. G. Johnson (1960*a*, 1962*b*) used further statistical methods in analyzing fossil assemblages, with a view to reconstructing the circumstances of their preservation (see page 37). He applied these methods to the fauna of the Pleistocene Millerton formation of Tomales Bay, California, which was particularly suitable for such a study because 36 per cent of its species are still living in Tomales Bay and its sediments closely resemble those now accumulating in the bay.

In other papers (1960*b*, 1962*a*), Johnson described a statistical study of sixty-three species of Pennsylvanian invertebrates in 152 collections from western Illinois, with the object of distinguishing natural associations. Nineteen significant associations were distinguished,[1] of which the most distinctive were associated with the upper limestone or black-shale members of cyclothems. The results were then compared with data from modern communities.

EXAMPLES OF COMPARISONS

When we look into the literature (or into our own experience) for direct comparisons between fossil assemblages and living communities, we find very few worthwhile examples. Obviously we are in a better position in the later strata, which contain many genera and species that still live today, but even here it is rarely possible to draw more than very rough parallels.

The London Clay of Sheppey

One of the closest resemblances that has ever been demonstrated between a fossil assemblage and a modern one is that between, on the

[1] Six main groups and thirteen minor groups related to them (see also p. 96).

one hand, the fauna and flora of the London clay (lower Eocene) of the Isle of Sheppey in the Thames estuary and, on the other, present-day life around the coasts of southeast Asia. This emanates from the work of several different authors, since many different specializations are involved. The fossil assemblage is very varied and abundant. The most common fossils are twigs and small fragments of wood, accompanied by large numbers of fruits and seeds. There are also large masses of wood (bored by *Teredo*), vast numbers of gastropods, pelecypods, *Nautilus*, occasional brachiopods, crabs, and rarer invertebrates such as simple corals and echinoderms. Vertebrates are unusually common and include abundant fish remains, crocodile scutes, turtle bones, and rare hippopotamus-like mammals and bird fragments. The fossils of the London clay have been summarized, with the relevant references, by Davis and Elliott (1957).

The plant remains from Sheppey were described in a large work by Reid and Chandler (1933), later supplemented by Chandler (1961). The forms identified in the earlier work consisted of a few diatoms, 7 species of conifers, and 220 species of angiosperms. These figures have been modified by continuing work (Chandler now estimates at least 500 species with more to come), but the essential principles remain the same. About 70 per cent of the species identified by Reid and Chandler are now extinct, but all of them were fitted into living genera such as *Magnolia*, *Sabal* (a palm), *Cinnamomum*, and *Vitis* (a vine). Of these genera, 73 per cent are forms which live today in the Indo-Malayan region, most notably the well-known *Nipa*, discussed earlier (Figure 11.6).

Among the living genera represented in Sheppey, the percentages given in Table 12.1 are very significant. From these modern comparisons

TABLE 12.1 *Comparison of the Sheppey Eocene flora with that of the Indo-Malayan region today*

Modern distribution of genera	*Sheppey, %*	*Indo-Malaya, %*
Exclusively tropical	11	14
Mainly tropical	32	33
Equally tropical and extratropical	46	33
Mainly extratropical	11	20
Exclusively extratropical	0	0

it can reasonably be deduced that, unless there has been a general and simultaneous change in habit of many different genera, the Sheppey flora must have grown in tropical conditions and was probably very comparable in life to a modern tropical rain forest. This has been strongly supported by the work of Richards (1952). It is also suggested by elements in the fauna such as *Nautilus*, the crocodiles and turtles, and the hippopotamus-like mammals, and by such common fish as sharks and *Myliobatis*, the eagle ray. But as climatic criteria, none of these are so dependable as the plants.

The Sheppey assemblage obviously accumulated in the sea, since there are a great abundance of marine gastropods and such unequivocal marine fossils as the brachiopods and cephalopods. We must therefore presume that the land and fresh-water organisms must have been washed down rivers and drifted out to accumulate on the sea floor. The nearest Eocene shoreline to Sheppey is thought to have been at least 80 km away to the northwest. It is also clearly significant that the Sheppey plants are entirely represented by resistant elements such as logs, twigs, fruits, and nuts. Except for a few fragments of leaves of the palm *Sabal*, there are no perishable parts such as leaves, which would not have survived the long journey.

It should be noted that the forms listed as mainly extratropical in Table 12.1 may live on higher ground in the tropics. This serves to explain the paradoxical suggestion in the table that the Sheppey flora is more tropical than the present tropics, since one would expect upland forms to be underrepresented in a marine accumulation, and shore-loving forms (such as *Nipa*) to be overrepresented. This would also explain the small percentage of conifers present.

Within the general Indo-Malayan region at the present day, Reid and Chandler (1933) drew attention to a remarkably close parallel to the Sheppey accumulation, at the mouth of the Ambernoh River in New Guinea. This was described by Moseley (1892) as follows:

On February 22nd . . . the ship was about 70 miles north-east of Point D'Urville . . . where the great Ambernoh River . . . runs into the sea . . . even at this great distance from its mouth, we found the sea blocked with the drift-wood brought down by it. . . . Amongst the logs were whole up-rooted trees. . . . The majority of the pieces were of small wood, branches and small stems. . . . Various fruits of trees and other fragments were abundant. . . . Amongst them were the usual littoral seeds. . . . But besides these . . . there were seeds of 40 or 50 species of more inland plants. . . . I observed an entire absence of leaves, excepting those of the Palm. . . . The leaves evidently drop first to the bottom, . . . the wood and fruits will sink to the bottom farther off land. . . . The fruits and wood were covered with the eggs of a Gastropod. . . . Two species of Crabs inhabit the logs. . . . Enormous quantities of small fish swarmed under the drift-wood . . . and small sharks. . . . The older wood was bored. . . .

Almost every word of the above quotation fits perfectly with the evidence at Sheppey. The parallel even extends to such details as the palm leaves, the bored waterlogged wood, and the abundant small sharks. Further remarkable details are provided by the finding of the pelecypod *Enigmonia* associated with *Nipa* at Bognor and Highgate, though not yet at Sheppey (Wrigley, 1936) and the finding of mangroves (Chandler, 1951, 1961). *Enigmonia* is a strictly tropical genus at the present day; it lives on the immersed roots, branches, and leaves of mangroves and *Nipa* along the shores of southeast Asia and North Australia.

Several other Tertiary assemblages have also been interpreted with fair confidence from modern comparisons, though not in as much detail. For example, Woodring (1928) made a very thorough interpretation of a Miocene fauna from Jamaica on this basis, reaching fairly definite conclusions about temperature, depth of water, salinity, and bottom type without even examining the fauna in the field.

As we move back in geological time, comparisons with the present day become more and more difficult; and in the Paleozoic, they become almost impossible. One example which may be quoted, however, is Ruedemann's comparison (1934) of the whole assemblage of rare organisms found in the black graptolitic shales of North America with the small organisms which live attached to floating weed in the present-day Sargasso Sea (see page 94).

Bone Beds

Very often it is the exceptional deposit that provides opportunity for modern comparisons rather than the more ordinary sediments and fossil assemblages. This is true, for example, of the remarkable deposits known as *bone beds*, which have provided endless opportunities for ecological theorizing.

Most of these accumulations of bony remains were formerly interpreted as having originated in catastrophes, and these were compared with the occasional catastrophes known in modern seas in which there is simultaneous extermination of vast populations (Brongersma-Sanders, 1957).

Such exterminations often coincide with the occurrence of what is called *red tide* or *red water*, produced by the fantastic proliferation of dinoflagellates or other plankton. Red tide occurs almost daily somewhere along the southern California coast during the summer, and on about half a dozen occasions this century has produced mass mortalities, in the region. Millions of fish or other organisms are killed off simultaneously, so that the sea is suddenly covered with floating bodies. Many other causes of mass mortalities are known, such as volcanic activity, earthquakes, severe storms, changes in salinity (as in lagoons after heavy rain inland), sudden temperature changes (including freezing of the surface), and the build-up of noxious gases in the bottom sediments.

The postulation of such catastrophes to explain bone beds followed the general geological theory of catastrophism into the realm of the unfashionable, and bone beds were explained by other concepts such as winnowing. In recent years, however, with the usual swing of the pendulum of fashion, catastrophism has come back again as a possible explanation of certain fossil occurrences. For instance, G. F. Elliott (1953) bravely returned to this line of thought in a study of the Rhaetic bone bed in England. He compared its original environment with the modern Baltic and lagoons in Tunisia, Texas, and southern France. In some of these, local aridity leads to high salinity in the absence of fresh-water inflow. Sudden downpours inland then produce sudden changes in the opposite direction. Thus the nektonic fauna may be killed off over and over again, only to be replenished each time from the open ocean. Their remains may accumulate much more rapidly than inorganic sediment. Such a picture certainly fits in with the general paleogeographical setting —low-lying deserts around, probably a low rainfall, unusual sediments, and restricted access to the oceanic Tethys—though this theory hardly explains the very extensive nature of Rhaetic beds of this facies across northern Europe.

A good example from the North American fossil record is in the Miocene of California—in the Monterey shale—where vast numbers of the herring *Xyne grex* have been found preserved on a single bedding plane in diatomaceous earth (Ladd, 1957*b*, 1959). Such beds have been compared by Brongersma-Sanders (1948) with modern deposits on the sea floor near Walvis Bay, South-West Africa, where fish remains are extremely abundant in unusual, highly organic sediments, including diatom ooze. These deposits are thought to have been formed as a result of periodic upwelling of cold water, with the production of vast concentrations of diatoms (dark water) or dinoflagellates (red water); and these in turn have a catastrophic effect on the local fish population. "Catastrophic" explanations of this sort are therefore clearly uniformitarian in approach.

Hoppe (1932) discussed four possible modes of origin for the bone beds which occur in the Upper Silurian of the island of Oesel in the Baltic. These were as follows:

1. Catastrophic annihilation and burial of a contemporaneous fauna
2. Concentration of bony remains by the washing out of inorganic material

3. Concentration as a result of a halt in sedimentation
4. Concentration of scattered material by moving water

Of these possibilities only the first can be regarded as of ecological significance, and this was completely rejected by Hoppe as a possible cause for the Oesel bone beds, as it was by J. W. Wells (1944) in his brilliant study of the Middle Devonian bone beds of Ohio. Undoubtedly, a "catastrophic" explanation must be rejected for most of the famous bone beds of Europe and North America in favor of concentration by sedimentary processes. However, catastrophic accumulations undoubtedly do occur in the stratigraphical record, and cannot be completely ignored. The mere number of remains is not in itself significant, as was once thought, since the fleeting nature of life makes it inevitable that all the animals in the sea at any one time must be dead before an appreciable amount of sediment has accumulated. Significant, however, are first, the way in which they have been preserved, and secondly, that they have been preserved at all.

In a study of the upper Miocene Beida stage in Algeria, R. V. V. Anderson (1933) maintained that the abundant, varied, and well-preserved fish provided evidence of catastrophic annihilation.

Death was evidently sudden and abnormal. There is not the dispersal of individuals or of skeletal parts that would be expected in the case of normal death. . . . Several factors suggest that many of the fish were overcome on the bottom, one of these being the even distribution of individuals in some layers as if there had been a deliberate occupation of the available space. . . .

Anderson went on to discuss ten possible causes of death, among which he favored the effects of volcanic eruptions, of which there is evidence in the same beds.

It is interesting to note that we have here the same association of fish and diatoms which has already been mentioned. It is tempting to prefer one of the other possibilities suggested by Anderson, that is, that the great proliferation of diatoms killed the fish, by poisoning, suffocation, or mechanical clogging of the gills.

Other occurrences of large numbers of well-preserved fish may also be attributed to catastrophic causes. An example is the famous Old Red Sandstone occurrence at Dura Den in Fifeshire, Scotland, mentioned earlier (see page 76), where thousands of specimens of *Holoptychius* occur crowded together in what was an ephemeral desert pool. Hennig (1923) described comparable terrestrial concentrations of the small thecodont reptile *Aetosaurus* from the Upper Triassic of Württemberg, Germany.

As pointed out by J. W. Wells (1944), the hypothesis of catastrophe is not necessarily eliminated even when the remains are broken and worn. It would apply, for example, if a temperature change or epidemic which did not affect the bottom fauna killed off many fish, and their fallen carcasses were then worked over by scavengers on the sea floor. It would also apply if the annihilation occurred in very shallow, rough water.

Summing up, although some bone beds and similar deposits may have had a catastrophic origin, it is usually the slow game of fossilization rather than the fast gamble of mortality which is responsible for such accumulations.

STUDIES OF THE PRESENT DAY

One of the main difficulties of modern comparisons in paleosynecology, as in palaeoautecology, is the lack of adequate modern studies on comparable assemblages. This is especially true for the shallow marine environments in which so much of the fossil record was buried.

Since the classic work of Petersen (1913, 1914, 1915, 1918, 1924) in Danish waters, there have been many detailed ecological studies which are *potentially* of great applicability in the interpretation of fossil marine assemblages. These studies have been ably summarized by Thorson (1957) in the *Treatise*. Credit may also be given here to the work of Parker (1956, 1959) in the Gulf of Mexico and to that of Newell et al. (1959) in the Bahamas. But while much lip service is paid to such studies by paleontologists, it is rare indeed to find them being used for direct comparisons in the paleontological literature. This arises partly from the fact that communities, like individual lineages, evolve and change with time. Thus many of Petersen's bottom communities are characterized by ophiuroids, which can hardly be regarded as common elements in the fossil record, except in special circumstances. The chief difficulty, however, is certainly the lack of adequate descriptions of modern "death assemblages." This gap is only just beginning to be filled by work such as that of van Straaten on Dutch tidal flats, the Rhone delta, and other shallow marine areas. These represent exactly the sort of area where a great part of the stratigraphical record must have accumulated and which concerns the majority of potential paleoecological studies.

In a paper on the Dutch Wadden Zee (1952), van Straaten showed how concentrated shell beds (of *Hydrobia* and larger mollusks) were formed by the burrowing action of the lugworm *Arenicola*. Later (1956) in a discussion of tidal-flat shell beds in the Netherlands and France, he carried out various quantitative measurements of great potential application for the paleoecologist. The following are the data which he plotted in his tables of modern shell assemblages:

1. the quantitative distribution of the various species;
2. the reliability of the data, given by the size (weight of sample and number of identified specimens) and by the percentage of shell fragments which could not be identified;
3. the coarseness of the sample, following from the percentage of material smaller than 2.5 mm, from the average weight (given in grammes) of the double valves of *Cardium edule* and from the relation between weight of sample and total number of identified specimens;
4. the degree of fracturing of the shells, given by the crush factor;
5. the number of living specimens, admixed to the (surface) samples.

One point here needs further explanation—the value which van Straaten calls the *crush factor*. This is simply the ratio between the total weight of *Cardium edule* material (both broken and unbroken) and the weight of unbroken valves only. The crush factor is used by van Straaten as a measure of the wear suffered by the specimens during transport. It is related to one species because shells of different species vary in their fragility. *Cardium edule* was chosen here because of its solid shell and great abundance.

Van Straaten suggested that the factor was not so significant in fossil studies because of the breakage of shells by compaction after deposition. This is obviously true in the vast majority of cases, but an attempt is now being made to apply van Straaten's methods to Eocene beds on the Isle of Wight in the south of England, with *Venericor planicosta* taking the place of the cockle for the determination of the crush factor. When the sediments are not too consolidated, it is possible to extract all the shell fragments with reasonable ease and to separate those which were obviously whole when buried, even if they have become fragmented since.

In a third paper (1960), van Straaten described a study of assemblages on the Rhone delta. He related the assemblages to differences in bottom type, current conditions, and rates of sedimentation. This will be referred to again later.

A simpler type of study of the present day was that of Miyaji and Habe (1947). They studied the accumulations of dead shells in Japanese bays and came to a number of conclusions which are of great interest to paleontologists. They found, for example, that the number of species present tended to be relatively large at the mouths of the bays, and that pteropods were particularly good indicators of the proximity of the open sea. One surprising conclusion was that transportation by currents was generally unimportant.

The great usefulness of this kind of work from the paleoecologist's point of view arises from the fact that these workers were studying "death assemblages" comparable to ours. We must accept the fact in marine paleoecology that epibiontic communities will almost invariably be moved and dispersed before fossilization. The only common exception to this rule is the reef community of massive, fixed colonies. Reefs have received more than their fair share of paleoecological study, but it is well to remember that—apart from endobiontic associations—they are the only bottom living communities that are at all likely to be fossilized in position of life.

THIRTEEN

Other geological evidence

I NOW propose to consider briefly other aspects of geology which may contribute, directly or indirectly, to synecological syntheses.

SEDIMENTOLOGY

In the part on paleoautecology, I dealt with the relationship between individual fossils and the sediments in which they are found. The same approach can obviously be used for whole assemblages of fossils, and the methods remain the same.

General Studies

First we may consider studies of regional scope in which the faunas and/or floras of large stratigraphical divisions are related to major facies changes. These are the standard observations of every good general geologist since the time of Gressly, but the more subtle gradations are commonly overlooked.

The broad synecological observations I have in mind are exemplified by the work of the Russian paleoecologist Gekker (1957), who plotted diagrammatically the relation between facies changes in sediments and

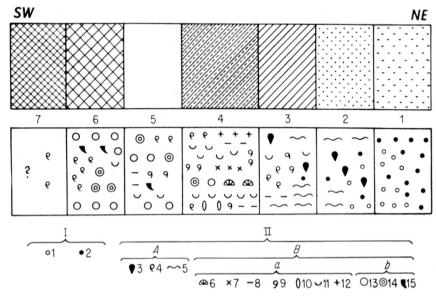

Figure 13.1   Lateral changes in sediments and fossil assemblages along the main Russian outcrop of the Upper Devonian series. (From Gekker, 1957.)

SEDIMENTS

1. Terrigenous red beds
2. White quartz sands
3. Clays
4. Argillaceous and marly limestones
5. Limestones
6. Dolomitic limestones
7. Dolomites

FOSSILS
I. Fresh-water forms

1. Trochiliscids
2. Old Red Sandstone type fish

II. Marine forms
   A. Euryhaline

3. *Lingula*
4. *Platyschisma*
5. Worm tracks

   B. Stenohaline
     a. Normal salinity

6. Tabulate corals
7. *Spirorbis*
8. Pelecypods
9. Majority of gastropods
10. Nautiloids
11. Most articulate brachiopods
12. Crinoids

     b. Salinity normal or a little above normal

13. Blue algae
14. Stromatoporoids
15. Rugose corals

those in fossil assemblages along the main Upper Devonian outcrop in Russia (Figure 13.1). The diagram illustrates the use of conventional symbols for different faunal and floral elements, which not only provides an immediate pictorial guide to the different kinds of fossils present but also shows, very approximately, their relative abundance. Also, the diagram matches in a remarkable way many of the vertical changes seen in the transitional Silurian-Devonian beds in the Welsh borderland.

Gekker's was a very broad study and obviously very generalized, but Figure 13.2 illustrates a more specific study—also from the U.S.S.R., by Ivanova and Khvorova (1955)—in which finer distinctions were drawn in the sediments and the distribution of the fossils was plotted in detail. This was a study of Middle and Upper Carboniferous rocks in the Moscow region.

In general studies, merely naming all the fossils accurately is usually an immense task, especially for the paleoecologist who is not in direct contact with large national collections, libraries, and specialists. Modern ecologists have expressed the same concern when faced with diverse communities, and Elton has discussed their need for a national identification service. The problem for the paleoecologist is vastly greater.

One solution might be to follow the lead of some field ecologists and simply not attempt to name everything accurately. We would then have to be at least temporarily content with "*Monograptus* sp. A" and "turreted holostomatous gastropod," rather than bury the paleoecological results under a mountain of undigested forensic literature. This would be an inadequate step, however, and perhaps the only acceptable solution lies in the team research project, with several different specialists working side by side on the same problem, as in the study of the Permian reef complex in Texas and New Mexico (Newell et al., 1953) which will be discussed later (Chapter 18).

Comparative Studies

Though detailed studies of broad scope are still unfortunately rare, there are more examples in the literature of comparative studies on the faunas and floras of different facies. The example of the "shelly" and "graptolitic facies" in lower Paleozoic rocks immediately springs to mind, though this is clearly an overgeneralization.

In this field, Ruedemann (1926, 1935) made an interesting comparison between the fossil assemblages of the black Utica shales of New York and the succeeding gray Lorraine shales, both of Ordovician age. The comparative figures and percentages (recalculated) are given in Table 13.1. It will be seen that the black shales are characterized by a preponderance of plants ("seaweeds"), sponges, graptolites, worms, cepha-

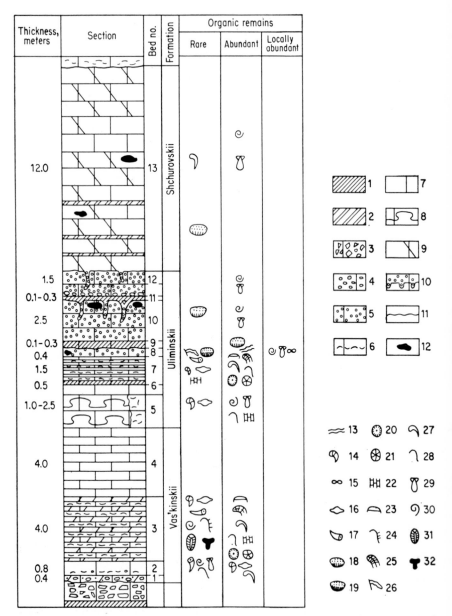

Figure 13.2 A section in the Carboniferous near Moscow, with conventional signs used to indicate the different kinds of sediments and fossils. 1, clays; 2, chemically deposited clays; 3, calcareous breccias; 4, calcareous conglomerates; 5, coprolitic limestones; 6, finely stratified and argillaceous limestones with intermediate beds of organic debris; 7, micro-oölitic and argillaceous limestones; 8, limestones

lopods, and merostomes, and by the absence of crinoids and corals. The gray shales, on the other hand, show a preponderance of bryozoans, brachiopods, pelecypods, and gastropods.

Another line of research on the same principles is that on Paleozoic spores. It is just becoming possible to attribute these spores to their parent plants and to extract them from all kinds of sediment. Neves

TABLE 13.1 *Analysis of assemblages in Utica shales and Lorraine shales.* (*From Ruedemann, 1935, with slight amendments*)

	Utica shales Number	%	Lorraine shales Number	%
Plants	5	4.7	1	0.5
Sponges	11	10.3	—	—
Corals	—	—	1	0.5
Graptolites	23	21.5	8	3.8
Crinoids	—	—	4	1.9
"Worms"	9	8.4	4	1.9
Starfish	1	0.9	—	—
Bryozoans	4	3.7	32	15.3
Brachiopods	12	11.2	33	15.8
Pelecypods	5	4.7	63	30.1
Gastropods	4	3.7	30	14.3
Cephalopods	13	12.2	6	2.9
Trilobites	7	6.6	11	5.3
Ostracods	4	3.7	13	6.2
Cirripedes	1	0.9	2	1.0
Phyllocarids	2	1.9	—	—
Merostomes	6	5.6	1	0.5
TOTAL	107	100%	209	100%

(1958) has compared the spores from a coal seam in the Upper Carboniferous of north Staffordshire, England, with those from the overlying carbonaceous shales and those from a marine band higher up. He found that the spore assemblages are markedly different in the different lithologies (Figure 13.3), and this is presumably related to the local geography and to the growing positions of the different plant types.

with algal bioherms; 9, dolomitic limestones; 10, deep animal burrows; 11, erosion levels; 12, chert concretions; 13, stromatoliths; 14, diverse small forams; 15, Paleonubeculariidae; 16, fusulinids; 17, solitary rugose corals; 18, Chaetetids; 19, colonial rugose corals; 20, crinoids; 21, echinoids; 22, bryozoans; 23, *Chonetes;* 24, *Linoproductus;* 25, *Dictyoclostus;* 26, *Meekella;* 27, *Choristites;* 28, other brachiopods; 29, pelecypods; 30, gastropods; 31, trilobites; 32, fish debris. (From Gekker, 1957, after Ivanova and Khvorova, 1955.)

Particularly notable was the dominance in the marine shale of the "gymosperm" spores *Florinites,* which constituted 58.3 per cent of the whole assemblage, compared with only 1.0 per cent in the coal.

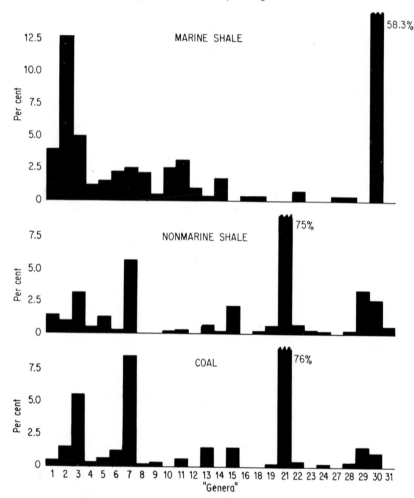

FIGURE 13.3   Relative abundance of spore "genera" at three horizons in an Upper Carboniferous cyclothem in north Staffordshire, England. The high peak on the right of the top histogram represents the supposed gymnosperm *Florinites.* (From Neves, 1958; by courtesy of *Geological Magazine.*)

In a discussion of this paper, Chaloner (1958) suggested that the "gymnosperms" (Cordaitales and Coniferales) dominated the vegetation of the higher ground adjacent to the coal swamps. During the deposition of the coal seam, the spores of the swamp-living plants would far out-weigh everything else. At the time of a marine invasion, however, the swamps would be considerably reduced, and the general spore "rain" from the upland areas would dominate the assemblage. Thence there is the paradoxical situation that the spore assemblages in a shallow marine deposit are more likely to be representative of the general land flora than are those of nonmarine deposits, in which the immediate local flora is probably overrepresented. Chaloner compared this situation with that described in the Tertiary of Venezuela by Kuyl et al. (1955).

Geochemistry of Sediments

Many new developments in the field of geochemistry are potentially of great value to the paleoecologist, but these are only just beginning to be used.

Trace Elements Ernst et al. (1958) have shown how the boron content of argillaceous sediments may be a clear guide to the original salinity of the water in which they were deposited. In Carboniferous shales of the Ruhr coal field in Germany, they found a sharp contrast in boron content between sediments with marine faunas and those with non-marine faunas. In the former, the B_2O_3 content ranged from 0.03 to 0.06 per cent, while in the latter it ranged from 0.005 to 0.015 per cent. These percentages seem to be stable through diagenetic changes and weathering, but are affected by metamorphism.

Other elements, such as lithium, have been used in a similar way, and a great deal of work has been done on the strontium/calcium ratio in both sediments and fossils. This will be discussed later.

Every year brings fresh advances in this field, and it is difficult for the paleontologist to keep up to date. But in all these studies and in those which follow, it must be emphasized that geochemistry alone cannot provide a magic wand which will solve every paleoecological problem. It is no use blindly analyzing sediments or fossils as a chemical problem without also considering the underlying geological situation. It is no use measuring the percentage of a certain element present without also considering all the different ways in which it may have got there.

Organic Chemistry Another new development in sedimentology in recent years has been the detection of small quantities of organic compounds still preserved in quite ancient rocks and fossils. I could quote many papers which have simply identified various compounds (even, very recently, in meteorites), but this type of information is only just beginning to be used in the elucidation of environment. For instance, Prashnowsky et al. (1961) recorded various sugars in the sediments of the Santa Barbara basin in California and suggested that the small proportion of glucose present might be an indication of marine conditions, since marine organisms show a preference for galactose, mannose, or the pentoses.

In a sequel to the above paper, the same collaborators (Degens et al. (1961) recorded nineteen amino acids in the same sediments and showed that each of these had an irregular distribution related to depth of water.

Swain (1961), in a study of Jurassic rocks in the Gulf of Mexico region, found that the amino compounds were highest in quantity and variety in samples from alluvial and deltaic mudstones, carbonaceous sandstones, and offshore black shales. Conversely, trace amounts of furfurals (probably derived from pentoses and hexoses) were present in rocks of many different types, but were scarce in algal limestones and evaporites.

The significance of observations of this type is not yet understood, but the results suggest that organic chemistry is another potential tool in the study of past environments.

Clay Mineralogy

As is well known, many clay mineralogists believe that the proportions of kaolinite, illite, and montmorillonite in argillaceous sediments are directly related to the physical chemistry of their depositional environment. Kaolinite, for instance, appears to dominate only in sediments which suggest a low pH at the time of deposition, such as fire clay. However, I know of remarkably few studies in which clay mineralogy has been related to fossil distributions. One of the rare examples is the study by Pryor and Glass (1961) on Cretaceous and Tertiary sediments in the upper Mississippi embayment of the United States. The proportions of the three main clay minerals were related to fluviatile, inner neritic, and outer neritic fossil assemblages. This is summarized in Figure 13.4. The area covered was very large for the number of samples studied, and as yet, no one seems to have used clay mineralogy in a detailed study of fossils as related to their containing sediments.

There are also lines of evidence which suggest that the rarer clay minerals, such as sepiolite, certain chlorites, saponite, and attapulgite, tend to occur in restricted associations where other evidence indicates high alkalinity.

BIOGEOCHEMISTRY

Following naturally on the chemistry of the sediments, there is the chemistry of the fossils themselves. The larger chemical constituents of fossil shells and skeletons and their crystallography may have an indirect bearing on paleoecological matters, in that they may determine the likelihood of particular elements in an assemblage being preserved. Thus the

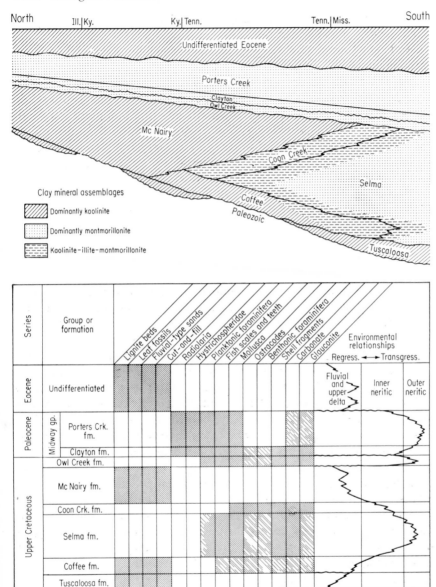

FIGURE 13.4 *Top*, generalized distribution of clay-mineral assemblages in different stratigraphical units of the Cretaceous and Eocene of the upper Mississippi embayment. *Bottom*, criteria observed and interpretations of environments for the same stratigraphical units. (From Pryor and Glass, 1961; by courtesy of *Journal of Sedimentary Petrology*.)

aragonitic nature of their shells may explain the absence of gastropods from certain assemblages.

Indeed, aragonitic shells are perhaps the most notorious, and the most instructive, in this respect. Jefferies (1962) has pointed out that, given present-day atmospheric pressures, sea water in the laboratory will dissolve aragonite but not calcite at temperatures lower than 5°C. He applied this kind of knowledge to a study of the faunas of one sub-zone of the Upper Cretaceous Chalk in the Anglo-Paris basin. He was able to relate the occurrence of normally preserved aragonitic fossils to variations in original temperature, turbulence of the bottom water, and length of exposure on the sea floor.

There is here, then, a preservation control of fossil distribution which is not related to the ecology of the organisms themselves, i.e., they may be independent of the factors which control their preservation or non-preservation. That this is so is proved by the occurrence of what Jefferies called *oyster-casts*. These are the impressions of gastropods and other aragonitic fossils on the attachment area of oysters, which are often found in areas where the aragonitic fossils themselves are completely absent. Such casts are sometimes found in the same beds as the calcitic aptychi, or opercula, of ammonites.

Aptychus beds are well known in the Mesozoic rocks of south and central Europe, particularly at the Jurassic-Cretaceous boundary, and it was long regarded as an anomaly that there should occur such large numbers of aptychi without the corresponding shells, or phragmocones. In many cases the explanation seems to be original nonpreservation, as suggested above, and the deposits concerned were probably laid down in relatively deep water. This may have a considerable bearing on the ecology of associated fossils. Thus at Gorna Luka, near Vrattsa in north-west Bulgaria, I collected a large fauna from Valanginian (Lower Cretaceous) shales which consisted of abundant and varied aptychi, belemnites (also calcitic and presumably pelagic), and a few of the strange aberrant brachiopods of the *Pygope* group (see page 157). Such associations seem to indicate a deep-water habitat for these specialized benthonic brachiopods.

Apart from such comparatively simple considerations of gross chemical-mineralogical composition, there is a whole new field of exciting paleoecological research opening up in the study of trace elements and isotope ratios.

Quantitative Analysis

A long series of papers has been written on the importance of the strontium/calcium ratio in fossils and sediments, most notably by Odum

(1950, 1951*a*, 1951*b*), Kulp, Turekian, and Boyd (1952), Lowenstam (1954), and Turekian (1955, 1956). These show first that the Sr/Ca ratio in shells is proportional to the ratio of these elements in their water media, and secondly that these ratios reflect the salinity of the water concerned. Temperature probably has very little effect on the ratios, except in those shelly structures, such as the tubes of serpulids, which vary their aragonite content with temperature, since aragonite takes up strontium more readily than does calcite. Recrystallization always reduces the ratio and destroys its significance, but in the right circumstances, the Sr/Ca ratio in fossils and sediments is a clear indicator of original salinity, being perceptibly higher in the sea than in fresh water.

I must refer again at this point to the work of Imbrie (1955) which was mentioned in Chapter 8 (see page 130 and Figure 8.5). In this pioneering work, he related the abundance of many different elements in the fauna of the Permian Florena shale of Kansas to Sr/Ca ratios.

Isotope Studies

Perhaps the most promising new technique in paleoecological research is that of estimating the proportions of the different isotopes of a particular element present in a fossil. The three stable oxygen isotopes O^{16}, O^{17}, and O^{18} have been used most. For instance, perceptible differences have been observed in the ratios between these three in rain water, lake water, and sea water. Thus the O^{18} content of oceanic water is said to be 0.9 per cent higher than that of ordinary fresh water. The ratio is partly controlled by temperature and when the oxygen is incorporated in a fossil, the ratio may give an indication of the temperature at the time.

Lowenstam (1960, 1961) described the use of both oxygen-isotope ratios and trace-element ratios in a study of fossil and modern brachiopods. In a number of fossil forms, ranging back to the Mississippian, he found O^{18}/O^{16} ratios comparable with those in modern brachiopods from oceanic waters of average salinity. Lowenstam's general conclusion was that his results are best explained if it is assumed that the O^{18}/O^{16}, strontium/calcium and magnesium/calcium ratios and the strontium and magnesium contents of the oceans have remained essentially constant since Mississippian times.

The pioneer work in the field of isotope studies on fossils was that of Urey et al. (1951), who used oxygen isotopes to study the paleotemperatures of belemnites from Upper Cretaceous deposits in England, Denmark, and the southeastern United States. They studied the ratio between the "normal" oxygen isotope O^{16} and the much rarer isotope O^{18}. At the present day there is a perceptible rise in this ratio as one passes into warmer water. The difference per degree centigrade in the usual temperature range is about 0.0172 per cent, so clearly very accurate measurement is necessary, and the whole method is fraught with possible experimental errors.

Urey's work showed that the Danish belemnites lived at a temperature of 12 to 14°C, the English belemnites at between 14 and 23°C, and the American ones at between 11 and 20°C. The general conclusion was that the temperature, averaging about 15 to 16°C, was remarkably uniform throughout the latitudes concerned, suggesting warm-temperate to subtropical conditions.

One fossil that was specially studied was an Upper Jurassic belemnite from the island of Skye, west of Scotland. Studies of the C^{13} and O^{18}

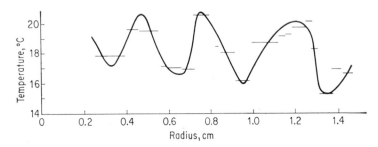

FIGURE 13.5 Paleotemperature estimates for different seasons during the life of an Upper Jurassic belemnite from Skye, Scotland. (After Urey et al., 1951.)

isotopes of this specimen showed that it lived through four winters and three summers after its youth (Figure 13.5), and that it inhabited warmer water in its youth than in its old age. The mean temperature was 17.6°C and the maximum seasonal variation about 6°C.

Lowenstam and Epstein (1954) continued this line of research, studying a variety of Late Cretaceous fossils from all parts of the world, including belemnites, brachiopods, the pelcypod *Inoceramus*, and oysters, as well as the sediments themselves. They concluded that results obtained from belemnites were relatively dependable as direct reflections of the local sea temperatures. The generally higher temperatures obtained from the other fossils may be the result of a different mode of skeletal synthesis and the presence of secondary calcite.

On the basis of these measurements, the authors concluded that there was a progressive rise in temperature from the Cenomanian to the Coniacian-Santonian and then a general decrease to the Maestrichtian. In a later paper (1959), the same authors related these temperature changes to the changing distributions of belemnites through Late

Cretaceous times that were demonstrated by Jeletzky (1948). They also used the same methods to demonstrate that the limiting temperatures of the rudistid pelecypods (see page 154) were roughly the same as the temperature at the margins of the subtropical belts today.

Bowen (1961a) used belemnites from Germany and Poland for similar paleotemperature studies. On the basis of oxygen-isotope ratios he worked out a large number of temperature estimates which showed an oscillating climate through Late Jurassic and Cretaceous times. A general decline in average temperatures during the Cretaceous was suggested as a cause of the multiple extinctions at the end of that period.

In a second paper (1961b), Bowen applied the same technique to Jurassic belemnoids from all over the world. He found a temperature range for these nektonic animals of about 20°C, which is much less than the range in modern seas. He deduced, therefore, that in Jurassic times the tropical and subtropical belts were wider than at present with smaller seasonal variations. He also maintained, from the distribution of his higher-temperature results, that the Jurassic equator lay obliquely across North America and western Europe, while India lay in the temperate zone, and Alaska and New Guinea were areas of cool water. The highest and lowest temperatures recorded by Bowen were 39.3 and 15.6°C respectively. They may have been completely absent from the cooler polar waters of the time. This might explain, for example, the complete absence of belemnoids and rudistid pelecypods from the west African Cretaceous.

Though these examples are autecological matters in so far as they refer to only one group of organisms, they are included here because the organisms were investigated, not for their own sakes, but to provide direct evidence of their environment and thence of the environment of all their associates.

DIAGENESIS

Diagenetic changes and metamorphism, though fascinating to some, are only a nuisance to the paleoecologist. In some cases, however, diagenetic changes may be related to the fossil content of the rock; and care must be taken to avoid cyclic reasoning. Thus in a study of the *B* member of the Redwall limestone (Mississippian) in the Grand Canyon region, McKee (1960) showed that fossils are far more common in the irregular beds of chert than in the carbonate rock. A careless paleontologist might suppose that this would imply an original relationship between sediment type and organisms, but as McKee showed, the silicification probably followed the zones of maximum permeability provided by the fossils themselves.

A similar example is that referred to earlier (see page 16) in which Ohle and Brown (1954) described lead mineralization following the axes of algal reefs in the Cambrian of Missouri.

Reefs are notoriously susceptible to diagenetic changes because of their porosity and because of the way in which they stand up among other sediments and provide an easy passageway for solutions. In the Mesozoic coral reefs of the Jura in southeast France, all organic structures are commonly obliterated by dolomitization, and it is only very locally that the interesting associations are preserved. Similarly diagenetic changes involved in the formation of high-rank coal commonly destroy all trace of the spores and other organic remains, or may produce a very distorted picture of the contemporary flora.

Diagenetic changes may also considerably affect the composition of a fossil assemblage through the preferential removal of certain forms. It is a common observation in unconsolidated Cenozoic rocks that some shelly genera are much better preserved than others and are therefore more easily collected, giving the collector a biased view of the assemblage.

GEOMORPHOLOGY

The study of geomorphology is often very relevant to research on certain fossil faunas and floras, since altitude and landform are essential aspects of their environmental setting. This is especially true of late Cenozoic continental assemblages.

A long series of papers by the Indian paleobotanist G. S. Puri [e.g., 1943, 1945, 1948; see also anonymous communication about his work (Puri, 1946)] has served to relate the ecology of the lower Pleistocene floras of Kashmir to the uplift of the Himalayas, which has been studied by geomorphological methods. Lake deposits in Kashmir at elevations of 1,675 to 3,230 m have a rich flora of hill trees and shrubs, lowland aquatics, gymnosperms, and algae which (by comparison with modern Himalayan floras) suggest an elevation of not more than 1,520 m. This requires an elevation of at least 1,500 m since the early Pleistocene, which corresponds with the local geomorphological evidence.

Puri repeatedly demonstrated the tropical or subtropical nature of the early Pleistocene Karewa flora in Kashmir. Thus he recorded a number of distinctive tropical plants such as *Woodfordia fruticosa* (1943), *Mallotus philippinensis* (1947a), and *Ficus cunea* (1947b) in the Karewa deposits, and showed how uplift of the Himalayas brought about a change to temperate conditions by elevation and the cutting off of the hot winds from the Punjab.

On the other side of the world, Frye and Leonard (1957) showed how the late Cenozoic fauna and flora of the Great Plains region in the west of North America could be correlated with both sedimentary and geomorphological changes. The relationship between sedimentation and the fossil populations is illustrated in Figure 13.6.

Frye and Leonard's interpretation of the record may be summarized as follows:

1. In mid-Neogene times there was a mature topography and a moist, humid climate with stable conditions of plentiful water. The fauna

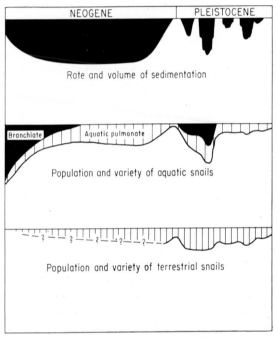

FIGURE 13.6 Correlation between intensity of sedimentation and gastropod faunas in the central Great Plains area during late Cenozoic times. (After Frye and Leonard, 1957.)

consisted of a great abundance of aquatic pulmonate and branchiate, i.e., gill-bearing, gastropods and terrestrial pulmonate gastropods; the flora was essentially a tree vegetation with types better suited to a warm climate than those which live in the area at present.

2. By the beginning of late Neogene times the climate had clearly become dryer, with a lowering water table and a general reduction of topography to an alluvial plain. The branchiate gastropods disappeared, and the flora was dominated by prairie grasses.

3. By the end of Neogene times the water table was very low, semi-arid conditions prevailed, and an erosional equilibrium had been reached.

The gastropod fauna was now sparse; only a few pulmonates were capable of surviving the long periods of desiccation. The flora was also reduced; there were only a few species of prairie grasses and one tree.

4. At the beginning of Pleistocene times there was a sharp reversal of climate with a return to damper conditions, and the topography was modified by the incision of streams. Coinciding with this change in geomorphology, the branchiate gastropods reappeared, together with a wide variety of aquatic pulmonates. At the same time, belts of trees and shrubs appeared on the prairie.

5. Finally, during the late Pleistocene, there was a return to aridity. There were some fluctuations, which are reflected in the relative abundance of aquatic pulmonates, but in general, desiccation continued until the present day. The branchiate gastropods again disappeared; the terrestrial pulmonates declined in number, variety, and density. Today, only very hardy species among the gastropods and the restricted prairie flora can stand the extremes of temperature experienced in the region.

Obviously the geomorphology of an area must always have been an important factor in its environment, but it is only at the top of the stratigraphical column that it can be fully appreciated.

STRUCTURAL GEOLOGY

An unlikely branch of geology to have any bearing on paleoecology is the study of tectonics; but even here, under special circumstances, there may be significant evidence. Obviously we cannot study fossil orientations without considering the structural setting. Even if the folds are "flattened out" in the conventional way, the results may be very misleading. My colleague J. G. Ramsay (1961) has shown that the precise nature of the folding must be considered in detail before there is an attempt to "put things back" as they were before the disturbance; otherwise it is possible to make an error of more than 90° in the reconstruction of original fossil attitudes.

In another way, structural geology may provide more direct evidence of value in interpreting past environments. In their study of the Permian Delaware basin in Texas and New Mexico, Newell et al. (1953) cited estimates of the precise original depth of the basin, which had been calculated on the basis of its later structural history.

FOURTEEN

Density
and diversity

IF one set out to make an alphabetical list of all the nationalities represented in the population of London or New York, it would probably
start like this:

Abyssinians
Afghans
Albanians
Algerians
Americans
Andorrans

. . . It is doubtful that such a list would be much more misleading
than the average faunal or floral list found in paleontological papers.
Just as the sedimentary petrologist tends to concentrate on the 1-m band
of limestone and ignore the 2,000 m of shale, so the paleontologist tends
to concentrate on the sole fragmentary ammonoid and ignore the 2,000
pelecypods. Faunal and floral lists may be useful stratigraphically (if
we believe in the identifications), but they are virtually useless from
the paleoecological point of view unless they give some indication of
the abundance of the different species present.

Paleoecology is, in essence, a very democratic subject; that is, though
we must never ignore the minorities, our primary consideration must
be for the majority. Thus the one damaged ammonoid *may* be significant paleoecologically (it may, for example, provide a clue about a mi-

217

gration route); but the 2,000 pelecypods are much more important when it comes to considering the environment of the immediate area.

There are really two separate ecological considerations here. First we are concerned with the population density of the different species present; secondly we are concerned with the diversity of the population as a whole.

DENSITY

The population density of an organic community is a very important facet of its ecology. It is obviously directly related to the conditions under which the organism lives, and populations must always be in a state of balance with their environments. This balance was discussed at length by Nicholson (1933) and has been the subject of a book by Lack (1954).

For every species there is an optimum density for any one place and time. This optimum density is controlled primarily by the food supply and secondarily by the predators which feed upon the organism concerned. Nevertheless, even under constant conditions there tend to be oscillations in population density, such as the well-known roughly four-year cycles of the lemmings in Norway, Greenland, and Canada.

If the number of individuals in a particular population drops too low, then the population becomes very vulnerable to predators, epidemics, or slight variations in climate, and may easily become completely extinct within a particular area. Carpenter (1919) noted that islands below a certain size on Lake Victoria did not have any tsetse flies, although the conditions were apparently suitable for them. The explanation was probably that the populations which theoretically could have lived on these islands would have been too small to survive the periodic setbacks produced by slight variations in their environment.

Islands are a special case, but even in a more or less continuous environment there is obviously a minimum level of density below which a species will not survive in a particular area. One factor is reproduction. It has been calculated that if there were only one of each sex of a particular tiny spider to the acre, then the male would have to walk an average of 310 km before he chanced upon the female. Obviously no species could survive and perpetuate itself under such trying circumstances!

On the other hand, if numbers grow too large, they may soon exhaust the food capacity of the area available. Again they become increasingly vulnerable and ultimately suffer a catastrophic reduction in numbers from one cause or another. Thus the mule deer of the Kaibab National Forest in Arizona (see page 8) increased in numbers so much after the killing off of their natural enemies that they stripped the vegetation.

All became so severely undernourished that many were not able to survive the winters, and a large majority died in a very few years. It has
been recorded that sheep in certain parts of Tibet have to feed on the
run in order to get enough nourishment from the sparse vegetation available! Clearly these poor creatures are just about at their upper limit of
density.

Predatory animals are controlled just as surely as the animals and
plants which provide their food. Thus the numbers of foxes and owls
can often be shown to vary in direct proportion with the abundance of
the rodents which provide their main nourishment.

Few of these things are likely to concern us as paleoecologists, but
they help us to appreciate how slight changes in the organic or inorganic

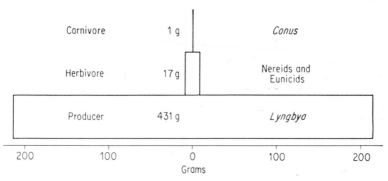

FIGURE 14.1 Biomass pyramid for the algae-polychaete-*Conus* food chain at
Kahuku, Oahu, Hawaii. (From Kohn, 1959; by courtesy of Duke University Press.)

environment can produce very violent changes in the populations of
particular species; and no one knows better than a geologist how rare and
fleeting a thing is a so-called "constant" environment!

What we can appreciate in terms of density is that a given area of
habitat will support only a certain number of organisms. A land surface
will grow only so much vegetation, and that vegetation will support
only a smaller weight of herbivorous animals, and those herbivorous
animals will support only a smaller weight of carnivores. This is what
is called a *biomass pyramid*. Kohn (1959) has calculated such a pyramid
with the gastropod *Conus* as its top stage (Figure 14.1). In simpler
form there may be merely a pyramid of numbers of organisms. Usually
we think of this as decreasing in size upward as in the *predator pyramid*,
but Noble (1959) has pointed out that the direction is reversed in the
parasite pyramid (Figure 14.2).

The size of the organism is important, since a small animal usually
does not require so much food as a large one. This is also related to

the problem of stunting, discussed earlier, since physiological retardation of growth can sometimes be related to overcrowding. Many cases are known of fresh-water pelecypods becoming stunted because of the density of the population in small lakes and ponds.

Island populations are also well known in this connection, since the restricted food supply sometimes leads to the development of stunted races. This extends back into paleontology, for example, to the stunted elephants of Malta and the Channel Islands off the coast of California. The largest known specimen of the southern mammoth (*Archidiskodon imperator*) from the California islands is only about 3 m tall, compared with specimens up to 4½ m tall on the mainland. Stock (1935) suggested that the difference in stature between the island and mainland

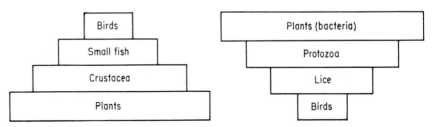

FIGURE 14.2 A predator pyramid (*left*) and a parasite pyramid (*right*). (After Noble, 1959; by courtesy of the Linnean Society of London.)

forms may be an index of the relative length of their racial exile. The small island of Pianosa, a few kilometers southwest of Elba, could only have been separated from the Italian mainland for a very short time before many of its Pleistocene vertebrates became stunted.

Most paleontologists are concerned with less spectacular fossils, and must have had the experience of searching fruitlessly in a bed where a previous worker had recorded fossils as "abundant." Such adjectives are always highly subjective—purely relative to the immediate past experience of the man who uses them. If he has been working for years on the Old Red Sandstone, then lower Paleozoic black shales may seem to be extremely fossiliferous; but this would not be the opinion of the man who has been working on Tertiary shell sands. Geological literature abounds in lists of fossils noted as "very rare," "rare," "common," and so on, but almost always without any quantitative estimate.

Absolute Density

The absolute density of a fossil species in life is difficult to determine from the evidence usually available, but this drawback can be partly

overcome by studying only individual bedding-plane surfaces. Here—
as is often the case in paleoecology—the methods of the plant ecologist
are particularly applicable.

One potentially useful technique for macrofossils is that of the
quadrat. This is a standard area marked out or otherwise delimited on
a bedding plane, such as is used for counting or mapping plant distributions. Obviously, there are limitations. This procedure can be based only
on the assumption that the bedding-plane assemblage is reasonably contemporaneous; but if the bedding plane represents a halt in sedimentation, then
the fossils may have gone on accumulating for a very long period. There is
also an obvious danger of sampling error, and we must clearly avoid
choosing a particularly fossiliferous area. In practice there are further
difficulties, such as broken shells and the separated ossicles of crinoid
stems. As a convenient compromise we may count whole fossils and
fragments separately, and treat as a fragment every completely separate
entity. It is usually necessary to select a minimum size of specimen that
will be recognized. This is not as difficult as it sounds, providing we do
not try to apply it to unsuitable horizons. For example, it is useless to
expect to learn anything from such a study on a purely detrital crinoidal
limestone. A quadrat is probably most helpful and most significant when
used on indigenous assemblages such as sessile benthos.

The size and shape of the quadrat have to be decided for each individual problem. There has been much discussion on this in the biological literature. Cottam et al. (1953) experimented with an artificial population of 1,000 randomly distributed individuals, trying sampling
methods which involved either fixed areas or fixed numbers of individuals collected. They decided that the samples attained reasonable
accuracy, regardless of method, when there were more than 30 individuals in the total sample. Bormann (1953) considered the statistical
efficiency of various sizes and shapes of sample plots in the study of
forest ecology. He concluded that a rectangular plot should be used,
with its longer axis normal to any obvious banding. Obviously the samples should be taken at random to eliminate any personal bias in the
selection of sites. Both of the above papers made the general recommen-
dation that samples taken should be larger than those generally employed in such studies.

I have found that a standard quadrat of 1 sq m is most useful in
studies on Mesozoic and Cenozoic shelf-sea benthonic faunas (Figure
14.3), but larger quadrats are desirable for sparser assemblages and
smaller ones for exceptional concentrations or small forms.

If we are studying sessile or endobiontic associations which are still
in life position, then clearly there will be complications due to the original concentrations of the organisms in life. Skellam (1952) has pointed

out that several different population models may produce the same distribution pattern in quadrat studies. The three cases which he discussed were (1) organisms randomly distributed with no interaction, (2) organisms in compact clusters smaller than the quadrat size, and (3) noncompact clusters much larger than the quadrat size. Many paleoecological studies involve organisms which are concentrated in lenses, e.g., brachiopod "nests," which seem to be original colonial associations.

When dealing with complex assemblages, there is always the problem of how many quadrats of minimal size need to be studied to ac-

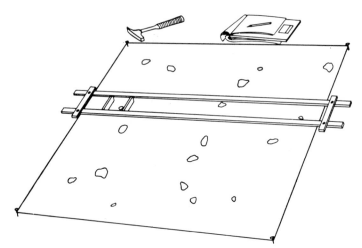

Figure 14.3   A 1-m cord quadrat being used in a bedding-plane study in conjunction with a frame 1 m by 10 cm. (From a photograph taken by the author.)

quire an adequate sample. This may be deduced from a simple *species-area curve*, in which the number of species observed is plotted against the number of quadrats used. The point at which the curve becomes asymptotic with the x axis is usually taken to indicate the minimum area to be studied, but as Cain (1938) pointed out, this depends on the way the information is plotted, i.e., the ratio between the x and y axes. He suggested that instead, the point should be taken where a 10 per cent increase in area gives a 10 per cent increase in the number of species. His simple method for finding this point is illustrated in Figure 14.4.

In practice, in the field, the most convenient material form for a paleontological quadrat is probably just four skewers or spikes with cords between, though a folding wooden frame is more usable on hard rock surfaces (Figure 14.3). I find that, for the average shelf-sea assemblages of the British Mesozoic, it is useful to employ the 1-m quadrat in conjunction with a frame 1 m by 10 cm, having the frame marked off at 10-cm intervals along the longer sides.

A more detailed study was carried out on exceptionally fossiliferous bedding planes in the Wenlock limestone (Middle Silurian) of Dudley, near Birmingham, England (Plate 8, *top*). In this case, a 20-cm quadrat

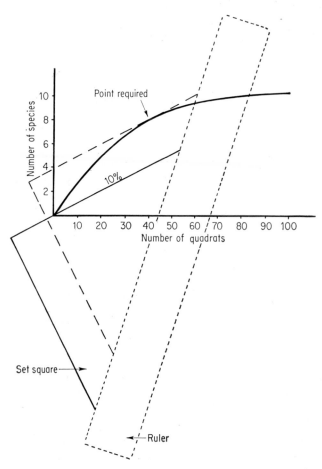

FIGURE 14.4   Species-area curve, showing simple method for determining the minimum quadrat area required for an adequate sample.

was used. The value of such studies lies entirely in their use for comparing densities from one locality to another or from horizon to horizon. Figures 14.5 and 14.6 illustrate the field records of two such studies on the Wenlock limestone. As in ecological studies, provisional identifications are usually sufficient at this stage.

Such comparisons may be done at a single level with the object of determining lateral facies change, or at completely unrelated levels with the object of comparing environments. In the first category, it would be interesting to compare an adequate coverage of the Wenlock limestone

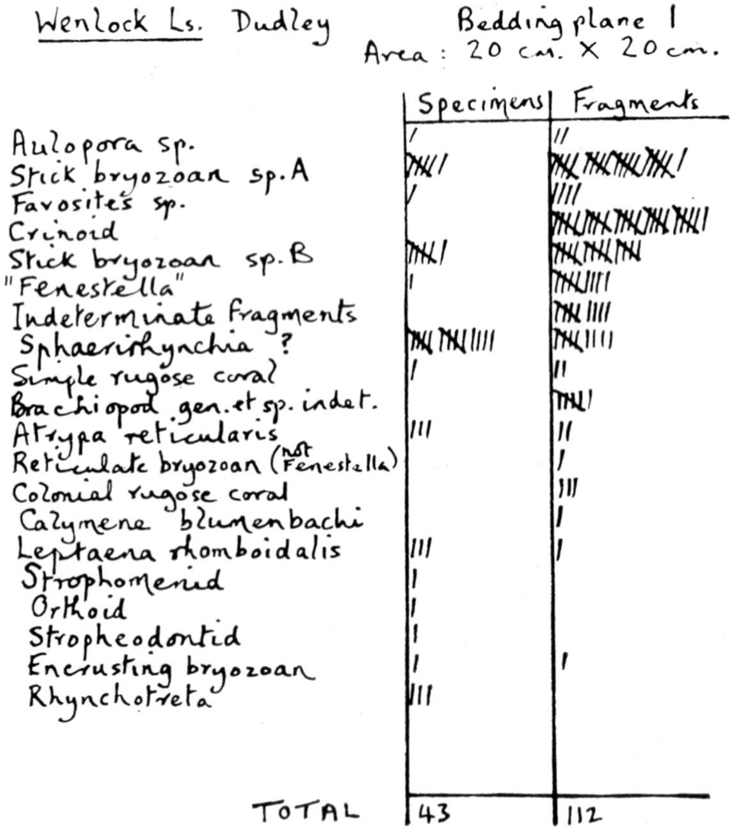

Wenlock Ls.   Dudley   Bedding plane 1
                              Area : 20 cm. X 20 cm.

	Specimens	Fragments
Aulopora sp.	/	//
Stick bryozoan sp. A	////I	//// //// //// ////I
Favosites sp.	/	////
Crinoid		//// //// //// //// ////
Stick bryozoan sp. B	//// I	//// //// ////
"Fenestella"	I	//// ////II
Indeterminate fragments		//// ////
Sphaerirhynchia ?	//// //// ////	//// ////
Simple rugose coral	/	//
Brachiopod gen. et sp. indet.		//// I
Atrypa reticularis	///	//
Reticulate bryozoan (not Fenestella)		/
Colonial rugose coral		///
Calymene blumenbachi		/
Leptaena rhomboidalis	///	/
Strophomenid	/	
Orthoid	/	
Stropheodontid	/	
Encrusting bryozoan	/	/
Rhynchotreta	////	
TOTAL	**43**	**112**

Figure 14.5 Field record of a bedding-plane count on a horizon in the Wenlock limestone (Middle Silurian) of Dudley, near Birmingham, England. (From the author's field notebook.)

at Dudley with a similar study of the same formation at Wenlock Edge, about 40 km farther west. Certain differences in the fauna are apparent from ordinary collecting, notably the scarcity at Wenlock Edge of the trilobite *Calymene blumenbachi*, which is so common at Dudley that it was incorporated in the town's coat of arms.

As an example of a study of densities at different stratigraphical levels, we may compare the densities of asteroids and ophiuroids in various starfish beds figured by different authors, and we may even compare them with modern assemblages. This is illustrated in Table 14.1. Such isolated counts have little statistical validity, but would be more significant if a number of separate slabs were counted in each case. It is

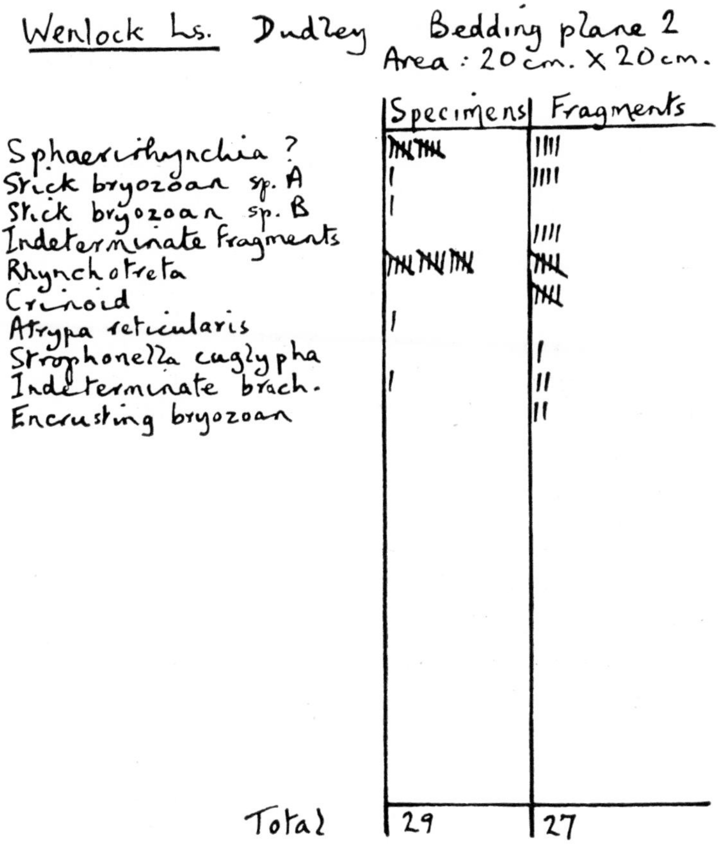

Wenlock Ls. Dudley Bedding plane 2
Area : 20 cm. X 20 cm.

	Specimens	Fragments
Sphaerirhynchia ?	卌 卌	IIII
Stick bryozoan sp. A	I	IIII
Stick bryozoan sp. B	I	
Indeterminate fragments		IIII
Rhynchotreta	卌 卌 卌	卌
Crinoid		卌
Atrypa reticularis	I	
Strophonella euglypha		I
Indeterminate brach.	I	II
Encrusting bryozoan		II
Total	29	27

FIGURE 14.6 Field record of an equivalent area of a different bedding-plane in the Wenlock limestone at Dudley.

necessary to produce somewhat contrived examples of this kind because so few have been published in the geological literature. All that usually reaches publication is an occasional remark such as that of Scott (1940) that "in one *Gryphaea* shell bed three inches thick, twelve large ammonites were counted in a distance of 15 feet." Occasionally such observations have been used for extrapolation, as in Jordan's estimate (1920) of the number of fish killed and preserved on a single bedding plane in the Miocene Monterey shale of California. He calculated the remarkable total of 1 billion herring within 4 square miles.

An outstanding example of the usefulness of this method is provided by Chaney's study (1924) of the upper Oligocene Bridge Creek flora at the type locality near Mitchell, Oregon. Chaney had earlier demonstrated the remarkable similarity which exists between the Bridge Creek flora and that of the modern California redwood forests. Nineteen out of the twenty-six genera recorded as fossils are present in the modern forests.

Chaney made three careful excavations of fixed size at Bridge Creek and from these counted a total of 20,611 specimens, mostly leaves. At the three localities he estimated densities of 261, 215, and 108 specimens per cubic foot, respectively.

TABLE 14.1 *Comparative starfish densities in various starfish beds.*

Locality and horizon	Number of individuals*	Area of specimen	Calculated number per square meter
Devonian, New York (a)†	72	0.25 sq m	288
Jurassic, Germany (o)	9	100 sq m	900
Cretaceous, Texas (o)	7	64 sq cm	1,092
Cretaceous, Texas (a)	62	90 sq cm	1,700
Recent, California (o)	11	1.04 sq m	11

* In each case an individual was only counted if the greater part of its central disc was visible.
† a = asteroids; o = ophiuroids.

He then wanted to determine if the numbers of leaves and fruiting parts found were an accurate indication of the relative abundance of the species which they represented. This would obviously be controlled by a number of factors. He therefore set out to obtain similar data for a comparable modern community, choosing Muir Woods redwood forest on the other side of the Golden Gate from San Francisco. Through this forest flows Redwood Creek, which is intermittent, so that for much of the year the water lies in a series of separated pools. Chaney thought that these were comparable to (though smaller than) those in which the Bridge Creek flora accumulated. He therefore made quantitative studies of the leaves in the pool basins, using a stiff-wire quadrat of 1 sq ft, which was thrown into the lower end of each basin where the leaves were most abundant. Forty-two basins were studied in this way, and in each case a count was also made of all plants within a radius of 50 ft.

The resemblances between the fossil and modern accumulations were quite remarkable. Nineteen species were represented by leaves and six also by fruits in Redwood Creek, out of twenty-seven species present locally; this compares with twenty-one species represented by leaves and five also by fruits, out of the twenty-six which have been recorded from the Bridge Creek beds. The four most abundant species make up a total of 85.44 per cent in the modern forest, and species of the same four genera constitute 86.44 per cent of the fossil flora. These are the following:

MUIR WOODS	BRIDGE CREEK
Sequoia sempervirens	*S. langsdorfi*
Alnus rubra	*A. carpinoides*
Quercus densiflora	*Q. consimilis*
Umbellularia californica	*U.* sp.

Chaney then sought to determine if there was a definite relationship between number of leaves and number of adjacent trees. For this purpose he applied the following equation to modern species which have fossil equivalents:

$$r_{XY} = \frac{\Sigma XY/n - M_X M_Y}{\sqrt{\Sigma X^2/n - M_X{}^2} \sqrt{\Sigma Y^2/n - M_Y{}^2}}$$

where r_{XY} = correlation between X and Y
X = number of leaves in 1 sq ft
Y = number of plants in a 50-ft radius
M = mean
n = number of stations

Chancy calculated r_{XY} for each genus common to both floras. Thus for the red alder—*Alnus rubra*—this worked out at .486, which indicates the not surprising conclusion that there is a distinct tendency for the number of *Alnus* leaves to be high where *Alnus* trees are most numerous, and small where the trees are few in number. Similar good correlations were obtained for most of the common species. Chaney was then able to make predictions about the number of trees in the Oligocene forest, on the assumption that 1 sq ft at Muir Woods (yielding an average of 200 leaves) was the approximate equivalent of 1 cu ft of the Bridge Creek shale (which yielded an average of 210 leaves). On this basis he was able to calculate that within a radius of 50 ft in the Oligocene forest there were 9.373 alders, 7.327 oaks, 5.416 redwoods, and so on, all within a margin of error of ±3 to 4.5.

There is rarely any point in paleoecology in actually mapping the distribution of individuals as in botanical studies, but I can imagine exceptional circumstances under which it might be worth trying. I know of one formation, for example, where it is possible to plot the areal distribution of brachiopod colonies on succeeding bedding planes. This is then a study of the density of colonies as distinct from the density of individuals, and changes in that density with time may be ecologically significant. Figure 14.7 shows the distribution of indigenous sessile sponges on a single bedding plane in the French Cretaceous. The same form can be observed in the same way in the English Cretaceous, and it might be instructive to compare the density of these sponges at different localities.

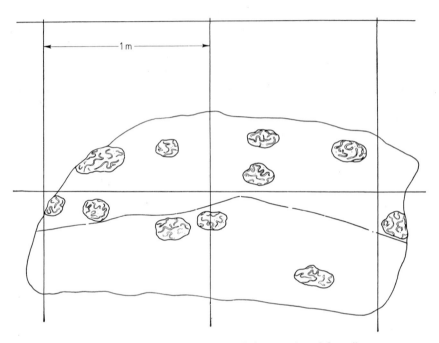

FIGURE 14.7 Distribution of the sponge *"Plocoscyphia labrosa"* auctt. on a bedding plane in the Cenomanian (Upper Cretaceous) near Wissant, northwest France.

The quadrat method is less suitable for vertical sections, but can be employed with value if it is restricted (for each count) to a single bed. A rectangle is then certainly preferable to a square. In special circumstance a *screen-testing* method can be used, as is sometimes done in sedimentary petrology; for example, there is the *Raster-Messverfahren* of Wurster (1958), who hung a net of 20-cm mesh over sections, in a study of the geometry of false-bedded sandstones.

A more convenient method for studying vertical sections is that of the *stretched line or line transect.* Here a line of standard length is stretched along a section parallel to the bedding planes, and every specimen which it crosses is counted (Figure 14.8). This method was

Figure 14.8 Stretched line, 4 m long, being used in a study on a vertical face. (From a photograph taken by the author.)

used by Johnson (1960*a*) in a study of the Pleistocene Millerton formation of Tomales Bay, California. He studied eight variables in a series of eleven line samples. These were:

1. Line density
2. Percentage of fragments
3. Percentage of articulated pelecypods
4. Percentage of pelecypod valves with concave side down
5. Median size of sediment
6. Coefficient of sediment sorting
7. Median size of fossils
8. Coefficient of fossil sorting

There are limitations in the line-transect method, some of which were discussed by McIntyre (1953). He observed that in plant-density studies, this method was ". . . well established in theory and practice as giving a level of precision in the estimate for a given effort which compares very favourably with other methods." The chief deficiency of the method is that counts made along a line will be proportional not only to abundance but also to the diameter of the specimens. A large specimen is more likely to be cut by the line than a small one. This drawback is of no great significance when the population studied is moderately uniform in size. Another snag about the line-transact method is that it is only usable when the fossils are very abundant. Below a certain density the method ceases to be practical.

Relative Density

Even when paleontologists do record the number of specimens they find in a particular bed, it is usually only a relative measure because we do not know how wide an area was searched or how long was spent in the searching.

Many micropaleontologists count the exact number of fossils in a standard weight or volume of sediment and then plot the relative abundance of the different species. Examples have already been given of such studies in forams (page 134), minute mollusks (page 187), and spores (page 206). This approach is, of course, the whole basis of palynological correlation. Sometimes such results are plotted in absolute numbers; more commonly they are plotted in percentages. Both methods have advantages in particular circumstances. Schott (1935) introduced the term *foraminiferal number* for the number of forams in 1 g of dry sediment, and Said (1950) expanded this into the more useful *pelagic number* and *benthonic number*, both still applying to foraminifera.

Stehli (personal communication, 1963) has drawn *isoratio* contours on the Upper Cretaceous rocks of West Texas, Louisiana, and south Arkansas, based on the ratio between planktonic and benthonic forams. This has proved extremely useful in deducing Cretaceous depth zones in the region.

Whatever the method and presentation, such estimates inevitably reflect relative and not absolute abundances at any one moment of time. Any counts based on bulk samples of sediment are as much a measure of the rate of sedimentation as of the absolute faunal or floral density. It is comparatively easy to count the number of a particular foram in a given sample of sediment, but it is almost impossible to estimate with reasonable validity the number of dinosaurs per square kilometer of Cretaceous jungle.

Relative-abundance counts are so well known in the micropaleontological literature as to hardly need discussion here. Unfortunately they are almost invariably confined to a single group and so hardly come into the category of synecological studies. Even more unfortunately, there have been very few comparable studies of macrofossils, and again, those that have been made, such as my own work on British Domerian brachiopods (Ager, 1956a), have been confined to one group.

One great difficulty about making counts of larger fossils is the fragmentation of the specimens, but a great deal can be done by counting only specific parts of each species, for example, the apical whorls of a gastropod or the right hinge of a pelecypod. Such counts are often difficult and time consuming, but very much worthwhile. They are vastly preferable to such subjective remarks as "very common" and "rare," and they are infinitely more desirable than the simple faunal list.

In the first of the two assemblages which Craig (1954) described (see page 304), the macrofauna consisted of more than nine hundred specimens of *Posidonia corrugata*, fifty-seven specimens of *Loxoceras* (?), one productid fragment, four bellerophontids, one fragment of another nautiloid, and one fragment of a rhynchonellid. In terms of relative density, the completely false impression which would be given by a faunal list of such an assemblage is immediately apparent. Another method sometimes used is that of measuring relative abundance in terms of weight (Figure 18.6).

In this field as in many others, the paleobotanists have been more ecologically minded than the paleozoologists; and although the latter tend to regard fossil plants as just one more group (and an unimportant one at that), they should remember that plants constitute half the organic world. Comprehensive studies of varied floras are therefore well within the realm of synecology.

One of the most interesting ecological studies of fossil plant communities, carried out by a south Wales miner, David Davies (1921), was based on the experience of more than twenty-five years of work in the mines of Clydach Vale and Gilfach Goch in Glamorgan. With great patience and care he collected no less than 45,000 Upper Carboniferous plants from bands which lie just above each of ten successive coal seams. He utilized the census approach for each horizon and estimated the relative abundance of each major group of plants—Equisetales, Sphenophyllales, Lycopodiales, Filicales and Pteridospermae (together), and Cordaitales. He found that the relative abundance of the different groups varied markedly from level to level and seemed to be interdependent (Figure 14.9). Thus the numbers of fernlike plants (Filicales and Pteridospermae) proved to be inversely proportional to the numbers of lycopods, while the primitive gymnosperms (Cordaitales) remained fairly constant throughout. If we compare the "Six Feet" horizon with the "Two Feet Nine," we see in the former 0.45 per cent lycopods compared with 44.36 per cent ferns and seed ferns, whereas in the latter there are 66.69 per cent lycopods and only 1.71 per cent ferns and seed ferns.

The deductions Davies drew from these figures were based partly on the opinions expressed by the leading paleobotanists of the time about the habits of the various groups. He suggested that the lycopods were essentially swamp-dwelling plants and that the ferns and seed ferns were dry-land forms. This would account for their varying inversely with differing conditions. The Equisetales presumably lived along the margins of the drainage systems and so persist throughout, and the

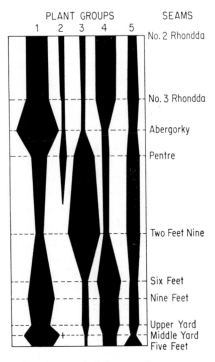

FIGURE 14.9   Relative abundance of different plant groups in beds overlying six coal seams in south Wales. 1, Equisetales; 2, Sphenophyllales; 3, Lycopodiales s.l.; 4, Filicales and Pteridospermae; 5, Cordaitales. (After D. Davies, 1921.)

Cordaitales were upland forms which are only represented by far-drifted parts.

The limitations of such an approach are obvious, since fossil floras are inevitably fragmental and the number of fragments produced by a single plant will vary considerably from one group to another. It is also unlikely that all members of a group had the same habits. Nevertheless, the differing proportions are presumably significant of some general factor; and in this regard it is instructive to compare Davies's results with figures for the famous Mazon Creek horizon in the Pennsylvanian of Illinois. Taking the figures quoted by W. N. Stewart (1950) for large collections made here, the comparable percentages are Equisetales,

9.0 per cent; Sphenophyllales, 0.5 per cent; Lycopodiales, 6.0 per cent; Pteridospermae and Filicales, 83.0 per cent; and Cordaitales, 1.5 per cent. The great dominance of ferns and seed ferns at this horizon was confirmed through personal inspection, and by Davies's arguments would seem to indicate dry conditions in the neighborhood. Particularly surprising is the dominance of one genus—*Pecopteris*—which constitutes more than 42 per cent of the collections from Mazon Creek (compared with not more than 0.56 per cent in Davies's collections in Glamorgan). It is interesting to recall that *Pecopteris* only comes in, in force, at the very top of the British "Coal Measures," where all the evidence points to comparative dryness or even aridity. On the other hand, in his study of coal balls, W. N. Stewart (personal communication) has found that many Pecopterids seem to have root structures suggestive of wet conditions. This suggests that other factors may be involved. Confirmatory evidence of Davies's views may be derived from the nature of the plant parts which occur. The roots of lycopods are commonly found in position below coal seams and clearly lived there, while the Cordaitales are known almost entirely from leaves and wood fragments which may have been washed long distances down streams.

In the case of the Mazon Creek assemblage, we are fortunate in also having a fairly complete picture of the contemporary animal population, though its fossils are by no means as abundant as the plants. Moodie (1916) made estimates of the relative abundance of the various species of vertebrates and insects present, and Richardson (1956) has recorded the numbers of the various Mazon Creek animal fossils in the Chicago Natural History Museum and the Walker Museum of the University of Chicago combined, as an indication of their relative abundance. He pointed out that more than two hundred species of small animals have been recorded and about five hundred named species of plants (including form species), ranging from fungi to trees. The list of animals in the museums may be simplified as follows:

Kind of fossil	Number of specimens
Amphibians	3
Fishes	88
Insects	19
Arachnids	5
Crustaceans (miscellaneous)	327
Ostracods	45*
Xiphosurids	309
Arthropleurids	2
Myriapods	45
Annelids	19*
Pelecypods	298*

* These are the number of concretions, each of which may contain many individuals.

Such a list is completely inadequate for anything more than the roughest of indications of the relative abundance of the various elements. Apart from the vagaries of preservation, there are very disproportionate chances of the various forms reaching the museums. The three amphibians were hardly likely to have been overlooked or ignored by the collectors, whereas hundreds of pelecypods were probably missed, rejected, or forgotten in private collections for every one that reached the Chicago museums. Other forms—for example, the coprolites mentioned by Richardson—were usually discarded in the field.

When, however, such a list is based on careful collecting and is as unbiased as is possible in the subjective world of paleoecology, then we can proceed to another kind of ecological study—that of diversity.

DIVERSITY

In recent years a number of papers have appeared in the ecological literature about "diversity as a measurable character of an animal or plant population," to quote the actual title of one of them (C. B. Williams, 1951).

At the simplest possible level of diversity study, we may consider nothing more than the total number of species present in a particular formation in a particular area. This in itself may be highly significant, since we know, for example (Sorgenfrei, 1958), that there is a progressive decrease in the number of molluskan species present as one goes farther into the decreasingly saline waters of the Baltic Sea (Figure 14.10). A comparable paleoecological observation is that by Tappan (1960) on Upper Cretaceous foraminifera in Alaska. She noted a progressive reduction in the number of species as one passed from "offshore" through "sublittoral" to "coastal" facies, though this did not mean a reduction in the number of individuals. I noted (Ager, 1956a) that a similar reduction in the number of brachiopod species occurred when the Marlstone rockbed (Lower Jurassic) was traced into an ironstone facies in southern England. This is illustrated in Plate 1.

A fossil example on a broader scale is the *Glossopteris* flora of the Southern Hemisphere and India. Generally speaking this late Paleozoic flora consists simply of *Glossopteris*, *Gangamopteris*, and a very few other forms. It contrasts markedly with the vast Upper Carboniferous and Permian floras of North America, Europe, and northern Asia. The largest flora in South Africa, for example, is in the Ecca series (?Lower Permian) in which Du Toit (1954) recorded only 39 species, of which the maximum number recorded from any one locality was 18 from

Vereeniging, south of Johannesburg. This contrasts with the 103 species recorded by Stewart (1950) and the more than 500 mentioned by Richardson (1956), all from one locality, Mazon Creek, in Illinois. It has often been suggested that the restricted nature of the *Glossopteris* flora may have been connected with the adverse climatic conditions implied by the preceding Permocarboniferous glaciation.

Mere numbers of species in themselves are not an adequate ecological guide, however, for obviously a flora of three species may be quite as dense as one of fifty. Generally speaking there tend to be fewer species

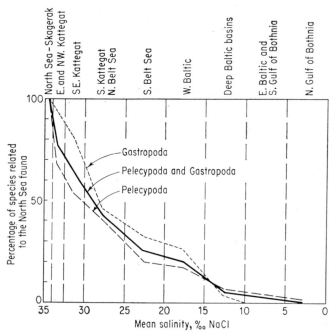

FIGURE 14.10 Decrease in number of molluskan species in the North Sea–Baltic transition area, related to mean salinities. (From Sorgenfrei, 1958; by courtesy of the author.)

in cold climates than in warm ones, but it does not follow that there are fewer individuals; in fact the opposite is often the case. Thus we have the vast shoals of cod and the great swarms of lemming in the north to compare with the much greater variety of fish and mammals in the south. Similarly we may compare the uniform and monotonous conifer forests of the north with the extraordinarily diverse tropical rain forests.

Fischer (1961) has developed the concept of diversity gradients as a potential tool in paleontology. He has suggested that the high diversities at present existing in low latitudes may be due to more rapid evolution here and freedom from disastrous climatic fluctuations.

To refer once more to Heer's classic work on the Miocene Oeningen beds of Switzerland (1865), we may remember that he pointed out that the Miocene flora there was far richer in species than the flora of present-day Switzerland and more comparable in variety with floras much farther to the south.

Sorgenfrei (1958) has emphasized the desirability of estimating the total numbers of molluskan species present in Tertiary marine faunas, for comparison with what are known at different latitudes today. The comparative modern figures he quotes, from various sources, are as follows:

Location	Number of species
North Norway	549
Great Britain	552
Portugal	784
Northwest Mediterranean	745
Mediterranean in general	1,000

He estimated the total numbers of molluskan species from two Danish Miocene faunas as 587 and 547 respectively, which fits in very well with his estimation on other grounds that his faunas lived under conditions comparable to those north of the Iberian Peninsula at the present day.

Sorgenfrei's estimate of the total number of species in a fauna was not founded on simple observation, as in the cases quoted previously, but was derived algebraically, since the true total is unknown for most fossil assemblages, but can be estimated from the number of species in two independent faunules of the same age. The essential equation, in its simplest form, is

$$n = \frac{rs}{a}$$

where n = total number of species in the fauna

r, s = numbers of species in two independent faunules

a = number of species common to both faunules

It is instructive to apply this technique to older fossil assemblages, though the number of species known is usually much smaller. Hallam's work (1960a) on the Blue Lias (lowermost Jurassic) of southern Britain provides a suitable comparison of two faunules from Dorset and

Glamorgan for several successive horizons in well-correlated strata (Figure 14.11). This shows very clearly the greater diversity of the later faunas (corresponding perhaps with the contemporaneous marine transgression), though this is masked in practice by the falling off in the number of species actually found fossil at either locality.

F. G. Stehli is at present applying the concept of diversity gradients to the taxonomic composition of various fossil families in different parts of the world (personal communication, 1963). He has to rely on comparatively few well-monographed faunas and treats his data statistically to check their significance. The results seem to indicate, in Permian and

Ammonite subzones	Total number species recorded	Total number species estimated
planorbis	20	21
johnstoni	25	26
laqueus	38	41
angulata	45	47
conybeari	40	52
rotiformi	36	50
bucklandi	35	58
gmuendense	37	45

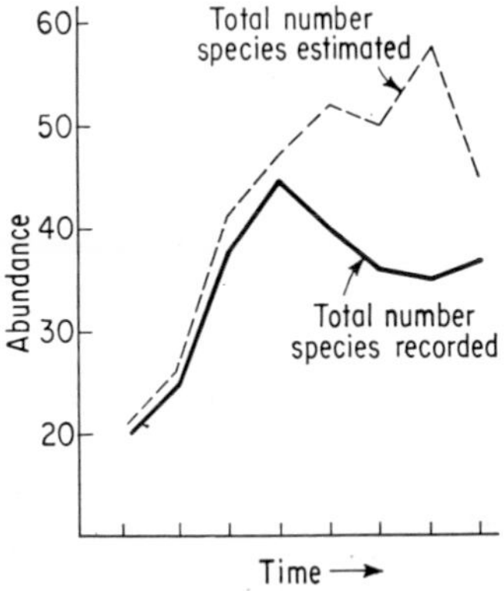

FIGURE 14.11 Estimate of species abundance in the lowermost Jurassic rocks of southern Britain. (Founded on data in Hallam, 1960a.)

Cretaceous rocks, for instance, an upward trending diversity gradient toward the present equator.

So far I have been concerned only with diversity in terms of the number of species present, but there is much more to it than this. If there is an assemblage of 1,000 fossils in which 10 species are represented, there can be, at one extreme, 100 specimens belonging to each species or, at the other extreme, there can be 991 specimens belonging to one species. Clearly the two extremes have quite different ecological implications.

In his study of the marine mollusk shell assemblages of the Rhône delta, van Straaten (1960) showed that the relation between the numbers of species having equal frequencies of specimens and their total frequencies in the combined coarse fractions from all sampling stations was approximately logarithmic. If there are y species each with a total abundance of x, then this relation is approximately

$$y = 26 - 12.2^{10} \log x$$

The greater the number of specimens contained in a sample, the greater is the average number of specimens per species—though there are exceptions to this rule.

When the number of species and the total number of specimens were plotted graphically for each station, they were found to fall into four main groups, as shown in Figure 14.12.

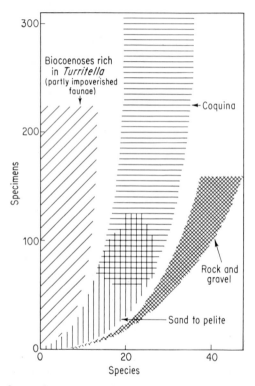

Figure 14.12 Relation between numbers of species and numbers of specimens (larger than 2.5 mm) for different assemblages on the Rhone delta. (From van Straaten, 1960; by courtesy of *Geologie en Mijnbouw.*)

Kornicker and Odum (1958) studied the diversity of certain modern marine faunas, as represented by their hard parts, with the object of comparing them with fossil assemblages. They examined three assemblages on the coast of southern Texas (Figure 14.13) and found a marked decrease in diversity as they passed from the open waters of the Gulf of Mexico into the enclosed, highly saline waters of the Laguna Madre, and a further decrease when they encountered the exceptionally high salinity of Baffin Bay on the landward side of that lagoon.

In each case they counted 1,000 specimens and used the number of new species found after 100 had been identified as their *diversity index*. On this basis they found that the Gulf of Mexico assemblage had a diversity index of 26, the Laguna Madre proper had one of 11, and Baffin Bay had one of 5. In other words there was a marked decrease in variability with an increasingly adverse environment.

Diversity may be illustrated graphically by plotting the cumulative number of species (in the order in which they were found) against

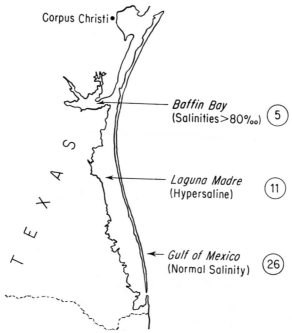

FIGURE 14.13 The coast of southern Texas showing, in circles, the difference in relative diversity of the fossilizable faunas at three localities. (Founded on data in Kornicker and Odum, 1958.)

the cumulative number of specimens. The slope of the curve is independent of sample size beyond a certain minimum number of specimens, and Kornicker and Odum found that 1,000 specimens was the minimum in their type of study. I found that this figure also applied in a study of the Upper Devonian Cerro Gordo fauna at Rockford, Iowa. Two assemblages were studied, one from the middle part of the Cerro Gordo member at Rockford Quarry (Table 14.2) and the other from the upper part at nearby Bird Hill (Table 14.3). At both places the specimens were collected by myself and Dr. A. L. Guber of Illinois, and our collections at each place are listed separately as a measure of the subjective element involved. Exactly 1,000 Bird Hill specimens were studied, and the cumulative total of species was plotted on semilogarithmic graph paper (Figure 14.14). It will be seen that the curve becomes asymptotic at the 1,000-specimen ordinate. No attempt was made in this study (or in that by Kornicker and Odum) to include microfossils in the count,

TABLE 14.2 *Macrofauna of the middle part of the Cerro Gordo member of the Hackberry formation (Upper Devonian), Rockford Quarry, Iowa.*

| | Number of specimens | |
	Ager	Guber
Spirifer hungerfordi Hall	156	83
Atrypa devoniana Webster	139	103
Schizophoria iowaensis (Hall)	57	31
Spirifer whitneyi Hall	23	20
Spirifer whitneyi subsidus Fenton and Fenton	22	15
Atrypa rockfordensis Fenton and Fenton	21	11
Douvillina arcuata (Hall)	15	14
Floydia gigantea (Hall and Whitfield)	15	3
Heliophyllum solidum (Hall and Whitfield)	13	11
Productella walcotti Fenton and Fenton	12	8
Diaphorostoma antiquum Webster	8	4
Petalotrypa formosa Fenton and Fenton	5	10
Strophonella reversa (Hall)	5	2
Lioclema occidens (Hall and Whitfield)	4	7
Paracyclas sabini White	4	1
Worm tubes	4	1
Stropheodonta thomasi Fenton and Fenton	2	2
Pachyphyllum woodmani (White)	2	1
Platyrachella cyrtinaformis (Hall and Whitfield)	2	1
Leptostrophia canace (Hall and Whitfield)	2	1
Crinoid fragments	1	2
Schuchertella prava (Hall) ?	1	0
Fenestella sp.	1	0
Cranaenella calvini (Hall and Whitfield)	1	0
Bellerophon sp.	1	0
Platyrachella macbridei (Calvin)	0	2
Westernia gigantea Webster	0	1
TOTAL	516	334

though Dr. Guber (being a micropaleontologist) made large and significantly varied collections of microfossils from bulk samples.

In the Iowa investigation, a diversity index different from that of Kornicker and Odum was applied to the two faunas. This was the formula, suggested by E. H. Simpson (1949):

$$\frac{N(N-1)}{\Sigma n(n-1)}$$

where N is the number of individuals in the population and n is the number of individuals in a group (here a species) within that population. This formula is much used in modern ecology, notably by C. B. Williams (1954). It is simply the average number of pairs that have to

TABLE 14.3 *Macrofauna of the upper part of the Cerro Gordo member of the Hackberry formation (Upper Devonian)* = Strophonella hybrida *zone of Belanski, Bird Hill, near Rockford, Iowa.*

	Number of specimens	
	Ager	*Guber*
Productella walcotti Fenton and Fenton	146	33
Douvillina arcuata (Hall)	135	50
Atrypa rockfordensis Fenton and Fenton	103	35
Spirifer whitneyi Hall	73	23
Schizophoria iowaensis (Hall)	67	29
Heliophyllum solidum (Hall and Whitfield)	43	20
Spirifer hungerfordi Hall	38	10
Strophonella hybrida (Hall and Whitfield)	27	4
Spirifer whitneyi subsidus Fenton and Fenton	25	8
Undetermined stick bryozoans	22	8
Cranaenella navicalla (Hall)	13	2
Charactophyllum nanum (Hall and Whitfield)	12	2
Strophonella reversa (Hall)	10	13
Atrypa planosulcata Webster	8	4
Crinoid fragments	6	2
Platyrachella cyrtinaformis (Hall and Whitfield)	5	0
Atrypa devoniana Webster	2	1
Stropheodonta thomasi Fenton and Fenton	2	1
Pugnoides calvini Fenton and Fenton	2	0
Tabulophyllum sp. ?	2	0
Straparollus argutus Fenton and Fenton	2	0
Petalotrypa sp.	2	0
Paracyclas sabini White	1	1
Camarotoechia saxatilis (Hall)	1	0
Bellerophon sp. ?	1	0
Fenestella sp.	1	0
Westernia gigantea Webster	1	0
Undetermined encrusting bryozoan	1	0
Spirifer rarum Webster	1	0
Paracyclas parvula Fenton and Fenton	0	1
Grammysia sp.	0	1
TOTAL	752	248

be selected from a population to obtain a pair of the same species. If all the members of a population were of the same species, then only one pair would have to be selected, whereas if every member of the population belonged to a different species, then an infinite number of pairs would fail to produce two conspecific individuals. This formula, then, is a very good measure of the diversity of a population. Williams used it to demonstrate, for example, that there is a steady fall in diversity with depth in marine benthonic faunas (Figure 14.15).

When this formula was applied to the Cerro Gordo faunas, a diversity index of 5.57 was obtained for the lower beds and one of 8.82 for the higher. This suggests a sharp change in environment for these ben-

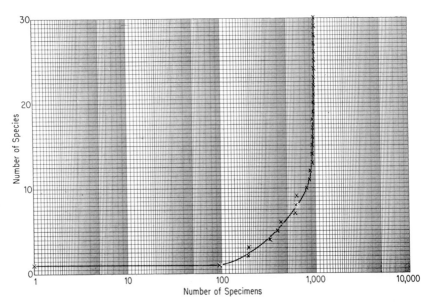

Number of Specimens

FIGURE 14.14   Cumulative curve for 1,000 specimens from the upper part of the Cerro Gordo member of the Hackberry formation at Bird Hill, near Rockford, Iowa.

thonic forms, and this may be relatable to changes within the faunas. If the two individual collections at each place are treated separately, then it may be noted that my own collecting gave figures of 5.45 and 8.69 respectively, whereas that of Dr. Guber gave 5.71 and 9.04. These figures are close enough to each other and to the general figure to substantiate the alleged contrast between the two faunas, but they provide an interesting reflection of the subjectivity of the sampling. As with most such subjective methods, the possible errors are considerably reduced when comparisons are made only of various results obtained by the same investigator or among a group of investigators. This also eliminates the subjectivity of species identification, which becomes an impossible barrier if we wish to use the results for general application. On these grounds it would be completely unwise to attempt to define absolute limits of diversity for a particular environment.

Several other methods of estimating diversity have been used in various contexts. Fisher's index of diversity a takes the form $a = n_1/x$, where n_1 is the number of groups with one unit and x is a constant (for the sample) less than unity. In this the assumption is made that the frequency distribution sampled is of a precise mathematical form—in simple cases a logarithmic series. Yule's characteristic K is a similar

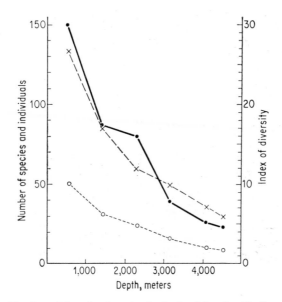

FIGURE 14.15 Number of benthonic animals dredged by the *Challenger* at different depths, showing a steady fall in specific diversity with depth. *Solid line,* number of individuals. *Broken line with circles,* number of species. *Broken line with crosses,* index of diversity. (After C. B. Williams, 1954.)

measure of diversity applied to a totally different type of problem—the frequency distribution of different nouns in random samples from the work of different writers. In this case the logarithmic series does not apply. C. B. Williams (1946) showed that completely different results are obtained when these two measures are applied first to the moths caught in a light trap at Harpenden, Hertfordshire, which are in a logarithmic series, and secondly to the nouns in Macaulay's essay on Bacon, which are not.

In other words, there are several different ways of estimating diversity, and we have to be explicit about what is meant when we use terms such as "index of diversity." In view of the inevitable subjectivity of paleoecology and the disinclination of most geologists toward mathematics, I prefer the simple Simpson formula demonstrated above. It is probably best not to attempt the higher flights of statistical fancy in paleoecology. The original observations are so subjective and fraught with uncertainties that to use them as the basis of complex statistical analyses is comparable, in the Biblical simile, to building a house on an unconsolidated arenaceous deposit.

FIFTEEN

Relationships between species

No man is an island, entire of itself; every man is a piece of the continent, a part of the main"; and the same is true, and apparently always has been true, for every organism on the earth's surface.

I have already pointed out how dependent organisms are, one on another, and discussed this in a general way in Chapter 6; but this chapter is concerned specifically with the harmful and helpful relationships which exist in organic communities. There are some very intricate relationships known at the present day, and we cannot hope to sort out such complexities in most fossil assemblages, but from time to time we find hints of what was going on.

A large number of terms have been applied to the different relationships which exist between species, many of them contradictory, but it is proposed to follow here the usage of G. L. Clarke (1954). He defined the relationships on the basis of gain ($+$), loss ($-$), and neutrality (0).

There are two basic types of relationship:

1. *Antagonism,* in which one species suffers through the actions of another.

2. *Symbiosis,* in which one or both species are benefited but neither is harmed.

We can, however, add an intermediate category:

3. *Toleration,* in which neither species gains or loses, and which is not really a relationship at all.

From this there follows a simple classification, using the symbols presented above:

$$
\text{Antagonism} \quad
\begin{cases}
\text{Antibiosis } (-\ 0) \\
\text{Exploitation } (-\ +) \\
\text{Competition } (-\ -)
\end{cases}
$$

Toleration (0 0)

$$
\text{Symbiosis} \quad
\begin{cases}
\text{Commensalism } (0\ +) \\
\text{Mutualism } (+\ +)
\end{cases}
$$

It must not be thought that this is a rigid system, since, as will be shown later, one type of relationship may pass imperceptibly into another. Also, there are some curious relationships which defy classification altogether.

ANTAGONISM

Antibiosis $(-\ 0)$

This is the relationship in which one species suffers and the other is not affected. The phenomenon is relatively uncommon and is hardly likely to be seen in fossils. The usual situation is for one organism to produce a substance which is harmful to the other or in some other way makes life difficult for it. It is chiefly known on a microscopic scale; for example, a certain alga may inhibit the growth of diatoms. Here I may again quote the cases where the proliferation of some microorganism kills off thousands or millions of fish, either by the production of a toxic substance or by simple suffocation through the removal of oxygen from the water. In such cases, the proliferation of the microorganisms is probably brought about by the upwelling of cold water rich in nutrients. Brongersma-Sanders discussed this matter at some length (1948, 1949, 1957). As stated earlier, she compared Recent with ancient deposits, quoting particularly a deposit on the sea floor near Walvis Bay, South-West Africa (1948). The sediments here include diatomaceous ooze with a high organic content, very abundant fish remains, and very few benthonic invertebrates. The last observation suggests anaerobic bottom conditions in which the fish remains would be likely to fossilize —conditions unlike those in the majority of marine deposits, where fish remains are·very rare.

Paucă (1934) describes an Oligocene fish fauna from Roumania in which many of the fish had been buried with their mouths open, suggesting asphyxiation. This is particularly interesting because the strata concerned are thought to be the source of the oil of the famous Ploesti oil field.

A different form of antibiosis in the fossil record (which is more debatable) is suggested by the small dinosaurs which are thought to have been poisoned. There is, for example, the specimen of *Struthio-*

mimus altus from the Upper Cretaceous of Alberta which was discussed by Moodie (1923). The thrown-back head, the curvature of the spine, and the backward-directed limbs all suggest the opisthotonic attitude of animals suffering from tetanus or strychnine poisoning. The former would be produced by bacteria and the latter by the eating of the seeds of *Strychnos nux-vomica*. We have no way of proving that this particular dinosaur died of poisoning, though it seems possible. Other cases, such as that of *Compsognathus longipes* from the Upper Jurassic of Bavaria, which has a similar attitude, may be explained simply as mechanical rearrangement after death.

At one point in the late Quaternary there is a sudden decline in elm pollen in the palynological profiles. This decline is so marked that it is often used as a marker for the boundary of Atlantic and Subboreal times. It has been suggested (Iversen, 1956) that this decline might be attributable to an early incidence of the Dutch elm disease which has caused such widespread destruction of elms in Europe and, especially, in the eastern United States in recent years. Troels-Smith (1960) re-examined the problem and preferred the theory that the collection of elm leaves and shoots by early farmers for fodder brought about the elm decline.

Both explanations provide an example of an antagonistic relationship, but the second alternative brings us to the next category.

Exploitation $(-+)$

This is a far more common phenomenon than the last; it involves simply gain by one species at the expense of another. This may happen in a number of different ways, but most commonly through predation and parasitism.

Predation This is the relationship in which one species feeds on the other. Obviously this is the most common of phenomena and one which has always been fundamental to animal life.

The paleoecologist should always ask himself, "What did this fossil animal eat?" and "What animal (if any) ate it?" This often presents very intriguing problems. It has been suggested many times that the appearance of the first fossil shells and exoskeletons in the Cambrian was a response to the evolution of the first predatory animals. But what could have been the large predators of the early Cambrian? Burling (1917) reported a partly healed injury to the Lower Cambrian trilobite *Paedeumias robsonensis* and suggested that an early fish was responsible. There are no known fish or giant arthropods in the Cambrian rocks, and even if we postulate early chordates without skeletons, we still have the negative evidence of the Burgess shale.

A popular evolutionary dictum is that there was a close relationship between the spread of grass in the early Tertiary and the rapid expansion of the grazing mammals. Grass today, either directly or indirectly, provides the bulk of the food of the great majority of the land tetrapods, and the whole system of predation on land must have been very different before it evolved.

Similarly, microscopic planktonic plants form the main basis for life in the sea, but these are practically unknown in the fossil record apart from diatoms. Seaweed—the larger brown algae—is surprisingly little used as a direct source of food. At the present day it is eaten by a few gastropods and arthropods, and it was eaten by Steller's sea cow until this was exterminated about two hundred years ago. However, seaweed does provide a major indirect source of animal food, via bacteria, when it decays on the sea floor.

To come to concrete examples of predation among fossils, we have the clear picture of such interrelationships presented by D. M. S. Watson (1957) in describing the *Cistecephalus* zone of the Beaufort formation in South Africa (?Upper Permian). At the top of the food pyramid here we have the Gorgonopsids, which were carnivorous reptiles ranging from giants, with skulls up to 60 cm long, down to forms smaller than a cat. Below them were the very abundant herbivorous Dicynodonts, more than a hundred species of them, again ranging from large ungainly forms down to very small ones. Also at this level were the more active herbivorous Pareiasaurs and smaller reptiles such as crocodiles and lizards. Lower down still were plants, fish, insects and other small animals.

An important point here is that the herbivores—the Dicynodonts—were far more common than the carnivores—the Gorgonopsids. This is as one would expect in a true food pyramid. The whole balance of nature depends on the fact that herbivorous animals tend to be gregarious, living together in large numbers, whereas predators are fewer and usually more solitary. This has a bearing on their occurrence as fossils. We have the famous discovery of twenty-nine Iguanodons in a Lower Cretaceous ravine near Bernissart in Belgium. Though it is now thought that they did not fall into the ravine but were washed down into it, the concentration does suggest a dense population of these large herbivores somewhere in the region.

On the other hand, we can consider the famous Rancho La Brea tar pits of California, which have now been surrounded by the spread of Los Angeles. Here there is a Pleistocene vertebrate association in which 91 per cent of the skeletons are of carnivores and only 9 per cent herbivores. This is obviously a completely distorted picture of the contemporary fauna. The tar pits trapped many different kinds of herbivorous mammals—horses, bison, camels, deer, ground sloths, mastodons, elephants, peccaries, and tapirs, plus a large number of birds and a few reptiles and amphibia. These in turn attracted vastly greater numbers of carnivores—both mammals and birds—which came to feed on the trapped animals but instead were trapped themselves.

Shotwell (1955) compared the carnivore/herbivore ratio at Rancho La Brea with that at two other late Cenozoic vertebrate localities (Figure 15.1). At both of the other localities—McKay Reservoir, Oregon, and Coffee Ranch, Hemphill, Texas—the proportions were much more what one would expect in a living population. The diagrams were produced following the principle of the *minimum number,* that is, by inclusion

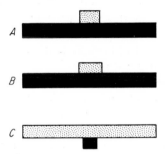

FIGURE 15.1 Relative abundance of carnivores and herbivores at three Quaternary localities in the United States. Carnivores, stippled; herbivores, black. *A,* McKay reservoir, Oregon. *B,* Coffee Ranch, Hemphill, Texas. *C,* Rancho La Brea, California. (After Shotwell, 1955.)

of the smallest number of individuals which could have produced all the bones found. This approach makes up for inaccuracies caused by one species having more vertebrae or a more easily broken skeleton than another.

More direct evidence of predation is provided by the remains found in the stomachs of the carnivores, such as the belemnites, reptile ribs, fish, and decapod hooks found in a pliosaur from the Upper Jurassic of Russia described by Juravlev (1943).

Perhaps the best evidence of all is the fossil predator actually "caught in the act," as seems to be the case with the slab from the Devonian of Saugerties, New York, figured by Ladd (1957*b*). On this, the starfish *Palaeaster* seems to be feeding on the pelecypod *Grammysia.* J. M. Clarke (1912) described an association from Mount Marion, New York, in which many specimens of the starfish *Devonaster eucharis* were found attached to the pelecypods *Grammysia* and *Pterinea,* actually in the act of feeding. In my own collection I have a lobster from the Solenhofen stone of Germany which was apparently fossilized in the act of catching a small fish!

There is also fossil evidence from the remains of victims which escaped complete mastication. L. B. Tarlo (personal communication, 1961) has observed a specimen of the Old Red Sandstone fish *Psammolepis venyukovi*, from Estonia, with the tooth of a crossopterygian fish embedded in its dorsal plate. Several other specimens have their protruding branchial plates bitten and healed, showing that they were attacked during life.

Kauffman and Kesling (1960) described and figured a Cretaceous ammonite from South Dakota that clearly shows the teeth marks of a mosasaur which bit it at least sixteen times and lost two teeth in the encounter! The reptile attempted to swallow the ammonite whole but finally crushed the body chamber and ate the soft parts. Sardeson (1929) noted that *Rafinesquina* shells in the Late Ordovician of Minnesota are frequently damaged. The concave valves are broken in centrally, and the fracture outlines often resemble the shape of the labrum of a trilobite, probably some species of *Asaphus*.

Parasitism   This is another very common phenomenon; nearly every animal and plant has its parasites, both external and internal. This state of affairs was probably established very early in the history of life, as shown by J. M. Clarke (1908, 1921). Perhaps this point is best exemplified by the fact that the famous plant remains of the Middle Devonian Rhynie chert of Aberdeenshire, Scotland, which were long regarded as the remains of the earliest land plants, had their living tissues penetrated by fungal hyphae. At the other end of the stratigraphical scale we have the parasites found on the Tertiary insects from the Baltic amber.

I could go on almost indefinitely quoting examples of apparent parasitic attacks on fossils. It is often difficult to distinguish, however, between a parasitic relationship, in which the host suffered, and a commensal one, in which the host was not affected. In every collection there are numerous examples of mollusk or brachiopod shells with other organisms attached, but these were not necessarily parasitic. They may have been commensal, or they may have been there purely accidentally, or they may have arrived after the death of the host shell. We must look for further evidence in every case.

Thus the best-known supposedly parasitic relationship among fossils is perhaps that of the "worm" *Hicetes innexus*, which almost invariably occurs in the center of the Devonian tabulate coral *Pleurodictyum problematicum*. Figure 15.2 shows this relationship as originally figured by Goldfuss (1826) in the first description of this coral from Germany. It is interesting to note that *Pleurodictyum* itself is found attached to larger creatures such as brachiopods, crinoids, and mollusks, so that we have here something comparable to the modern parasite chains or pyramids. In this case the coral presumably benefited from the solid

substratum provided by an older organism, and the "worm" presumably benefited from the food collected by the coral. However, we have no evidence, suspect it though we may, that any of the organisms suffered from the relationships and it may be that these are cases of commensalism rather than parasitism.

Pleurodictyum also provides an example of an apparent careful selection of hosts. J. M. Clarke (1908) pointed out that *P. problematicum* in the German Lower Devonian is always attached to the brachiopod *Chonetes sarcinulatus*, whereas *P. styloporum* in the New York Middle Devonian is always attached to a gastropod—usually *Loxonema*. This may be taken as evidence that the coral required more of its host than just something hard to sit on. It is not suggested that there was

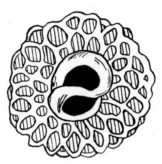

FIGURE 15.2 The association of the tabulate coral *Pleurodictyum problematicum* and the "worm" *Hicetes innexus*. (After Goldfuss, 1826.)

necessarily deliberate selection by the younger organism in its larval stage, but rather that the larva only prospered and grew to a full colony on the right kind of host. I have suggested a similar form of selection by the tabulate coral *Aulopora* in its attachment to brachiopods in the Upper Devonian of Iowa (Ager, 1961*b*). The species commonly found here on *Spinocyrtia iowensis* is the flat-lying *A. elleri*, whereas that found on *Eosyringothyris calvini* appears to be *A. multiramosa*, which is a completely different species with an erect portion in each corallite (Plate 7A and E).

There is even evidence in this fauna of constancy in the nature of the attached coral species in one family as distinct from another. Clay (e.g., 1947) has shown among modern birds that it is sometimes possible to identify a genus with a particular family on the evidence of its parasites. This was done, for example, with the flamingos. Pruvost (1930) used this kind of evidence in arguing that the Carboniferous pelecypod *Anthraconauta* was more closely related to *Naiadites* than to "*Anthracomya*," since the first two commonly carry *Spirorbis*, whereas the last named does not.

PLATE 7   Brachiopods and their epifaunas.
A–D, Spinocyrtia iowensis, Upper Devonian, Vinton, Iowa, with symbiotic associates.
A, with coral *Aulopora elleri* in characteristic position on the dorsal value; ×1.5. **B,**
bedding plane view of a specimen in supposed life position; ×2. **C,** young individual

Again, in all the fossil examples quoted so far there is no evidence of the host suffering, and the relationships may be symbiotic rather than antagonistic, and even when there has been damage to the host, we have to be sure that this happened during its life. Fenton and Fenton (1932*a*, 1932*b*) showed that the sponge borings in *Atrypa* in the Devonian of Iowa were only found in the dorsal valve, which they therefore interpreted as uppermost in life, though this could also be interpreted as the position of greatest mechanical stability after death.

Bored shells are common in every system from every part of the world, and the borings have been referred to a wide variety of organisms, though sponges, gastropods, and "worms" are probably the most popular. To quote merely one example, there is the bored brachiopod *Dalmanella meeki* from the Richmond group (Upper Ordovician) near Oxford, Ohio, which was figured by Bucher (1938). The holes were attributed to the acid-assisted action of the gastropod *Holopea*. Immense damage is done to modern oyster beds by the oyster drill, *Urosalpinx cinerea;* but since the shell is completely penetrated and the oyster killed, this is predation rather than parasitism. The boring sponge *Cliona*, on the other hand, weakens rather than kills its oyster host and is more truly parasitic (Plate 6*F*).

More likely to represent true parasitism are the examples of the coral *Cyclolites* from the Cretaceous of Hungary described by Géczy (1954) which contain tubes or cystlike structures around which the coral skeleton has been considerably deformed (Figure 15.3). Similar structures in brachiopods (again in *Atrypa*) from the Polish Devonian were described by Biernat (1961). In these, the parasites formed V-shaped tubes opening on the interior of the ventral valve, and the irritation so caused induced the hosts to secrete thick ridges of calcium carbonate to contain them. Similar also are the galls in Russian Devonian crinoid stems described by Yakovlev (1926). There are many other examples in the literature.

Competition (— —)

Competition is the natural state of affairs in an uncontrolled society, but while supposedly beneficial for the society concerned, it is almost invariably detrimental for the individuals involved. We have every-

with valves twisted as a result of partial overgrowth of the commissure by the encrusting bryozoan *Paleschara incrustans* (seen in bottom left-hand corner); ×2. **D**, symbiotic nature of the association proved by the cessation of growth of the encrusting bryozoan along a growth line on the brachiopod; ×2.
E, *Eosyringothyris calvini* from the same locality and horizon, with the symbiotic coral *Aulopora* cf. *A. multiramosa;* ×1.5. (Data in Ager, 1961*b*.)

where continuous competition for food, light, and space between species and within species. The more closely alike two forms are in needs,
the more they will compete. G. F. Elliott (1948) has discussed the effect of intraspecific competition in closely packed brachiopod colonies
on species evolution. He came to the conclusion that it was anything
but beneficial for the group as a whole.

To turn to interspecific competition, there is the fascinating subject
of competition between species of the same genus. Allied species are
likely to have similar ecological requirements and are therefore more
likely to compete with one another than with species of other genera,
as was pointed out by Darwin in his *Origin of Species.* This has the important effect that very rarely are two species of the same genus found

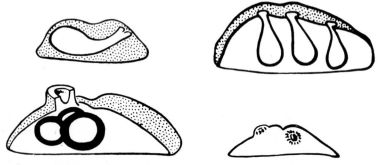

FIGURE 15.3   Cystlike structures formed around parasite borings in the Cretaceous
coral *Cyclolites.* (From Géczy, 1954.)

living together in the same environment. This is the *Gause,* or *Volterra-
Gause, principle* which has been the subject of a great deal of argument. In simple terms it states that, in a stable community, two or more
species with the same ecological requirements cannot exist together.
The reason is obvious: one species will inevitably be the more successful and drive the other out.

Some time ago, when writing on this subject, I chanced to look out
of my study window and was slightly demoralized to see four species
of the same genus, all feeding happily together on my lawn. These were
the blue tit *Parus caeruleus,* the great tit *P. major,* the coal tit *P. ater,*
and the marsh tit, *P. palustris.* However, when I read the relevant literature, it soon became obvious that, in natural circumstances, these
species do in fact have different habits and habitats. Betts (1955)
showed that their food tends to be different, and Hartley (1953) showed
that they tend to feed at different levels in the trees. The only time that
they are likely to feed together is when there is a great abundance of
food, as on the crumb-strewn lawn.

Similarly, the two British rats, both of which were introduced from abroad, tend to be separated in their feeding habits. The brown rat (*Rattus norvegicus*) tends to occupy the ground floor and basements; the black rat (*R. rattus*), which is a more agile climber, tends to occupy the upper stories.

Such examples are not, of course, likely to concern paleoecologists, but an excellent study of a modern genus of obvious paleoecological application has been published by A. J. Kohn (1959). This was a comprehensive study of the ecology of the gastropod genus *Conus* in the shallow water around Hawaii. At least twenty-one species of *Conus* are known here within the restricted environment of the reefs and marine benches; and presumably, in a geological equivalent of such an environment we might expect to find a comparable number of species associated in a single bed. However, Kohn's detailed study revealed that, though all these *Conus* species are associated in a general sort of way, there are many subtle differences between them in the details of habit and habitat. For example, the species *C. marmoreus* appears to eat only other species of *Conus*, whereas its associate *C. pennaceus* will not touch its relations but only eats other gastropods.

Table 15.1 summarizes the ecological characteristics of six species of *Conus* living on marine benches. Each can be seen to have some particular ecological characteristic which distinguishes it from the others. Thus 90 per cent of the population of *C. sponsalis* were observed to live on a substratum of algal turf, compared with much lower percentages of the other species. *Conus catus* was the only one of the six to feed only on fish. Both *C. ebraeus* and *C. chaldaeus* were found to feed mainly on Nereidae, but differed from each other in that the former was able to withstand stronger water currents and the latter tended to concentrate at a greater distance from shore. *Conus rattus* was found to be unable to withstand strong currents at all, and *C. abbreviatus* differed from all the others in that the greater part of its population remained partly buried in the substratum by day. These are only some of the more obvious differences among the habits and habitats of the six species, but they suffice to show how related species living together in space may be separated ecologically.

Such fine distinctions in the habits and habitats of closely related species may explain the close association of such forms in apparently indigenous fossil assemblages. These circumstances may, however, be exceptional; most field paleontologists would probably agree that it is very rare to find more than one clearly recognizable species of any genus in a particular noncondensed assemblage. This is where the big divergence commonly occurs between the man who has collected the specimens and the specialist who studies them.

TABLE 15.1 *Ecological characteristics of six species of* Conus *living on marine benches around Hawaii.* (*After Kohn, 1959*)

	sponsalis	abbreviatus	ebraeus	chaldaeus	rattus	catus
Relative abundance at all bench stations	1	2	3	4	5	6
Population density on a solution bench (Sta. 5), no./100 sq ft	0.41	0.66	1.02	0.15	0.02	0.00
Population density on a water-leveled bench (Sta. Kl), no./100 sq ft	0.48	0.85	0.55	0.18	0.09	0.24
Population density at abrasion-ramp stations, no./100 sq ft	0.25	0.21	0.00	0.07	0.33	0.00
Distance from shore of density peak at Sta. 5 (% distance across bench)	8	8	50	73	—	—
Distance from shore of density peak at Sta. Kl (% distance across bench)	22	18	26	48–70	47	53
Per cent of population on substratum of algal turf on bench, binding ± sand	90	65	65	45	62	(45)
Per cent of population on sand patches on bench	5	26	15	28	11	(18)
Per cent of population exposed to air at low tide	55	35	29	32	17	29
Per cent of population partly buried in substratum during day	30	63	31	42	10	(44)
Ability to withstand strong water currents, arbitrary units	+	+	++	+		
Active period in nature and in laboratory	All species actively crawl about at night, are quiescent during day					
Per cent of diet represented by Nereidae	52	26	93	85	50	Eats only
Per cent of diet represented by Eunicea	44	69	6	15	50	fish

Sorgenfrei (1958) produced what seems to be a clear demonstration of the Volterra-Gause principle in operation in the fossil record. He showed that four species of *Nassa* were more or less mutually exclusive in the Middle Miocene of South Jutland in Denmark. This is expressed graphically in Figure 15.4.

In Sorgenfrei's example, the mutual exclusiveness is demonstrated through time in a small area. The same phenomenon can be demonstrated in space if contemporaneous faunas can be traced over large

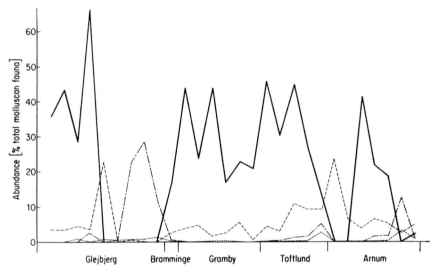

FIGURE 15.4 The relative abundance of four species of *Nassa* in well sections in the Middle Miocene of South Jutland. (Drawn from data in Sorgenfrei, 1958; observations omitted when total number of mollusks was less than seventy-five.)

———— *N. cimbrica*   ------- *N. facki*

— — — —*N. schlotheimi*   — · — — -*N. fuchsi*

enough areas. Thus in my work on the brachiopods of the *spinatum* zone of the British Lower Jurassic (Ager, 1956*a*), I found that the genus *Aulacothyris* was represented in the southwest by *A. resupinata*, whereas in the northeast this species was completely replaced by *A. fusiformis* and *A. pyriformis* (Figure 15.5). In turn, these two were separated stratigraphically.

Another fossil example of such mutual exclusiveness is provided by the work of Laughbaum (1960) which was quoted earlier (see page 94). In this study of the Lower Cretaceous Denton formation in north

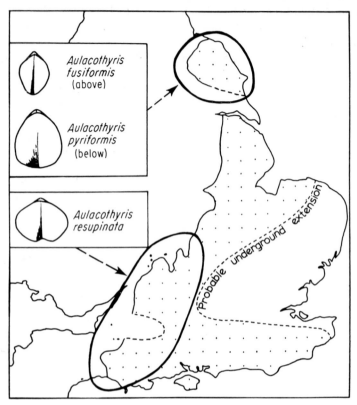

FIGURE 15.5   Distribution of species of *Aulacothyris* in the *spinatum* zone of the English Lower Jurassic.

TABLE 15.2 *Differences in tolerance of three environmental factors by three species of oysters in the Denton formation of Texas.* (*Data from Laughbaum, 1960*)

	REDUCED SALINITY	DEEPER WATER	TURBIDITY
Gryphaea washitaensis	X*	√√	√
Ostrea (*Arctostrea*) carinata	√	√	X
Ostrea (*Lopha*) quadriplicata	√	X	√

*X = not tolerant; √ = tolerant; √√ = highly tolerant.

Texas, he showed that three species of oysters had different ranges of tolerance (Table 15.2). Though the oysters are placed in different nominal genera or subgenera, these are undoubtedly artificial, and the species are closely related. Their variation in environmental adaptation clearly prevented them from coming into direct competition.

TOLERATION (0 0)

The state of toleration, or neutrality, is such a negative one that we cannot expect any definite evidence of it in the fossil record. We might indeed find a fossil lamb lying down with a fossil lion, but the cynical paleoecologist would inevitably interpret this as a "death assemblage." If we look at nature, living or fossil, with unbiased eyes, we must admit that one species will tolerate another weaker species only if the latter does not interfere with its own ends.

SYMBIOSIS

We come now to the other main type of relationship between species—that in which one or both species benefit but neither is harmed. Symbiosis is sometimes used in a stricter sense, but I accept it here in its simple literal sense of "living together."

Commensalism (0 +)

This is the very common relationship in which one species gains and the other is not affected. There are innumerable examples of this both at the present day and among fossils. Living examples already mentioned (Chapter 1) are the urchin fish living between the spines of echinoids and the clown fish living between the stinging tentacles of sea anemones.

Some animals act as host for many different commensals, such as the often-discussed sponge "the size of a washtub" which was found to contain more than seventeen thousand smaller animals. Another famous example is the species of echiuroid worm *Urechis* which lives in a U-shaped burrow in tidal mud flats on the Pacific Coast of North America. This is an untidy feeder, and there is plenty available for associates (besides the safety of its burrow). Commonly found with *Urechis* are a small fish, an annelid, two crabs, and a pelecypod. This burrow slum is particularly worth mentioning because a comparable burrow found in Pliocene diatomaceous shales near Monterey, California, contained a fossil crab identical with one of those which live with the modern worm (MacGinitie and MacGinitie, 1949).

The most abundant fossil examples of commensalism are in the form of one shelly organism attached to another. Usually, this must have been beneficial for the smaller creature involved and did not inconvenience the larger one.

For instance, Chapman (1929) described a species of the conical gastropod *Capulus* attached to the exoskeleton of the eurypterid *Pterygotus* in the Silurian near Melbourne, Australia. Several gastropods were

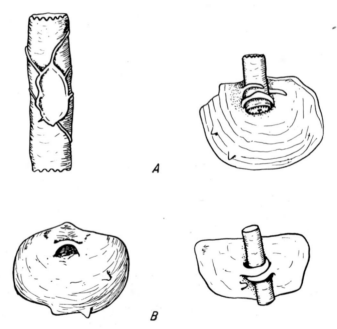

FIGURE 15.6 Small productoid brachiopods attached by their spines. A, *Etheridgina* attached to crinoid stems, Lower Carboniferous, Scotland (Redrawn from Etheridge, 1876). B, *Productella*, showing loop formed of convergent spines, attached to the spine of an adult brachiopod. Mississippian, Missouri (Redrawn from Unklesbay and Niewoehner, 1959).

present and each had a smooth area around it. Chapman compared the association with that of the allied genus *Hipponix* on *Chlamys* shells in present-day Australian seas.

Etheridge (1876) described productoid brachiopods (later called *Etheridgina*) from the Lower Carboniferous of Scotland which had attached themselves to crinoids (Figure 15.6A). Unklesbay and Niewoehner (1959) described minute specimens of *Productella* from the Mississippian of Missouri which had attached themselves in youth to crinoid stems by means of convergent spines (Figure 15.6*B*). This may have served to keep the poorly protected young away from bottom predators and in the food-bearing water currents. Similarly, Trechmann (1921) described two species of *Strophalosia* and a terebratuloid attached to the spines of another brachiopod, *Horridonia horridus*, in the Permian of northeast England. More recently, Grant (1963) has described what seems to be the only known productoid—*Linoproductus angustus* from the

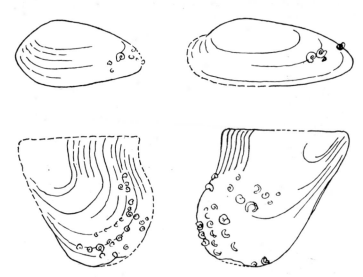

Figure 15.7 *Spirorbis* tubes concentrated near the exhalant currents of two Upper Carboniferous nonmarine pelecypods. *Top, Carbonicola; bottom, Naiadites.* (From Trueman, 1942; by courtesy of *Geological Magazine.*)

Permian of Texas—which lived attached in this way to crinoid stems in adult life.

A more directly beneficial arrangement is exemplified by Trueman's description (1942) of *Spirorbis* tubes concentrated near the exhalant current on the shells of Upper Carboniferous nonmarine pelecypods (Figure 15.7).

A common comparable association in the Devonian and Mississippian of North America is that of the gastropod *Platyceras* and various crinoids. The former is always found in position over the anal opening of the crinoid, and it is assumed that it was coprophagous (Figure 15.8). The same association in the U.S.S.R. was described by Yakovlev (1926).

Another very familiar fossil association is that of the tabulate coral *Aulopora* on the shells of Paleozoic brachiopods, already described in this chapter. R. F. Gekker (1935) showed that such associations in the

Devonian of Russia occurred during the life of the host and were therefore probably symbiotic. Chang Shou-hsin (1959) described a specimen from China which provided the same kind of evidence. In my study of more than three hundred Devonian spiriferids from Iowa (Ager, 1961b),

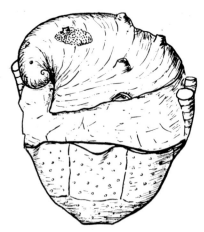

FIGURE 15.8 The gastropod *Platyceras* in its characteristic position over the anal opening of a crinoid; Devonian, New York. (Drawn from a specimen in the author's collection.)

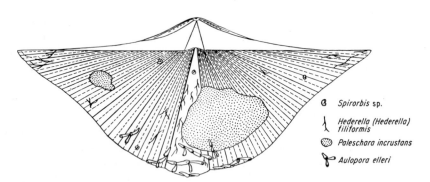

FIGURE 15.9 A hypothetical specimen of *Spinocyrtia iowensis*, showing the characteristic positions of the epifaunal elements. (From Ager, 1961b; by courtesy of the Geological Society of London.)

I found *Aulopora* and three other epifaunal elements on nearly 90 per cent of the shells. This is summarized in Figure 15.9 and illustrated in Plate 7. I found that the four elements—*Aulopora*, two bryozoans, and a serpulid—tended to attach themselves to their host in a definite order and all while it was still alive. Some of them also tended to favor certain parts of the shell. I suggested that the epifauna derived benefit from the firm substratum, the freedom from sediment, and the feeding streams of the brachiopod.

In only two exceptional specimens was there any evidence of harmful effects on the host. In both of these an encrusting bryozoan colony had grown over the anterior commissure, preventing the valves from opening and so causing the death of the spiriferid (though both specimens showed evidence of the final struggle of the brachiopod to escape the smothering embrace). Thus it will be seen that, though these relationships have been dealt with under commensalism, they may pass into antagonistic relationships in which the host suffers. This can often be seen at the present day. Anyone who has been to the southern states of the United States knows the so-called "Spanish moss" (*Tillandsia*) which hangs from the branches of the swamp cypress, the live oak, and other trees. This is a commensal relationship for the benefit of the moss, as is shown by the fact that it also hangs from telegraph poles, on which it could hardly be parasitic. But in time, the mere weight of the moss becomes sufficient to break down the branches of the trees, and the moss may prevent the light from reaching the leaves; so the relationship becomes an antagonistic one.

Mutualism $(+ +)$

This is a less common relationship in this hard world, being the one in which two species cooperate for their mutual benefit. The extreme version of this is seen in the lichens, which are intimate intergrowths of algae and fungi. Each is completely dependent on the other. The fungus forms the main body of the lichen, fixes it in place, and holds the essential water, while the alga photosynthesizes and produces the necessary carbohydrates.

A fossil example was described by Alan Wood (1948); he showed that the organism known as "*Sphaerocodium*" from Middle Silurian limestones of the Baltic was in fact a complex association of several organisms. The most obvious of these were the alga *Rothpletzella* and the foram *Wetheredella*. In an earlier paper (1942) Wood redescribed the Lower Carboniferous form known as "*Mitcheldeania nicholsoni*," which proved to be an admixture of at least these three algae: *Girvanella nicholsoni*, *Garwoodia gregaria*, and *Ortonella kershopensis*.

A comparable association from the Cretaceous of Guatemala was described by Johnson and Konishi (1960). In this study, the interspaces between the filaments of the siphonocladacean alga *Pycnoporidium sinuosum* were found to be occupied by a tubular alga referred to *Girvanella* cf. *G. tosaensis*. The same relationship had been observed in the Torinosu limestone of Shikoku, Japan, by Yabe and Toyama (1928). Johnson and Konishi discussed the nature of these relationships and suggest that a ". . . consistent association throughout the various localities where a form is found may lead to the assumption of a symbiotic relationship." In the case of the Guatemalan specimens, however, it was noted that the parts of the *Pycnoporidium* in contact with *Girvanella* appeared to have had their wall structure obliterated, suggesting parasitism.

A similar relationship between quite different fossil organisms is that postulated by Condra and Elias (1944) for the well-known bryozoan *Archimedes*. This, they maintained, is not simply a *Fenestella*-like bryozoan with a massive screwlike axis but is an intimate association of *Fenestella* with a plantlike organism, or *phytomorph*. The latter enabled the bryozoan to grow upward and to produce larger, more durable growth forms, and both organisms benefited from the association.

To return once more to the *Aulopora-Spirifer* association, this has also been described as a mutualistic arrangement. The Russian paleontologist Yakovlev (1926) suggested that the coral derived benefit from the feeding streams of the brachiopod (as I suggested for the Iowa specimens) and that the brachiopod may have derived benefit in the form of protection by the stinging nematocysts of the coral. This is the type of relationship that occurs at the present day between the hermit crab and the sea anemone, but there is no possible proof of it in these ancient fossils.

OTHER RELATIONSHIPS

Finally, there are a number of other strange relationships which are known at the present day and which may be found fossil.

The commonest of these is the utilization of the dead remains of one organism by another. On a soft sea floor any shell, living or dead, is a favored spot for other organisms to settle. Thus the *Gryphaea* in Plate 6E has large serpulid tubes on one valve and oyster spats on the other, and it is difficult to prove whether the host was alive when they arrived. More specific use is that of the dead whelk shell by the hermit crab. The strange fossil *Kirunia* from the Eocene of Egypt has been interpreted as a gastropod covered by a symbiotic hydrozoan and utilized—like the whelk—by a crab, the remains of which have been found inside.

Chatwin (1923) described gastropods from the English Chalk which were guests in dead echinoid tests. They grew there until they were too large to escape. In contrast with Trueman's example quoted earlier (Figure 15.7), Maclennan (1943) described *Spirorbis* tubes *inside* what must have been the dead shells of the Carboniferous nonmarine pelecypod *Carbonicola.*

Similarly, there are many borings in fossils which must have been made after the death of the attacked shell. Schlaudt and Young (1960) have described borings in the Cretaceous gastropod *Ceritella proctori* from Texas which they attribute to the acrothoracic barnacle *Rogerella cragini.* The attackers were not parasitic, since they did not usually penetrate the host shell but merely drilled holes along the sutures between the whorls. The evidence that this occurred only

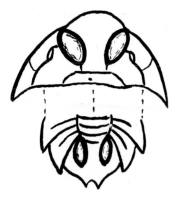

FIGURE 15.10 Silurian trilobite *Platylichas margaritifer* from the Porkuni limestone of Estonia, showing pseudo-eyes on the cephalon and pygidium, supposedly to discourage predatory enemies.

after the death of the gastropod is that the borings are restricted to the upper sides of horizontal specimens.

There are also the well-substantiated cases of the use of dead organisms, particularly dead wood, for an epiplanktonic mode of life. Crinoids are often found in the European Lias associated with wood fragments. Hauff (1953) figured several beautiful specimens from Holzmaden in Württemberg; the echinoderms can be clearly seen attached to the wood and presumably floated with it in life.

Two other categories of interspecific relationships may also be included here: those of saprophytes and those of scavengers. The former are plants living on dead organic material, like many of the larger fungi, and the latter are animals, ranging from ostracods to hyenas, which live in the same way. These are important ecological niches which must have existed since very early in the history of life. The saprophytes include the all-important bacteria, which even at the present day are known by their activities more than by their form.

Bradley (1946) described some very well-preserved coprolites from the Eocene of Wyoming which contained silicified bacteria very like the saprophytic bacteria which live in the intestines of modern animals. Scavengers were probably partly responsible for many of the gaps and distortions in the fossil record, for example, the scarcity of graptolites in early Paleozoic "shelly" sediments.

Even odder relationships are that of ants obtaining a sugary solution from aphids and that of man obtaining milk from cows.

The most extreme form of relationship (in the widest sense) is that of mimicry, as when a harmless animal resembles a much larger, fiercer one and so protects itself from attack. The larvae of the Tiger Swallowtail butterfly have small and inconspicuous eyes, but huge eyelike color markings, perhaps to frighten predatory birds.

Curiously enough, a closely comparable example from the fossil trilobites has been postulated by Lamont (1952). He suggested that the lobes of the glabella of *Lichas hendersoni* from the Silurian of southern Scotland, looked like the eyes of a much bigger creature and may have deterred predatory cephalopods. In another trilobite he found similar *pseudo-eyes* on the pygidium—supposedly to discourage attack from behind! Figure 15.10 shows similar structures in a related form.

SIXTEEN

Lateral and vertical changes in assemblages

I have already considered, with many reservations, changes in individual fossils in response to different supposed environments, but the study of such changes in whole assemblages provides a whole system of checks and cross-checks. Changes in one fossil species may not be significant—they may be explained in a hundred different ways—but if a whole assemblage changes, then we must clearly take much more notice.

LATERAL CHANGES

When we study the lateral variation of a single fossil species or group, the other fossils present may be used for correlation. Thus, in studying lateral changes in brachiopod faunas in the British Jurassic, I was able to use ammonites to prove contemporaneity. We are always using one ruler to measure another.

When the whole assemblage appears to change laterally, this problem of proving contemporaneity becomes much more difficult. Unless one suitable member remains constant throughout, the only hope is to use the faunas immediately above and below the one being considered. Absolute proof is, of course, impossible. Yet, bearing these limitations in mind, it is sometimes possible to trace the lateral changes of a particular assemblage over considerable distances.

L. W. Stephenson (1933) showed that the zone of *Exogyra cancellata* in the Upper Cretaceous of the eastern United States can be traced for more than 4,000 km, from New Jersey to Mexico, and down dip as much as 185 km. Different lines of evidence suggest shallow-water conditions throughout that distance, ranging from about 8 to about 50 m in depth. The zone itself varies in thickness from about 1.2 m in New Jersey to about 60 m in central Texas.

The zone fossil, *E. cancellata,* and fifteen other species, seven of them oysters, are found from one end of the belt to the other; therefore it can be argued that there were no geographical breaks. Stephenson concluded that food supplies, temperature, and salinity must have been fairly uniform throughout the belt for the same forms to occur all the way, though there may have been a range in toleration. There are, however, some notable changes, of which the most significant is the appearance of rudistid pelecypods at the south end of the outcrop in Texas. Stephenson suggested that the climate was probably tropical at the south end of the belt and subtropical to warm temperate in the north.

A much older example of lateral change in a fossil fauna was claimed by Dr. G. L. Elles (1939) in Lower Paleozoic rocks. She pointed out that the common assemblages in British Ordovician and Silurian sediments are each dominated by one of the following alternatives:

1. Graptolites alone
2. Graptolites and trilobites
3. Trilobites
4. Trilobites and small brachiopods
5. Large brachiopods

These may be interpreted as signifying a shoreward transition through successive bathymetric zones (Figure 16.1).

Graptolites almost certainly drifted landward in life but stood a much smaller chance of survival near land as fossils. In shallower water, their fragile skeletons were far more likely to be broken up or eaten by predators. The same transition can also be observed vertically in successions which record shallowing water, as in the View Edge escarpment of Shropshire.

Eva Hanzlíková (1956) has drawn attention to marked lateral changes in microfaunal assemblages in the Paleocene Magura flysch in Czechoslovakia. Some of the differences in the *Gaudryina* zone are summarized in Table 16.1.

These are all variations within the foraminifera, which constitute the whole of the microfauna in these regions. But Dr. Hanzlíková also noted that in another facies of the same zone—the Babice clay—a foram fauna dominated by the Anomalinidae is accompanied by an abundance of

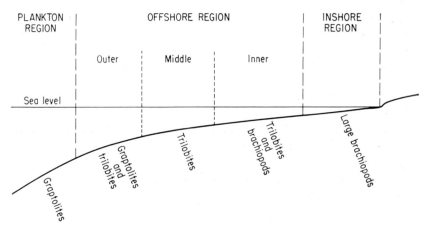

FIGURE 16.1   Lateral changes in fossil assemblages of Lower Paleozoic age in the marginal area of a geosyncline. (After Elles, 1939.)

other minute organic remains such as sponge spicules, echinoids, bryozoa, pelecypods, gastropods, and calcareous algae.

One phenomenon of lateral variation which we may consider with more confidence when dealing with whole assemblages is that of stunting. There are frequent examples in the fossil record of varied accumulations of small specimens; and the decrease in average size of a whole assemblage, if it is not merely the result of mechanical sorting, clearly

TABLE 16.1 *Lateral changes in microfauna of Magura flysch.*

Hluk	*Raca*	*Bílé Karpaty*
Rzehakinae absent	Rzehakinae abundant	Rzehakinae very rare and small
Dendrophrya small	*Dendrophrya* absent	*Dendrophrya* abundant and well developed
Hormosina abundant	Lituolidae and Ammodiscidae predominant	Ammodiscidae abundant
Saccamina uncommon	*Nodellum* common	*Glomospira* common

indicates a significant environmental change. Again we have to beware of regarding as stunted species which are naturally small. The Rhaetic fauna (uppermost Triassic) of northwest Europe consists chiefly of small pelecypods and gastropods but is not a stunted fauna, since the species present do not habitually attain a larger size elsewhere.

When we suspect that all or most of the members of a particular fauna or flora in one area are notably smaller than usual, then we may subject them to an objective test.

Tasch (1953, 1957) did this with a diminutive association in the Pennsylvanian Dry Shale of Kansas. The fauna consists of brachiopods, gastropods, cephalopods, pelecypods, and ostracods, amounting to twenty-one species in all. Tasch examined and measured about four thousand specimens and compared them with supposedly "normal" faunas elsewhere. He took great trouble to find whether the so-called "dwarfs" were in fact retarded adults or ordinary juveniles. For this he used criteria such as the crowding together of ammonoid sutures at maturity. His results were as follows:

CEPHALOPODS

Imitoceras grahamense: some stunted adults
Gonioloboceras goniolobum: all juveniles

BRACHIOPODS

Crurithyris planoconvexa: the majority juveniles, a few unstunted adults

PELECYPODS

Nuculana bellistriata: the majority juveniles, a few unstunted adults
Anthraconeilopsis kansana: the majority juveniles, a few unstunted adults
Pleurophorus ? dryensis: no conclusive evidence of stunting
Schizodus piedmontensis: both adults and juveniles, no conclusive evidence of stunting
Aviculopecten sp. 1: one specimen, juvenile
Aviculopecten sp. 2: one specimen, juvenile
Nuculanella piedmontia: all juveniles
Pleurophorus pseudoblongus: both adults and juveniles, no conclusive evidence of stunting

GASTROPODS

Kansana discoidalia: the majority juveniles, a few unstunted adults
Strobeus cf. *S. puludinaeformis:* all juveniles
Euphemitella emrichi: all juveniles
Straparollus gladfelteri: mostly immature
Bellerophon wabaunseensis: all immature

OSTRACODS

Hollinella gibbosa: one unstunted adult
Hollinella dissimilis: two juveniles
Bairdia beedei: one immature form
Bairdia subconvexa: two juveniles
Neobeyrichiopsis emporiensis: mostly juveniles, some unstunted adults

It may be argued that many of the species are represented by too few specimens for any significant conclusions, and it is not always clear what characters are held to signify immaturity, but it may be concluded that the fauna is predominantly juvenile and that there is little definite evidence of stunting. More than 90 per cent of the fauna is within the size range of 2 to 8 mm in diameter (mostly 4 to 8 mm), and Tasch suggested that they had been mechanically sorted by bottom currents after death. He also suggested that the entire fauna may have met a catastrophic death due to toxic conditions and that if so, this contributed to the predominance of juvenile forms. Only *Imitoceras* was truly stunted, perhaps because of an excessive iron concentration in the water. All three of Cloud's categories of diminutive assemblages (see page 141) are therefore thought to be represented in one fauna.

Most other alleged cases of stunting will also not stand up to detailed examination. Two other classic cases are the fauna of the Tully pyrite of the Middle Devonian and that of the Clinton hematite of the Middle Silurian, both in New York State. These are bedded ironstones, and the supposed stunting was blamed on the concentration of iron in the water at the time of deposition. The Tully pyrite fauna of gastropods, pelecypods, cephalopods, and brachiopods has been quoted as a stunted fauna since the work of Loomis (1903), but the possibility of true stunting due to iron concentration has been disputed on the grounds that the pyrite resulted from secondary replacement.

The Clinton hematite assemblage seems to be better qualified as a true stunted fauna, and there is plenty of evidence to suggest that the iron-rich sediments were being deposited while the creatures were living on the sea floor. Even here it has been suggested, however, that many of the diminutive fossils show signs of being water worn.[1]

Kummel (1948) also provided a case of wholesale stunting connected with iron deposition. He compared the normal faunas of certain Cretaceous formations in Texas with those of a local pyritic facies. He concluded that in the latter everything was stunted—mollusks, corals, crustaceans, bryozoans, brachiopods, echinoids, and ophiuroids.

My final example of stunting in an iron-rich environment is that illustrated in Plate 1. This relates to my work on the British middle Lias (Ager, 1956a). Several of the brachiopods in the south, such as the distinctive sharply folded rhynchonellid, become stunted as they approach the ironstone-depositing conditions of Midland England. This is confirmed by other groups, even the pelagic ammonites, which become very rare and stunted to the north.

On the other hand, Plate 8B illustrates what is undoubtedly a mechanical accumulation of small forms, in the Devonian of western Illinois. It shows small brachiopods, bryozoans, and mollusks drifted together in shrinkage cracks on the surface of a thin-bedded argillaceous limestone. It will be noted that the crinoid debris is much larger in size

[1] This may, of course, occur in completely indigenous assemblages.

PLATE 8   For descriptive legend see opposite page.

than the other elements in the assemblage. This probably relates to the different hydrodynamic properties of echinoderm skeletons which are due to their very porous nature. This point should be remembered, since it is important for understanding any water-washed fossil assemblage that includes echinoderms (see page 132).

VERTICAL CHANGES

Vertical changes in fossil faunas and floras are one of the chief concerns of the geologist; for this reason the most practical aspect of paleoecology is that which concerns itself with the possible environmental control of such changes. It is of primary importance to find out to what extent vertical changes are ecological matters and to what extent they are evolutionary and therefore stratigraphically useful. Clearly the probability is that for a whole assemblage to change its character in a vertical direction reflects an environmental change. Stratigraphical paleontology is founded on evolving lineages, not on contrasting assemblages.

An object lesson in the fallaciousness of correlation by environment-controlled assemblages is provided by the already-mentioned bitter controversy over the age of the Shenley limestone of Leighton Buzzard in Bedfordshire, England. The essence of the argument lay in the correlation of the brachiopod-echinoderm fauna of this impersistent limestone with similar faunas of undoubted Cenomanian (Upper Cretaceous) age elsewhere. The evidence that the limestone was overlain by upper Albian, i.e., pre-Cenomanian, clays with ammonites was rejected by the protagonists of a Cenomanian age, even though they had to explain this by an obviously improbable hypothesis of glacial overturning.

Ammonite evidence eventually proved a lower Albian age for the limestone; the misinterpretation arose through the comparing and contrasting of unlike assemblages. It is not sufficient to say, "This brachiopod-echinoderm fauna is like the brachiopod-echinoderm faunas of the Cenomanian but unlike the ammonite-pelecypod faunas of the lower Albian"; one has to be able to say, "This brachiopod-echinoderm fauna is more like the brachiopod-echinoderm faunas of the Cenomanian than the brachiopod-echinoderm faunas of the lower Albian"—and even then

---

PLATE 8   **Transported fossil faunas.**
A, Wenlock limestone (Middle Silurian), Dudley, England. Fauna almost indigenous, only slightly mixed and transported. Note the curious juxtaposition of the head of a *Calymene* with the tail of a *Dalmanites*. ×⅚. **B,** Cedar Valley limestone (Upper Devonian), Milan, Illinois. Fauna transported and sorted so that only small and uniform remains (apart from the echinoderms) are here concentrated in shrinkage cracks. ×1.

there are limitations due to ecological variations *within* such major fossil groups.

What is more, one type of assemblage is often much more stereotyped than another. Fresh-water associations, for example, have shown very little change since the Mesozoic, compared with marine associations. Within the marine realm, Arkell (1928) showed that reef faunas tend to be far less variable in a vertical direction than associated nonreef faunas. He noted this both in the Upper Jurassic of Oxfordshire and in the Quaternary reefs of the Red Sea.

In their simplest form, vertical changes may be nothing more than progressive alterations in some morphological feature. A large part of a fauna may get progressively bigger with improving conditions. More subtle changes also occur, such as changes in the proportions of different constituent elements. W. N. Edwards (1936) showed that there was a progressive decrease in the proportion of woody plants in the Cenozoic floras of western Europe. A high proportion of woody plants is characteristic of tropical climates, and the figures in Table 16.2, based on

TABLE 16.2 *Changes in proportion of woody plants in Cenozoic floras.* (*Data from Edwards*, 1936)

Age	Locality	Percentage of woody plants
Lower Eocene	Sheppey, England	97
Upper Eocene	Hordle, England	85
Oligocene	Bembridge, England	57
Mio-Pliocene	Pont-de-Gail, France	51
Pliocene	Reuver, Netherlands	57*
Pliocene	Tegelen, Netherlands	28*
Lower Pleistocene	Cromer, England	22
Recent	Britain	17

* The contrast in the two Pliocene floras from the Netherlands presumably reflects local environmental differences.

Edwards's survey, suggest a climatic deterioration from the Eocene onward. A possible error here lies in the obvious fact that an oak tree is more likely to fossilize than a buttercup.

Cyclic Changes

An important feature of the life of modern communities is the succession of changes brought about by cyclic astronomical phenomena. These changes may be:

1. Tidal
2. Diurnal
3. Lunar
4. Annual
5. Of longer duration

Most of these periodic changes are too well known to require modern examples, but there are also a number of more unusual types of cycle. For example, swarming of the Atlantic palolo worm may be related to phases of the moon. The swarming is followed by the production of eggs, and the controlling factor is probably the number of hours of darkness each night. Figure 16.2 illustrates another little-known and com-

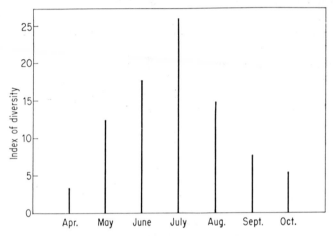

FIGURE 16.2   Seasonal variation in the diversity of the population of adult nocturnal Macrolepidoptera caught at Rothamsted. (Redrawn from C. B. Williams, 1954.)

pletely different type of cycle in which there is a seasonal variation in the diversity of the fauna.

None of these phenomena is at all likely to be preserved in the rocks, and there are very few records of seasonal changes in fossil assemblages, though mention may again be made of Heer's recognition (1865) of seasonal assemblages in the Oeningen beds of Switzerland (see page 98). R. Y. Anderson (1960) recognized seasonal changes in pollen and spore assemblages from Middle Pleistocene varved deposits in Texas. He also claimed a sunspot period of eleven years (or multiples of eleven years) in the same sediments, and a twenty-two-year sunspot period in Devonian shales, but these did not involve fossils.

Though rarely observed, these matters are important in paleoecology because of the long-term effect they may have on the nature of the communities present. The length of day and night may be critical for some groups of organisms, making it impossible for them to live in certain latitudes. It might be said, for example, that the Moslem faith could only prevail in the lower latitudes because the sunrise-to-sunset fast of Ramadan would make life extremely difficult in high latitudes and impossible within the polar circles.

The same argument has been used in discussions on polar wandering and continental drift. It has been doubted whether the various floras and other fossil assemblages of the arctic and antarctic could possibly have lived under conditions of six months day and six months night.

Seres and Climaxes

A great deal of modern ecological literature is devoted to the study of *seres*, or organic successions, and *climaxes*, or the ultimate communities of particular environments. In fact, Clements and Shelford (1939) have written: "Climax and sere have been the chief topics of study in plant ecology. . . ." A typical subject for such study is the successive changes from sand dunes along the coast of Lake Michigan to grassland, to open woodland of pines and oaks, to dense beech-and-maple forest.

Often the changes are brought about by the organisms themselves, as when the vegetable debris accumulating in a pond slowly transforms it into a marsh and then into dry land. Other changes are caused by the physical transformation of an area, say by erosion or flooding.

In the fighting of 1944, the dikes around the Dutch island of Walcheren were bombed, and the island was flooded for a year. During that time only the most rapid colonizers among the local marine fauna were able to establish themselves (Benthem Jutting, 1946). These included the commonest pelecypods—*Mytilus edulis, Cardium edule,* and *Mya arenaria*—but many of the slower-moving gastropods did not arrive. Such observations may be very applicable in the stratigraphical record.

In the British Upper Carboniferous "Coal Measures," there are several thin marine bands, which represent brief invasions by the sea. When clearly enough displayed, each marine band may record an almost perfect sere of colonization by marine organisms, followed by depopulation as the sea again retreated. In the Clay Cross marine band of the English Midlands, Edwards and Stubblefield (1948) demonstrated the following faunal cycle:

1. Nonmarine pelecypods
2. *Lingula,* occasionally associated with the marine ostracod *Hollinella*

3. Fully marine fauna containing goniatites, marine pelecypods, occasional gastropods, and horny brachiopods

4. *Lingula* with interdigitations of layers of nonmarine pelecypods and *Spirorbis*

5. Nonmarine pelecypods

This is a true cycle of the ABCBA form, with the "normal" marine fauna preceded by the more tolerant *Lingula*. More detailed successions within the marine phase have been recognized by M. A. Calver and R. M. C. Eagar. Corals may be regarded as the ultimate in an ideal cycle, requiring full oceanic salinity. They are significantly rare in European marine bands, and the only record I know in the British "Coal Measures" is in the thick Cwm Gorse marine band in Pembrokeshire, which seems to have been more marine than any other. Corals are much more abundant in the marine phases of Pennsylvanian cyclothems in the eastern United States, though mostly of the simple horn-coral type. This fits in with the fact of much better development of marine strata in that part of the world than in northwestern and central Europe.

A "Coal Measure" marine band may therefore be interpreted as a marine flooding with a faunal sere leading up to a climax community of the normal shallow-water marine association of the time. When the fully marine band is missing, there is often just a *Lingula* band in its place; here it may be said that the climax community was not established.

In marine bands, the increase in salinity led to the establishment of a more varied and abundant community. A continuation of that trend, as in the increasing salinity of an inland basin, might produce exactly the reverse effect with a "deteriorating" sere and perhaps ultimate extinction of the community. One of the classics of paleoecology—a series of papers on the life of the Upper Permian Zechstein sea in northeast England by C. T. Trechmann (1913, 1925, 1945)—is a study of just such a course of events.

The general paleogeographical picture is of a restricted sea which became more and more saline with time, so that a marine dolomitic limestone (the Magnesian limestone) is followed by evaporite deposits. The main fossiliferous horizon is a reef development in the middle Magnesian limestone. Trechmann recognized three later reef developments, in each of which the fauna is progressively more impoverished. Not only are there fewer species upward, but many of them become stunted. Table 16.3 summarizes the evidence for the four reef horizons, giving the number of species of each group present. Usually (but not always) they are the same species at all levels. It should be pointed out, however, that the collection for horizon D was from one locality only, compared with five localities for A, two for B, and five for C.

The reverse process, i.e., decreasing salinity, is seen in the Neogene of eastern Europe. There paleogeographical changes brought about the cutting up of a Miocene sea into a number of separate basins in what are now Austria, Hungary, Roumania, and southern Russia. The water became brackish and the marine faunas died out, except for some

TABLE 16.3 *Number of species of different fossil groups found at four successive reef horizons in the Permian Magnesian limestone of Durham, England.*[*] (*After Trechmann, 1945*)

	PORIFERA	ANNELIDA	ANTHOZOA	BRYOZOA	ECHINODERMA	BRACHIOPODA	PELECYPODA	GASTROPODA	CEPHALOPODA
TOP									
Horizon D	0	1	0	0	0	3 (3)	2 (2)	7 (6)	0
Horizon C	0	0	0	4†	1	6	13 (3)	12 (2)	2
Horizon B	2	0	0	4	1	8	12	9 (2)	2
Horizon A	4	3	5	6	2	20	25	21	2

[*] The number of stunted species in each case is shown in parentheses. Doubtful records are omitted.
† All rare.

adaptable elements such as *Cardium*. If life is possible at all, then an ecological vacuum is impossible; as the marine mollusks disappeared, they were replaced by fresh-water forms, which changed almost out of all recognition in adapting themselves to this unusual environment. The most startling change of all was that of the common fresh-water snail *Limnaea* to produce the coarsely corrugated, limpetlike form *Valenciennesia* (Figure 16.3). Particularly surprising is the fact that all these changes in the usually ultraconservative fresh-water mollusks were completed during the stratigraphical life on land of *Hipparion gracile* of the rapidly evolving horse family (Gorjanović-Kramberger, 1901, 1923; A. M. Davies, 1937).

In the various studies just discussed, it is difficult to disentangle the progressive changes of environment and fauna. In the ideal sere, we first change the environment and then study the way life adapts itself to that change. Such a situation is best displayed when the physical changes are so drastic that all the earlier population is killed off and we have a clear succession as the area is repopulated.

In 1883 the volcanic island of Krakatoa, between Java and Sumatra, exploded with great violence. Half the island was blown away, and every single animal and plant was destroyed. Nine months later the first traces of life returned to the island—a single small spider carried on the wind. Two years later a survey showed that many seashore plants had established themselves on the beach, but inland there were

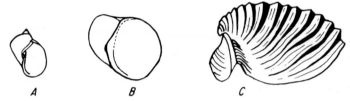

Figure 16.3 Adaptation of the fresh-water snail *Limnaea* to a brackish-water environment. A, *Limnaea* (*Radix*) *auricularia;* B, *Limnaea* (*Velutinopsis*) *velutina;* C, *Valenciennesia annulata.*

only blue-green algae (which can live under very adverse conditions), bacteria, mosses, and ferns. All of these had grown from wind-blown spores. After that grasses arrived, and thirteen years later there were coconuts around the shores, with scattered trees and many other plants inland. By 1906, twenty-three years after the eruption, Krakatoa was densely covered with vegetation, though the trees were still isolated. Larger animals had also arrived, most of them flying forms but some of them ground animals, perhaps rafted over on logs. In 1920 the island was half covered by trees, and by 1930 it was at last once more densely clothed with tropical jungle. It therefore took nearly fifty years for the bare ground of the devastated volcano to pass through all stages of the sere up to the forest climax. But this was quite a rapid succession, such as could only happen in a very wet tropical climate.[2] One could hardly expect such a sequence to make any showing in the fossil record.

In an arid climate the situation would be quite different. In Washington, Oregon, and Idaho there are vast areas of basic volcanic rocks,

[2] The proximity of large, densely populated landmasses must also have been an important factor.

thousands or even millions of years old, which show scarcely any signs of weathering or vegetation. Sunset Crater in Arizona is known to have erupted in A.D. 1064, but apart from a few trees in the crater itself, there are only very scattered plants on the ashy sides of the mountain and on the contemporaneous ash cones and lava flows round about.

The devastation caused by a volcanic eruption does not only provide a wonderful opportunity for the study of colonization; it may also tell us a great deal about the habits and tolerances of the different species involved. Sardeson (1926a, 1926b, 1929) made a detailed study of the recolonization of an area of Ordovician sea floor in Minneapolis, Minnesota, after a very widespread fall of volcanic ash. The Platteville limestone assemblage in the lower part of the Beloit formation (Upper Ordovician) was completely exterminated at a thin bentonitic layer. It included "fucoids" (probably brown algae and worms), trilobites, ostracods, cephalopods, gastropods, pelecypods, brachiopods, cystoids, crinoids, asteroids, bryozoans, monticuliporoids, a few corals, and at least one sponge. All these disappeared abruptly at the ash level.

Above the bentonite are the Decorah shales, the lowest bed of which is full of "fucoid" remains thought to represent floating plant material. Then, soon afterward, came trilobites, cephalopods, a few gastropods, a few species of brachiopods in great numbers, crinoids, monticuliporoids, and the one sponge. These are thought to have returned from outside the affected area (which extended as far as Virginia). Among the forms which did not return were all the ostracods, the pelecypods, nearly all the gastropods, some common brachiopods, the cystoids, and a formerly common coral. Sardeson wrote: "The circumstances would not be so remarkable if it were not that locally banished species return, some quickly and some tardily, until all groups are again represented. New immigrants are meanwhile few." The first to return were the free-swimming trilobites and cephalopods, together with those gastropods which may have attached themselves to floating weed. Sluggish bottom-living forms, such as the pelecypods and the majority of the gastropods, were the slowest to return. The brachiopods present the most interesting evidence since they fall into four distinct groups (Table 16.4). It is thus that repopulation of a devastated area may give us information about the habits of the different faunal elements.

Sardeson thought that the first to return after the catastrophe were those that could move about on the sea bottom and those that were attached to floating weed. The later arrivals were those that lived fixed to the substratum, such as *Rafinesquina minnesotensis*, which was the most abundant shell in the bed below the bentonite. The return of brachiopods such as *Crania* which lived attached to other shells was naturally controlled by the habits of their hosts. Five species disappeared

TABLE 16.4 *Distribution of brachiopods in the Beloit formation, above and below a bentonite layer.*

	Top of St. Peter sandstone	Platteville limestone		Bentonite layer	Decorah shales			Base of Galena formation
		1	2		3	4	5	
ATTACHED TO THE SEA BOTTOM								
Siphonotreta minnesotensis Hall and Clarke			X					
Orbiculoidea lamellosa Hall			X					
Pholidops trentonensis Hall						X		
Petrocrania halli Sardeson					X			
Leptaena halli Sardeson					X			
Rafinesquina inquassa Sardeson					X	X		
Rafinesquina minnesotensis Winchell		X	X		X	X		
Strophomena winchelli Hall and Clarke		X	X					
Scenidium anthonense Sardeson		X	?			X		
Orthis tricenaria Conrad		X	X		X	X		
Dalmanella rogata Sardeson					X	X		
Dinorthis pectinella Emmons						X		
Dinorthis deflecta Conrad		X	X					
ATTACHED TO FLOATING WEED								
Plectambonites sericeus Sowerby					X		X	
Strophomena incurvata Shephard*		X	X		X	X	X	
Pianodema subaequata Conrad		X	X		X	X	X	
Hebertella bellarugosa Conrad		X	X				X	
Platystrophia lynx Eichwald							X	
Zygospira recurvirostris Hall		X	?		X	X	X	
Zygospira aquila Sardeson		X	X					
Camarella panderi Billings							X	
Camarotoechia plena Hall							X	
Rhynchotrema ainsliei Winchell					X	X		
Rhynchotrema minnesotensis Sardeson		X	X		X	X		
Rhynchotrema increbescens Hall							X	
FIXED TO OTHER LIVING SHELLS								
Schizocrania filosa Hall						X		
Trematis huronensis Billings			X		X	X		
Crania setigera Hall		X	X		X	X	X	
Crania granulosa Winchell		X	?				X	
Crania trentonensis Hall		X	X		X	X	X	
MOTILE ON THE SEA BOTTOM								
Lingula elderi Whitfield		X	X		X	X	X	
Lingula iowensis Owen		X	X		X	X	X	

* Included here on circumstantial evidence only.

completely at the ash band, and Sardeson suggested that these may not have lived at all outside the area of the ashfall.

There are several obvious criticisms of Sardeson's conclusions. One may quarrel with the unprovable assumptions about brachiopod habits, as well as the disregard of the change in lithology between the Platteville limestone and the Decorah shales. A more serious matter is the possibility of a stratigraphical break at this level—now generally recognized, though denied by Sardeson.

A more recent and more acceptable study of a paleontological sere is contained in a series of papers by Lowenstam (1948, 1950, 1957) on the progressive development of Niagaran (Middle Silurian) reefs in the Great Lakes region. His papers, comparable to the climax-flora studies of botanists, provide a good example of a fossil faunal (and floral) succession.

Lowenstam's general thesis was that the reefs were built up from a soft substratum in relatively deep, quiet water. After establishing a solid base, the reefs grew up through increasingly rough water until they reached their maximum development as wave-resistant structures in the very rough surface water. As they did this, there were profound changes in the composition of the organic community which formed the basis of the structure (Figure 16.4). Lowenstam recognized three stages in reef development: (1) a quiet-water stage, (2) a semirough-water stage, and (3) a rough-water (wave-resistant) stage. In the *quiet-water stage*, the first pioneers were tabulate corals, notably *Syringopora* (80 per cent) and *Favosites*. These formed large boss-shaped colonies. The establishment of the initial reef surface and the start of upward growth was accomplished by *Favosites*. Next there developed a lacy open network formed by a problematical organism (variously interpreted as an alga and as a stromatoporoid) comparable to *Stromatactis*. These were all reef builders; there were also reef dwellers which lived in and on the growing mass. Predominant among the latter were crinoids belonging to the genus *Pisocrinus*. There were also bryozoans, trilobites, brachiopods, and sponges—in that order of importance. Generally speaking, the quiet-water stage is characterized by low population densities and little diversity, among both reef builders and reef dwellers.

The semirough-water stage is interpreted as beginning at the level of the deepest penetration by storm waves. *Stromatactis* was dominant as reef builder at this stage, but undoubted stromatoporoids appeared and became increasingly important. These formed an open lacy network as before. The tabulate corals *Favosites, Syringopora, Halysites,* and *Heliolites* were now merely minor accessories, usually forming low bosses on the reef surface. The reef dwellers increased in variety and density. They now included crinoids, brachiopods, bryozoans, trilobites,

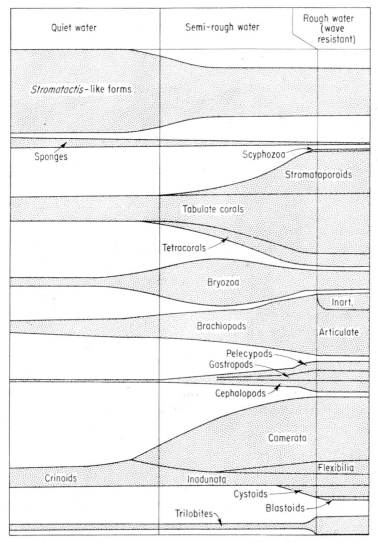

Figure 16.4 Vertical changes in the fossil assemblages of Niagaran reefs in the Great Lakes area. (From Lowenstam, Willman, and Swann, 1956; by courtesy of the Illinois State Geological Survey.)

and sponges (in that order of importance) with cephalopods, gastropods, and pelecypods as rare elements. The brachiopods were increasingly important, especially on the reef flanks, and the crinoids were much more varied—five genera instead of one. Some of the latter, notably *Pisocrinus*, seem to have persisted only in protected hollows on the reefs.

Finally, in the *rough-water stage*, there was a very great variety of species and a great abundance of individuals. Agitated surface waters are rich in oxygen and food particles, and in spite of the constant disturbance, provide a very desirable residence for many organisms.

In the Niagaran reefs at this level, stromatoporoids greatly increased in number at the expense of *Stromatactis*. Corals increased in population density, and new groups appeared, such as inarticulate brachiopods, cystoids, and blastoids. Crinoids were still by far the most important reef dwellers, but instead of the fragile "pea crinoids" of the quieter waters, the dominant group was now the camerates with their massive boxlike calices. The proportions work out, roughly, at forty Camerata to seven Inadunata to four Flexibilia. The other reef dwellers now comprised brachiopods, bryozoans, solitary corals, trilobites, cystoids, cephalopods, gastropods, pelecypods, sponges, blastoids, and conularids —in that order of importance. The cephalopods included a great variety of coiled and curved nautiloids in place of the earlier orthocones. Many species were recognized within the genera present. This was interpreted by Lowenstam as evidence of many microenvironments with the main reef setting.[3]

Smoot (1958) studied other Niagaran reefs known only in borings in the oil-field region of southern Illinois. He found that these were developed at the northeast end of previously existing (Ordovician) anticlinal ridges. He suggested that the position of the reefs resulted from the prevalence of winds, and thence currents, coming from the south or southwest. This fits in very well with the deductions made by Lowenstam working much farther north.

Changing Environments

The sere and the climax are related to the concept of gradual adjustment until a climax community suited to a particular environment is developed. In other words, the community slowly adjusts itself to a static environment. But geologists know very well that environments are never static. They have been changing through every moment of geological time, and fossil communities have been adjusting themselves all the time. We can usually assume that the individual sere was so short, relatively speaking, that it is not detectable in the record, so that all we study in practice are the changing environments.

Lowenstam assumed a sere in response to a basically static environment. As a contrast, Lecompte, in his work on Devonian reefs in

[3] Nicol (1962) also has now drawn attention to this as an example of a fossil sere.

Belgium, had the theory that the depth of water was changing with subsidence and the faunas were changing at the same time. Lecompte (1958), described the succession in Frasnian reefs on the south side of the Dinant basin. He recognized two types of bioherms. The first are

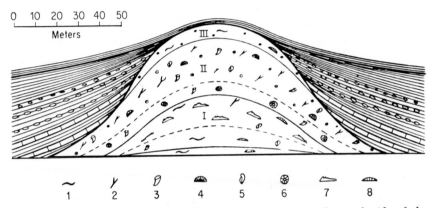

FIGURE 16.5 Vertical succession of faunas in a bioherm on the south side of the Dinant basin in Belgium. 1, lamellar *Alveolites;* 2, branching tabulate corals; 3, solitary rugose corals; 4, massive *Alveolites;* 5, brachiopods; 6, *Receptaculites;* 7, *Stromatactis;* 8, "*Acervularia.*" (From Lecompte, 1958; by courtesy of Ferdinand Enke, Stuttgart.)

of modest height—perhaps 80 m high and 100 to 150 m in base diameter. In these he distinguished the following stages (Figure 16.5):

A lower zone of lamellar corals.
A middle zone of small, subglobular corals, with brachiopods and some lamellar stromatoporoids.
An upper zone comparable to the lower zone but thinner.

For this type of reef, Lecompte postulated rapid subsidence in the lower and middle zones, with slower subsidence in the upper zone.

His second type of reef was much larger—1 to 4 km in diameter and 200 to 250 m high. Here the succession was thus:

A coral base as before.
A thin intermediate zone of lamellar stromatoporoids.
A much thicker upper zone, forming the main part of the reef and built essentially of massive stromatoporoids and, in an accessory role, the same species of corals as in the first type of reef, but much larger.

Unlike the smaller reefs, the reefs of the second type apparently grew into the zone of turbulent wave action and have talus accumulations around them.

In a more general way, Lecompte interpreted the Frasnian of this region in terms of faunal succession related to progressive subsidence. From the surface to the deepest level attained, the biological zones succeeded each other in the following sequence:

Zone I. Dominance of massive stromatoporoids, with numerous branching tabulate corals, rugose corals, and massive tabulates, globular brachiopods, and gastropods. This is the zone of turbulence in which the stromatoporoids are often worn and the brachiopods are often disarticulated and drifted together in lumachels.

Zone II. Dominance of lamellar stromatoporoids, with lamellar *Alveolites*, branching tabulates, and, sometimes, globular stromatoporoids. This is a thin transition zone with still some signs of turbulence.

Zone III. Dominance of compound corals, both Tabulata and Rugosa, with brachiopods but without stromatoporoids. It is sometimes possible to subdivide this zone on the basis of its corals. These were exclusively coral reefs which did not prosper in the turbulent zone which suited stromatoporoids; "*Acervularia*," for instance, is never found in the turbulent zone.

Zone IV. Dominance of brachiopods (though they are also found in other zones). This zone is always shaly, and there are no corals. The brachiopods are often stunted in the lower part.

Zone V. A zone of barren shales.

Zone VI. Dominance of goniatites and the pelecypod *Buchiola*. These were perhaps all pelagic forms. This zone represents deposition of fine-grained black shales in very calm water.

Such studies as those of Lecompte are regrettably few in number, but another example, which comes from a completely different ecological setting, demands mention. This is the study by Olson (1952) on the vertebrates of the Lower Permian Clear Fork group in north Texas. The sediments are those of a deltaic environment, and within this delta Olson recognized four principal physical subzones which provided habitats for these vertebrates: streams, ponds, pond margins, and "uplands." There were only minor migratory movements into the area from outside, and Olson disentangled a complex internal web of evolving lineages and changing environments.

Some stocks appear to have persisted unaltered in spite of changes in topography and rainfall. One of these was the burrowing amphibian *Lysorophus tricarinatus*, which lived in a very limited ecological niche. Another aquatic amphibian, *Trimerorachis insignis*, persisted without modification in spite of moving from pond to stream and back again to pond.

Other lineages, however, showed marked modifications, even within a single environmental subzone. Some such evolutionary changes can be directly related to the environment. Thus, at the end of early Clear Fork times, the pond-margin subzone disappeared from the record, and with it its inhabitants, since there were no refuge areas available. When the subzone reappeared, it was occupied by evolutionary radiants from the reptile group living in the "uplands."

Several other evolutionary modifications can be related to movements from one habitat to another. Thus the shark *Xenacanthus* produced a new species in the course of expanding its range from streams to ponds.

Olson observed a general tendency toward stability in faunas undergoing moderate environmental changes. "As long as the various ecological niches are effectively occupied little evolution occurs." On the other hand, changes might affect only a few species directly but through these might affect many others.

Fairly drastic changes in physical environment seem to have been beyond the range of adaptability of the indigenous fauna, and therefore such changes resulted in local extinction.

Olson's work was most important in that it related the evolution of new species to environmental changes. He concluded that a new species only appeared when there was a vacant niche available or when an existing niche was insufficiently occupied with respect to the usurper's potential. This recalls an example mentioned earlier (see page 95) in the work of Rózycki (1948) on the Polish Jurassic, in which, he claimed, one stock of brachiopods took over a reef niche from another and at the same time became homeomorphic externally with the former occupant.

Summing up, it may be said that the student of the ecology of living organisms usually seems to assume a fixed fundamental environment. He observes small physical changes, such as the silting up of a pond, and studies the effects produced by organic introductions (usually through human interference), but on the whole these are very local matters. In the vast majority of studies the ecologist, quite reasonably, takes for granted a static climate and geography as a background to his work.

This is not so for the paleoecologist. The one advantage that we have over the ecologist is that of geological perspective. We know and study the major physical changes that were always taking place through geological time. In this light it appears to be most exceptional for the sere to be preserved at all in the fossil record, and very good evidence indeed is required before such a succession can be accepted. Most of the fossil record is almost certainly one of successive climax populations, with their growth and decline foreshortened and obscured in the geological perspective.

Coupled with this we have the dynamic factor of evolution, and, as Olson emphasized, "the importance of considering evolution from an ecological viewpoint." As my last examples have shown, vertical changes in fossil assemblages in response to changes in environment may be intimately mixed with evolutionary changes within those assemblages. Sorting out these tangles is one of the most exciting prospects in paleoecology.

SEVENTEEN

Geographi-cal distribution of assemblages

IN Chapter 10, I considered the study of the geographical distribution of individual fossil genera and species. Distributional studies on whole assemblages are obviously much more difficult. Each species in an assemblage will have its own peculiar ecological limits, and the assemblage as a whole will be restricted to the much smaller area or areas where all these limits overlap. Leibig's law of the minimum (see page 10) applies from several different directions at once, so that only a very narrowly defined set of conditions will suit all the members of an assemblage. This makes their occurrence at widely separated places all the more significant from the ecological point of view.

It is very difficult to find suitable examples in paleoecology, but this is partly due to the fragmentation of the subject and the fact that experts tend to study only certain elements in fossil assemblages.

EXAMPLES OF DISTRIBUTIONS

Once more the overworked reef environment immediately springs to mind. For example, the assemblages of the "Waulsortian" reefs in the Lower Carboniferous of western Europe are remarkably constant. The same species of bryozoans, brachiopods, mollusks, and echinoderms turn up over and over again, and their distribution as a single assemblage reflects a special combination of geomorphological and climatic circumstances. The distributions I have in mind, however, are of broader scope and may be of world-wide significance.

One possible example is the *Eurydesma* fauna of Lower Permian age in various parts of Gondwanaland. *Eurydesma* is a distinctive and somewhat aberrant pelecypod with a very thick shell (Figure 17.1). It is almost always accompanied by the problematical fossil *Conularia* (probably a coelenterate) and by certain other mollusks. We know from other

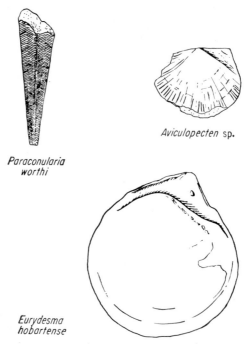

Aviculopecten sp.

Paraconularia worthi

Eurydesma hobartense

FIGURE 17.1   Typical members of the Permian *Eurydesma* fauna from Gondwanaland.

evidence that these forms lived in rather restricted environments. *Conularia*, for instance, tends to be abundant only in the more unusual sedimentary rocks where other fossils are rare. Thus it is common in Ordovician oölitic iron ores in Czechoslovakia (Bohemia), in France (Normandy), in Germany (Thuringia), in Morocco (Ougarta) and near Istanbul, Turkey (Ariç, 1955). In more "normal" marine sediments, it is usually only a minor element in the fauna. Other members of the *Eurydesma* fauna tend to be stunted. Apparently, therefore, this was a restricted assemblage which lived in unusual and perhaps unfavorable marine environments. Its distribution is all the more interesting for this reason. It has been found in all the continents of the Southern Hemisphere except Antarctica, and in India in the north (Figure 17.2).

Once more, paleobotanical work in an ecological field far exceeds that of paleozoology, though even here W. N. Edwards (1955) has written: ". . . we have . . . tended to lay emphasis on . . . individual genera . . . rather than plant formations or types of vegetation." Probably the most frequently mentioned of all fossil geographical distributions is that of the *Glossopteris* flora. It has long been known, however, that there were four distinct floras in Upper Carboniferous and Permian times. First there was the *Euramerian*, or Arcto-Carboniferous, flora which is found right across eastern North America from west of the

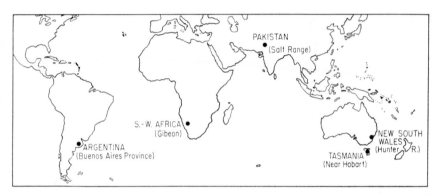

FIGURE 17.2 Geographical distribution of the *Eurydesma* fauna, showing well-known localities.

Great Lakes and then right across Europe from Ireland to Turkestan and south of the Aral Sea in Russia (Figure 17.3). Northward it extends to Spitsbergen and southward to northwest Africa. Throughout this belt are found familiar genera such as *Lepidodendron*, *Sigillaria*, *Pecopteris*, *Calamites*, *Cordaites*, and many others. As a complete nonspecialist, I still found it easy in Illinois to identify familiar European species such as *Neuropteris scheuchzeri* and *Alethopteris serli*—much easier, in fact, than to identify the species of living native plants.

Farther east, right across northern Russia and Siberia to Vladivostok and into northern China, there is another, less varied contemporary flora, which is especially well known in the fabulous Kuznetsk coal basin. This is the *Angaran* flora, still containing many of the Euramerian genera but differing very much in proportions and in species. The pteridosperm *Callipteris* is particularly noteworthy.

In China generally and in southeast Asia there is a third distinctive assemblage—the *Cathaysian* flora. Again there are elements of the Euramerian flora (enough to prove contemporaneity), but also a very distinctive native element, notably the large pteridosperm *Gigantopteris* with its angiosperm-like leaves. The Cathaysian and Angaran floras are said to intermingle at one point in Mongolia.

Finally there is the *Gondwanan* or *Glossopteris* flora of the southern continents and India. The impoverished nature of this flora has already been discussed (see page 234). It is dominated by the two pteridosperm genera *Glossopteris* and *Gangamopteris*. Records of these genera from Russia have been disproved.

In discussions of fossil distributions, the hypotheses of continental drift and polar wandering inevitably raise their heads. In many ways the paleoecologist is better qualified to discuss the second hypothesis than the first; any relative movement of the poles must have affected the world's climatic belts and therefore its life, whereas a river may be as effective a faunal barrier as an ocean, and the continents may have sailed merrily round and round for aeons without any great effect on their passengers.

The *Glossopteris* flora has figured prominently in discussion on these matters. It is argued that the *Glossopteris* assemblage was the flora of a formerly united Gondwanaland, separated from the Euramerian flora by the Tethys, but W. N. Edwards (1955) pointed out that the Euramerian flora is in fact found on the south side of Tethys, in northwest Africa and went on to suggest that there was a more or less uniform belt of abundant and varied vegetation extending around the world, with less varied floras on either side. This seems to be true not only for the plants but also for such animals as the insects.

Edwards pointed to the complete absence of fossil plants along a line from North Africa through Arabia into Central Asia—crossing the Tethys obliquely (Figure 17.3). He suggested that this was a great desert belt in late Paleozoic and Mesozoic times. He claimed that the differentiation of northern and southern floras was quite as distinct in the Mesozoic as in the Paleozoic. The postulated desert belt coincides with the main present-day desert belt of the Eastern Hemisphere. In other words, the main deserts have been in the same general area for a very long time, though more extensive at some times than at others.

That brings me naturally to Edwards's main argument, which was that, given the distribution of past floras, the climatic belts have always been roughly parallel with the present lines of latitude and the equator has always been approximately in the same position. This is not to say, of course, that the climatic belts have always been just as they are today. A great deal of evidence (some already quoted) indicates that the tropical belt was much wider during most of the fossiliferous geological past.

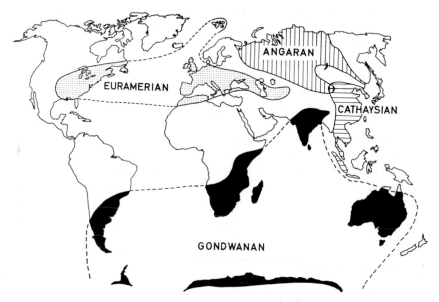

FIGURE 17.3   Geographical distribution of the major floras in Pennsylvanian and Permian rocks. (After Halle, 1937, and other sources.)

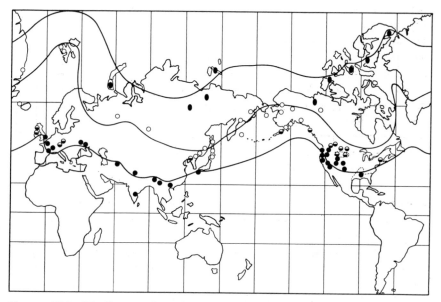

FIGURE 17.4   Distribution of northern floral belts during Eocene times. Black circles, subtropical; half-black circles, intermediate; open circles, temperate; ellipses, cool temperate. (From Chaney, 1940; by courtesy of the Geological Society of America.)

The story of Tertiary floras follows naturally from that of the Mesozoic. In Chapter 12 the tropical flora of the early Tertiary in southern England was considered at length. Farther north, in western Scotland, there is an early Tertiary leaf-and-pollen flora between basalt flows which is definitely more temperate in nature, with plants such as oak, plane, hazel, and *Ginkgo*. Similarly in North America, there are subtropical to tropical floras with figs and palms in the south and as

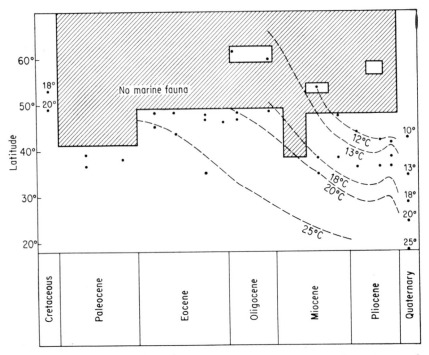

FIGURE 17.5 Postulated past positions of February isotherms along the Pacific Coast through Cenozoic times. Dots indicate the observations on which the diagram is founded. (After J. Wyatt Durham, 1950.)

far north as Oregon; whereas farther north, in Alaska, there is an Eocene flora with forms such as alder, beech, chestnut, and elm, which are distinctly temperate.

Chaney (1940) used such evidence to demonstrate three *isoflors*, or floral belts, around the Northern Hemisphere in Eocene times (Figure 17.4). The supposed *subtropical belt* ran through southern Britain, France, south Russia, south China, south Japan, and the western and central United States. North of this the *temperate belt* included Iceland, Spitsbergen, northern Russia, north Japan, Kamchatka, Alaska, and the west coast of Greenland. North again was a *cool-temperate belt*, with floras in northern Siberia and the Canadian Arctic Islands. These isoflors circle the North Pole and quite closely match the January isotherms at the present day, with a noteworthy northerly turn in the North Atlantic and a southerly bend over Siberia.

Supporting evidence came from a completely different field. J. Wyatt Durham (1950) summarized the evidence offered by the distribution of

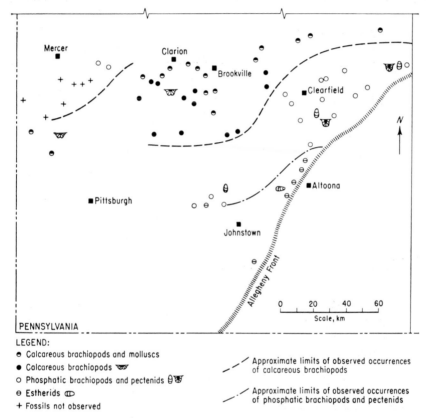

FIGURE 17.6 Distribution of faunas in the shales above the lower Kittanning coal, Pennsylvanian, in western Pennsylvania. (From E. G. Williams, 1960; by courtesy of the Society of Economic Paleontologists and Mineralogists.)

shallow marine faunas in various divisions of the Tertiary along the West Coast of North America. Most of these or their close relations are still living at the present day, and many of them are closely controlled by water temperatures, notably the reef corals. Durham's data were summarized in a diagram which is simplified in Figure 17.5. On this he was able to postulate the positions of past isotherms and so to demonstrate the well-known deterioration of climate through Tertiary times.

It may be noted that all this is founded on a supposed constancy of habit through a very long period of time, but the consistency of the results suggests that this assumption is justified. In a later paper (1952), Durham extended his analysis of early Tertiary marine faunas around the world and came to conclusions very similar to those of Chaney.

In considering all these fossil-distribution studies it must be remembered that there are great gaps in our knowledge of certain parts of the earth's surface, even in the continental areas, partly because of the existence of huge shields, as in Africa, and partly because of the lack of adequate studies, as in parts of South America and the Far East.

But the study of the geographical distribution of fossil assemblages need not be so grand in areal extent. We can learn a great deal by simply plotting our distributions on quite large-scale maps. For example, E. G. Williams (1960) published an interesting series of maps showing the distribution of marine and fresh-water assemblages in the Pennsylvanian rocks of western Pennsylvania. Figure 17.6 is Williams's map for the shales above the lower Kittanning coal, in which he distinguishes three faunal belts approaching the Allegheny front, with the progressive disappearance of first the calcareous brachiopods and most mollusks, then the phosphatic brachiopods and pectenids, and finally the estheriids.

Even more detailed was the work of W. E. Smith (1961) on the Upper Cretaceous (Cenomanian) in Devon, southwest England. Using an isopachyte map having a vertical interval of one inch, he was able to draw attention to faunal differences on either side of a Cretaceous sandbank within a distance of a mile or two. On the west side there was a fauna of "regular" echinoids, asteroids, and crinoids, suggesting a hard sea bottom and perhaps more protection; on the east side there was a fauna of mollusks and "irregular" echinoids, suggesting an unconsolidated floor.

There is, in fact, no limit to the detail which might be studied with profit in the realm of fossil distributions.

EIGHTEEN

Paleo-ecological syntheses

GENERAL PRINCIPLES

The synecology of a fossil community is the sum of the autecologies of all its constituent elements. A logical approach in paleoecology is therefore first to study the habits and habitats of all fossil species present—in as much detail as possible—and then to bring these studies together in a general picture of the life of the community.

By these means it should be possible to eliminate anomalies such as those of derived fossils, fossils which have been transported from their true habitat, and fossils which have changed their habits.

The vast majority of the contributory observations must, of necessity, be made in the field, and the paleoecologist must extract every possible tidbit of information from the natural occurrences of the fossils before he begins any subjective theorizing.

It has been with this in view that my field questionnaire (Appendix 2) has been prepared. Use of a field questionnaire, suggested primarily by Allan (1948), has been successful with student parties. Many of the questions are not, of course, answerable for every rock unit, but all present points which deserve careful thought. This is slow, painstaking work; but ultimately the only way in which paleoecology can progress as a contributory part of general geology.

It is very tempting to rush ahead with simple criteria and quantitative methods in the hope of speedy and exciting results, but it is more practical and more in keeping with the normal processes of natural science to aim first at the gradual building up of a great mass of observational detail. In the younger rocks there is some justification for extended analogies from present-day observations, but through the greater part of the stratigraphical column what are needed most are more and more records of observed facts.

Hallam's paper on the lowermost Jurassic of Dorset and Glamorgan (1960*a*) provides an example of the kinds of observations that are needed. In this study he surveyed the organisms belonging to twelve different major groups, including forams and trace fossils, and extracted all the information he could about their mode of life and environment. This was brought together to produce a clear picture of a warm, shallow sea with weak bottom currents and periodic stagnation.

A simple demonstration of the reasoning that should be used in a study of this kind is provided by Table 18.1, which is based on a study made by Richardson and Zangerl (1957) on a Pennsylvanian black shale in Parke County, Indiana. The table illustrates the valid progress of deduction in paleoecology from field observations, via postulates, to deduced environments.

Work of this kind can sometimes be carried out very effectively by simply pulling apart a large block of sediment in the laboratory, as was done in this case (Zangerl and Richardson, 1955), but usually the observations must be made in the field. It is then very difficult to be objective and to record exactly what is seen and not what we afterward think we saw. We may notice a distinctive orientation in one specimen and then keep seeing it in other specimens, while subconsciously overlooking orientations of other kinds. The same is true of differences in associations or in preservations. We need to keep a tight hold on our imagination the whole time.

The most desirable procedure is to photograph or draw every critical section as a permanent, objective record. Photographs are not often usable in this way because it is almost impossible to show clearly on a photograph every obscure fossil in an uneven rock face, but they may be used in special circumstances. Field drawings, however, are in every way more satisfactory. They were strongly recommended for field paleoecological research by Gekker (1955, 1957). Typical field sketches of this kind by the author are shown in Figure 18.1.

Following Dr. Gekker's lead, Russian paleontologists also commonly use conventional signs for different kinds of fossils in field records, with variants to indicate differences in preservation and orientation. This procedure is often used by paleontologists on the European Continent but is not often seen in British or American publications. Some examples have already been given (e.g., Figures 13.1, 13.2, 16.5), but the procedure is particularly well illustrated in Figure 18.2, which shows the general features of the fauna, flora, and lithology in a section of the

TABLE 18.1 *Paleoecology of a Pennsylvanian black shale, Parke County, Indiana. (From Richardson and Zangerl, 1957, slightly modified)*

Evidence	*Postulates*	*Deduced environment*
Early stage of transgression across nearly flat land.	Gentle change of level more probable than sudden change.	Shallow sea.
Shale very fine grained and finely laminated; elongated fossils show no preferred orientation.	Fine grain size indicates slow current, smooth laminae indicate lack of bottom disturbance; currents would produce preferred orientations in fossils.	Very quiet water.
Abundance of carbon; climate considered warm by paleobotanists.	Carbon indicates fast-growing and fast-decaying vegetation; rapid growth requires warmth.	Warm water.
Cephalopods abundant.	Cephalopods are exclusively marine.	Connected with open ocean.
Fauna of sharks, etc., not widespread; no evidence of rough water.	If these forms lived over normal marine sediments, they would be preserved elsewhere; open seas are disturbed by storms, tides, and currents.	Communication with open ocean restricted.
One shark's front part, presumably buried in mud, well preserved; hind part, presumably projecting into water, destroyed.	Anaerobic bacteria in mud and aerobic bacteria in water behaved like modern counterparts.	Bottom mud was toxic.

Mste River near Borovichi, U.S.S.R. In practice, such a variety of rocks and fossils in one section is extremely rare, and Figure 18.3 is a more typical example taken from my own work in the Jura of southeast France. This is intended to show the kind of detailed field recording which is necessary to build up an adequate paleoecological picture.

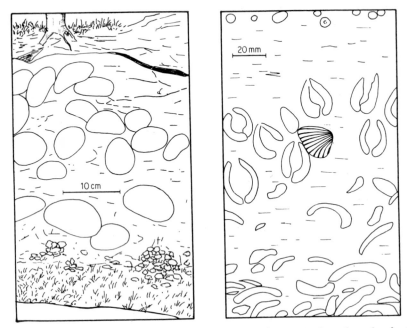

Figure 18.1   Examples of paleoecological field sketches. *Left*, bun-shaped colonies of *Isastraea oblonga* in Upper Jurassic limestone, Lac Genin near Cret d'Echallon, the Jura, southeast France. *Right*, *Venericor planicosta suessoniensis* (below) and *Turritella sulcifera* (above) in Cuisian (lower Eocene) clay, Whitecliff Bay, Isle of Wight, England.

Much subsequent laboratory work is still necessary, both on the sediments and on the fossils themselves.

EXAMPLES OF SYNTHESES

As the logical conclusion to my book, I propose to present four examples of well-founded paleoecological syntheses. These are different in scope, in approach, in age, and in nature, but they serve to illustrate the bringing together of many different lines of evidence in a series of convincing pictures of past life.

A Pleistocene River in England

The first example comes from the very center of London—Trafalgar Square—where excavations for deep foundations made possible a detailed analysis of the deposits of an earlier Thames River during the last interglacial period. The work has not yet been published, but it has

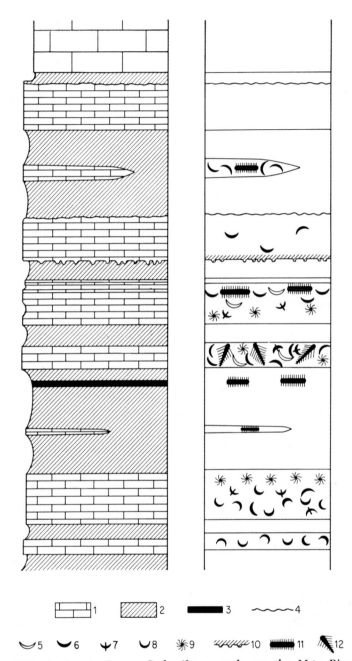

FIGURE 18.2 Section in Lower Carboniferous rocks on the Mste River above Borovichi, U.S.S.R., with conventional signs for different sediments and fossils. 1, limestones; 2, arenaceous-argillaceous rocks; 3, coal; 4, erosion surface; 5, bivalve shells of *Gigantoproductus;* 6, separated valves of *Gigantoproductus;* 7, *Productus;* 8, small brachiopods; 9, burrows of *Taonurus* (*Spirophyton*); 10, worm burrows; 11, horizontal *Stigmaria;* 12, vertical and oblique *Stigmaria.* The symbols used for brachiopods also indicate the orientation of the shells. (From Gekker, 1957; by courtesy of the author.)

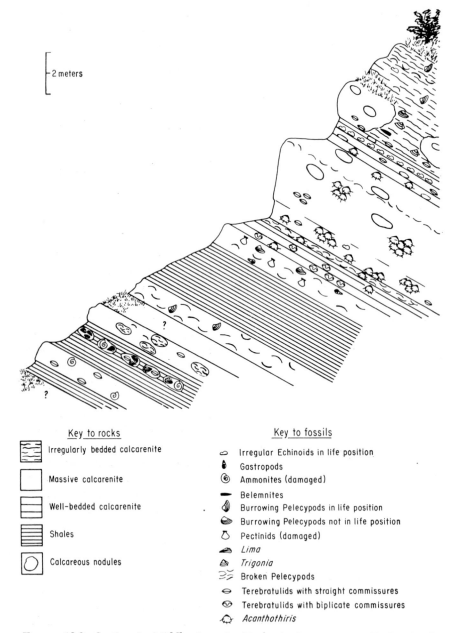

Key to rocks

Irregularly bedded calcarenite

Massive calcarenite

Well-bedded calcarenite

Shales

Calcareous nodules

Key to fossils

  Irregular Echinoids in life position

  Gastropods

  Ammonites (damaged)

  Belemnites

  Burrowing Pelecypods in life position

  Burrowing Pelecypods not in life position

  Pectinids (damaged)

  Lima

  Trigonia

  Broken Pelecypods

  Terebratulids with straight commissures

  Terebratulids with biplicate commissures

  Acanthothiris

FIGURE 18.3 Section in Middle Jurassic (Bathonian) strata near Cuzieu in the French Jura, showing distribution of fossils and general lithology. Field identifications only.

been summarized in popular form (Franks et al., 1958). A large and varied fauna and flora were collected from about 10 m of silt and sand. Clearly a great deal of the material, notably the bones of large mammals, had been washed down the river, though probably not for any great distance.

The vertebrates found were hippopotamus, straight-tusked elephant, rhinoceros, ox, red deer, fallow deer, lion, bear, and possibly hyena (represented only by dung). It should be noted that the elephant was of the southern (supposedly warmth-loving) type, not the northern mammoth. About thirteen thousand mollusks were also found, belonging to about sixty species of land and fresh-water gastropods and pelecypods. These included the large pelecypod *Margaritifera auricularia,* which is found today in rivers in southern Europe and North Africa, and the minute gastropod *Belgrandia marginata,* which now lives in streams in the foothills of the Alps and Pyrenees. There were several other species which are now extinct in England but still live farther south. The land snails present are mainly marsh-loving types at the present day, but some that now live on dry grassland were found as well.

Also collected were vast numbers of insect remains including many beetles and weevils, for example, the Rose Chafer beetle. Finally there were more than 150 species of plants, including the wild rose which provided the food for the beetle just mentioned, and many plants characteristic of more southerly climates, such as the cocklebur, the water chestnut, and the southern European maple. With these was a great variety of pollen.

From all this evidence produced by team research, a remarkably clear picture emerges of London 100,000 years ago. The river itself was warm, swiftly flowing, and highly calcareous, with a great deal of weed and a soft floor. This is shown particularly by the mollusks, which include many calciphiles and forms which attach themselves to weeds. Negative evidence is provided by the absence of forms which require a hard substratum. There were numerous backwaters or marshy areas along the sides of the river, with bulrushes, sedges, reed mace (cattails), water lilies and water chestnuts. This is also shown by some of the snails and beetles and by the wallowing hippopotamuses.

Beyond the marshes was open grassland—almost parklike—as indicated by other snails and by certain of the vertebrates such as the lions. The grassland was dotted here and there with oak, yew, hazel, and other trees and shrubs, and there were probably some patches of thicker woodland providing cover for the deer, though there was a marked absence of woodland mollusks in the deposit.

From the fauna and flora as a whole, it is clear that the climate was warmer than it is in the same place today, and altogether the Trafalgar

Square of 100,000 years ago sounds a much more delightful place in which to live than that of the nineteen sixties.

A Carboniferous Sea Floor in Scotland

The example just given came from strata in which every species is still living or is closely related to a living species. For contrast we may consider an example from the Paleozoic in which all the species and all of the genera except *Lingula* are now extinct, but in which it is possible to make a very convincing synthesis of the synecology.

This was the study made by Craig (1954) on 60 cm of Lower Carboniferous calcareous shales in a single quarry near Kilsyth in

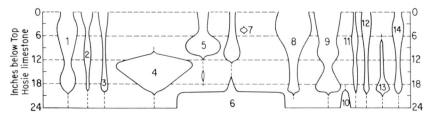

FIGURE 18.4   The relative abundance and distribution of macrofossils in the 2 ft (61 cm) of shale below the Top Hosie limestone in the Lower Carboniferous of southern Scotland, in 3-in. (7.6-cm) groupings. 1, *Lingula;* 2, *Productus;* 3, *Camarotoechia;* 4, *Tornquistia;* 5, *Pseudamusium?;* 6, *Posidonia;* 7, *Actinopteria;* 8, *Nuculopsis;* 9, *Sanguinolites;* 10, *Loxoceras?;* 11, other nautiloids; 12, *Bucaniopsis* and *Euphemites;* 13, *Glabrocingulum;* 14, other macrofossils. (From Craig, 1954; by courtesy of the author and the Geological Society of London.)

southern Scotland. From this band Craig extracted about five thousand fossils belonging to the following groups: forams, scolecodonts, conodonts, brachiopods, gastropods, scaphopods, pelecypods, nautiloids, ostracods, crinoids, fish, algae, and fragments of larger plants. His procedure was exactly as followed here, in that he considered first the autecology of each individual group and then put these conclusions together to form a general picture of the synecology of the assemblages. For every species he considered such factors as the form, preservation, orientation, and, where possible, the habits and habitats of their modern counterparts.

Craig's general conclusion was that two well-defined contrasted groups of macrofossils were present (Figure 18.4). These were a *Posidonia* assemblage in the basal 10 cm of shale and a more varied assemblage in the rest of the bed.

The *Posidonia* assemblage he interpreted as a mud-surface community, living in an area of gentle currents—sufficient to separate the valves of *P. corrugata* but not enough to break them. Both this species and the ostracod *Waylandella cuneola* were also represented in the bed by juvenile spats and molts, indicating that they lived all their lives in the area. The same may be true for several other species. The only common macrofossil besides the pelecypod was a nautiloid—*Loxoceras* ?—which was also present in several growth stages. Craig also noted the great abundance of juvenile stages of gastropods and other forms, without the corresponding adults, suggesting that the bottom environment was unfavorable for their development. It is also presumably significant that there were no burrowing forms, and Craig concluded that the mud was in all probability anaerobic below the surface.

The sediment containing the later assemblage was slightly different, being less fissile, coarser grained, and less pyritic. The *Posidonia* assemblage disappeared, and a number of burrowing forms invaded the area, notably the brachiopod *Lingula squamiformis*, the pelecypods *Nuculopsis gibbosa* and *Sanguinolites costellatus*, and the scaphopod *Coleolus carbonarius*. There were also sessile and crawling benthonic animals such as the brachiopod *Productus concinnus* (often found in presumed life position with the spiny convex ventral valve downward). The microfauna remained essentially the same as before, but the macrofossils were more abundant and varied. The latter tended to be concentrated and fragmentary, suggesting stronger currents than before, and burrowers were abundant, suggesting that the bottom mud was now better aerated.

A Jurassic Lake in the U.S.S.R.

Turning to more general syntheses, I can hardly omit mention of the nature reserve of Kara Tau in southern Kazakhstan, which has been preserved chiefly for its remarkable record of life in a Late Jurassic lake. This was described by Gekker et al. (1948), and their processes of reasoning about it were summarized by Gekker in the French edition of his book on paleoecology (1960).

The Kara Tau range stands up from the eastern shores of the Caspian Sea, and in Upper Jurassic times a great thickness of sediment accumulated here in a northeast-southwest–trending graben between Paleozoic rocks. The Jurassic sediments consist of alternations of sandstones, conglomerates, and "paper shales," which are in fact thin-bedded, finegrained limestones and dolomites.

Following the same process of observation, hypothesis, and deduction as has been outlined above (Table 18.1), Gekker and his associates produced a convincing picture of this Mesozoic mountain lake.

The general setting of the lake was proved by ordinary geological mapping. The Jurassic deposits are delimited by fault lines within the Paleozoic rocks, and there is a suggestion of seismic activity in the presence of intercalated boulder beds of Paleozoic rocks within the thin-bedded carbonates. There are also signs of subaerial and subaqueous landslipping.

That this was a lake and had no connection with the sea is shown by the complete absence of marine organisms and the presence of vast numbers of probably fresh-water fish. There are also a few fresh-water turtles, estheriids, and gastropods.

There is evidence of the nature of the lake margins from the intercalated sands and from certain of the fossils. Evidently the margins were often steep and rocky, but mostly well forested; little or none of the lakeshore was low lying and marshy, since hygrophilous land plants are few in number and variety and exceptionally poor in their preservation. Locally there were stretches of sticky, calcareous mud along the shore, as is suggested by the occurrence of fish remains, strung out as along a strandline. The bodies are twisted and oriented as though by the waves.

The climate was subtropical, on the chemical evidence of the deposition and of the composition and abundance of the fauna and flora. The xerophilous nature of the dominant plants suggests that it was dry in the region, though not arid enough to produce evaporites. There must have been rising currents of air over the lake and winds to carry in the plentiful insects, seeds (adapted for wind dispersal), and other small plant fragments. These occur as scattered specimens rather than in the concentrations that would be expected from water transport. Most of the insect species are only known from a single specimen.

The rivers feeding the lake were evidently seasonal, since very thin layers of fine sand are interstratified with the carbonates. They must also have brought down the larger masses of wood (without leaves), though some may have fallen directly into the lake from its forested borders. Rivers may also account for some of the rarer elements from other environments and odd items such as insect chrysalids.

The carbonates were laid down in very calm waters, as is shown by the beautiful preservation of most of the fish and insects. The fish sometimes still contain recognizable eggs. The clarity and hardness of the lake water and the sparsity of its aquatic vegetation are suggested by the nature of some of the invertebrates and the absence of others, such as pelecypods. Evidently conditions in the lake varied from place to place, since the faunas change laterally. The fish species, for example, are nearly always found separately, and in some areas are completely absent.

Occasional flying reptiles include both fish-eating and insect-eating types (on the evidence of their jaws), and so we have at least a hint of part of the local food chain.

All these observations and deductions, together with dozens of others, provide us with almost as clear a summation of this Jurassic mountain lake as we have of many modern lakes.

A Permian Reef Complex in the United States

Probably the most ambitious paleoecological synthesis so far attempted was the team project organized by N. D. Newell in the

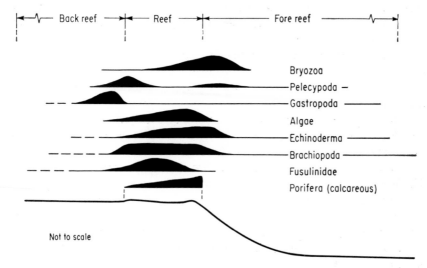

FIGURE 18.5 Inferred life distributions of Capitan reef organisms. (From *The Permian Reef Complex of the Guadalupe Mountains Region, Texas and New Mexico, a Study in Paleoecology,* by Norman D. Newell et al. San Francisco, W. H. Freeman, 1953.)

Guadalupe Mountains region of Texas and New Mexico. This investigation (Newell et al., 1953) covered a very large area and a great thickness of sediment, so cannot be compared in scope and content with the detailed studies so far discussed; but its generalizations are exciting, and its methods illustrate the need for joint efforts by teams of specialists in any worthwhile paleoecological project on this scale.

The authors were dealing particularly with the great Delaware basin of Permian times with its famous series of marginal reefs. Their study forms a suitable conclusion for my book in that it applies almost every method mentioned in previous chapters in a comprehensive synthesis.

For example, starting with the autecological approach, there is *comparison with living representatives* of some of the reef-forming algae

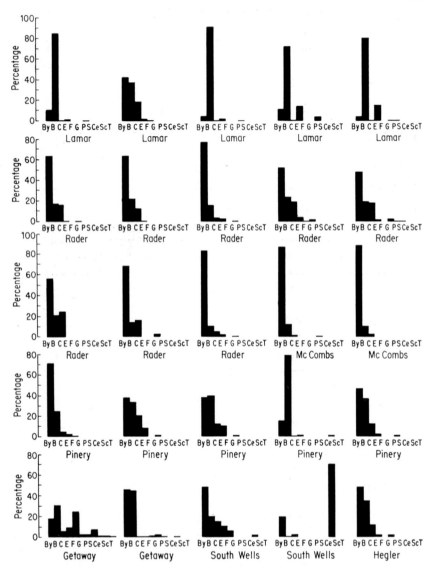

Figure 18.6   Relative abundance of major faunal elements, by weight, at various localities in different (named) Permian formations of the Guadalupe Mountains area. Based on siliceous residues, except the two South Wells histograms, which are based on surface counts. By, bryozoans; B, brachiopods; C, corals; Ce, cephalopods; E, echinoderms; F, fusulinids; G, gastropods; P, pelecypods; S, sponges; Sc, scaphopods; T, trilobites. (From *The Permian Reef Complex of the Guadalupe Mountains Region, Texas and New Mexico, a Study in Paleoecology,* by Norman D. Newell et al. San Francisco, W. H. Freeman, 1953.)

(Newell et al., 1953, p. 100). Also, there are observations on the *life orientation* of some of the sponges present (p. 112) and on the *organic associates* of the fusulinids (p. 148). There is *evidence of activity* of boring organisms in some of the shells (p. 108). Evidence from the *associated sediments* forms a major part of the work, including mention, for instance, of the common occurrence of the brachiopod *Leiorhynchus* in sediments of the deeper-water facies in the basin (p. 67). *Lateral variation* is recorded in the growth forms of certain bryozoa (p. 147), with a decline of fenestrate forms toward the basin. Finally, the autecological aspects of the work include a great deal of information on the *geographical distribution* of individual groups and genera (pp. 198 ff.)—

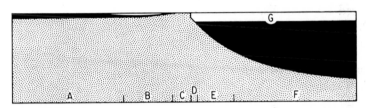

FIGURE 18.7 Inferred ecological zones of late Guadalupian (Middle Permian) times in the Guadalupe Mountains area of Texas and New Mexico. The Delaware basin is on the right. The zones, or biotopes, are explained in the text. (From *The Permian Reef Complex of the Guadalupe Mountains Region, Texas and New Mexico, a Study in Paleoecology,* by Norman D. Newell et al. San Francisco, W. H. Freeman, 1953.)

notably the distribution of reef organisms, as summarized in Figure 18.5.

Turning to synecology, there is the fundamental assumption, based on *comparison with living assemblages,* that the reefs grew in shallow water at or near sea level (e.g., p. 108). Following from this, *other geological evidence* is used to provide evidence of the depth of water in which the various organisms lived, since (p. 187) ". . . the basin has been subjected to little deformation since deposition of the rocks."

The *density and diversity* of the fossil assemblages are considered at length (pp. 141 ff.), using the evidence of abundance by weight of silicified organisms removed by acid from limestone matrices (Figure 18.6). *Relationships between species* are often significant—for example, the mutual exclusiveness of bryozoans and similarly shaped corals in the Rader assemblages (p. 148).

Lateral and vertical changes in assemblages were observed, notably in the way the deeper-water benthonic faunas became more restricted upward with increasing stagnancy of the basin (p. 197).

Finally there are the main paleoecological conclusions of Newell and his colleagues, contained in a survey of the *geographical distribution of assemblages* and bringing in all the previous aspects of the subject (pp. 194 ff.). They recognized seven distinct ecological zones, or biotopes, within the region (Figure 18.7). There are complications in space and time, but the essentials may be summarized as follows:

Shelf or backreef biotopes

A. Hypersaline lagoonal waters with an impoverished fauna or completely barren.

B. Lagoonward detrital area with fusulinids, brachiopods, gastropods, crinoids, various algae (mainly pisolite-forming types).

Reef biotopes

C. Reef flat with fusulinids, calcareous sponges, massive bryozoans, cemented brachiopods, and algae.

D. Reef front with pedunculate brachiopods, branching bryozoa, and a few algae.

Basin biotopes

E. Intermittently stagnant waters of the upper talus slope with monactinellid sponges, certain pelecypods, gastropods, and echinoids.

F. Deeper stagnant waters, barren except for scattered rhynchonelloids which as I have suggested elsewhere (Ager, 1962) may have been epiplanktonic.

G. Surface waters of basin with pelagic associations of radiolarians, ammonoids, and spores, all found in the bottom biotopes (E) and (F).

Postscript

PALEOECOLOGY is still in its infancy. What is its future?
The most startling advances will probably come in knowledge
of the chemistry of isotopes and trace elements, which will
put many new tools at our disposal. Studies of modern
environments will also provide many new standards with which
to compare our record. But we shall still have to study the
fossils themselves.

I have tried in this book to suggest many different ways in
which paleoecological problems may be approached. I hope
I have convinced the reader that the task has hardly begun
in the way of straight-forward observation and measurement,
quite apart from the latest fashions of laboratory equipment.
The first principle of practical paleoecology is that one should
go to the field and look at the fossils carefully.

Glossary of
paleoecological terms

Abyssal   pertaining to the sea floor in the greatest oceanic depths other than trenches, i.e., from about 4,000 to about 5,000 m in depth.

Anaerobic   without free oxygen.

Antagonism   relationship between two organisms in which one or both are harmed.

Antibiosis   passive action by one organism which is harmful to another.

Aphotic zone   that portion of a body of water not penetrated by light.

Arboreal   pertaining to trees.

Assemblage   all the organisms found together in a particular stratum. Cf. *community*.

Autecology   the ecology of the individual organism or group, as distinct from that of a whole community.

Bathyal   pertaining to the sea floor on the continental slope, i.e., from about 200 to about 4,000 m in depth.

Benthonic (or *benthic*)   pertaining to the sea floor.

Benthos   all those organisms which live on the sea floor.

Biocoenose   a living community.

Biomass   weight or volume of animal and/or plant material per unit area.

Biotope   an association of organisms characteristic of a particular geographical setting.

Boreal   northern.

Carnivorous   eating flesh.

Chorology (or *biogeography*)   the study of the geographical distribution of plants and animals.

Circalittoral   pertaining to the outer part of the sublittoral zone, i.e., between about 100 and about 200 m in depth.

Climax community   the ultimate community developed in a particular habitat under stable conditions.

Cline   graded series of variants in a population when traced laterally.

Clisere   succession of climax communities in an area resulting from major physiographical changes.

Colony   a group of individuals of one species living together.

Commensalism   relationship between two organisms in which one benefits and the other is not affected.

Community   any group of organisms living in a common environment and interdependent. Cf. *assemblage.*

Discontinuous distribution   a widespread distribution with large gaps.

Disphotic zone   zone between photic and aphotic zones, *q.v.*

Distribution   the geographical spread of a form. Cf. *range.*

Ecad   a form modified by the conditions of its habitat (the modifications not being heritable).

Ecotone   transition zone between communities.

Edaphic   pertaining to the soil.

Endemic   native to a particular restricted area.

Endobiontic   living within the bottom sediments.

Environment   the sum total of all the external conditions which act upon an organism.

Epi-   prefix meaning above or on.

Epibiontic   living on the surface of the bottom sediments.

Epifauna   animals living *on*, as distinct from *in*, a particular substratum, especially when this is another organism.

Epiphytic   of plants living on other plants.

Epiplanktonic   of organisms attached to floating material.

Eury-   prefix denoting a wide range of tolerance. Cf. *steno-.*

Euryhaline   tolerant of a considerable range of salinities.

Euxenic   pertaining to unoxygenated bottom conditions.

Exotic   nonnative.

Fluvial   pertaining to rivers.

-fuge   suffix denoting movement away from.

Geotaxis   movement stimulated by gravity.

Geotropism   growth stimulated by gravity.

Habitat   the type of place in which an organism lives.

Hadal   pertaining to the sea floor in deep sea trenches, i.e., more than about 5,000 m deep.

Halophyte   plant tolerant of very salty conditions.

Herbivorous   eating plants.

Hydro-   prefix meaning water.

Hygro-   prefix meaning moisture.

Hypersaline   having a salinity greater than sea water.

Indigenous   of native species, not introduced.

Infauna   animals living within the bottom sediments.

Infrahaline   having a salinity of less than 0.5‰.

Infralittoral   pertaining to the inner part of the sublittoral zone, i.e., between low tide and about 100 m in depth.

Insectivorous   eating insects.

Lacustrine (or *limnic*)   pertaining to lakes.

Laminarian zone   zone of sea floor characterized by the seaweed family Laminariaceae.

Limnology   the study of fresh-water environments.
Littoral   intertidal.
Meridional   southern.
Mesohaline   salinity of 3.0 to 16.5‰.
Microphagous   feeding on microscopic food particles.
Mutualism   relationship between two organisms in which both benefit.
Nanism   the phenomenon of stunting.
Nektobenthos   forms which swim just above the sea floor and sometimes rest on it.
Nektonic (or *nectonic*)   pertaining to swimming organisms.
Neontology   the study of present-day life.
Neritic   pertaining to pelagic organisms living beyond the littoral zone as far as the edge of the continental shelf.
Niche   an organism's place in the organic community to which it belongs.
Oceanic   pertaining to pelagic organisms living beyond the continental shelf.
Oligohaline   salinity of 0.5 to 3.0‰.
Optimum   most favorable.
Oryctocoenose   outcrop assemblage.
Paludal   pertaining to marshes.
Paralic   marginal.
Parasitism   relationship in which one organism derives its food from another living organism without actually killing it.
Pathological   pertaining to disease.
Pelagic   pertaining to swimming and floating organisms.
-phagous   suffix denoting eating; e.g., *coprophagous* = feeding on excreta.
-philous (or *-phile*)   suffix denoting attraction; e.g., *xerophilous* = "liking" dry conditions.
-phobic   suffix denoting repulsion; e.g., *hydrophobic* = "hating" water.
-photic and *photo-*   combining forms denoting light; e.g., *photophilous* = "liking" light.
Photic zone   that part of a body of water penetrated by sunlight.
Phyto- and *-phyte*   combining forms denoting plants; e.g., *phytoplankton* = floating plants.
Plankton   floating organisms.
Planktonic   of floating organisms.
Pluvial   pertaining to rain.
Polyhaline   salinity of 16.5 to 30.0‰.
Province   geographical unit containing a distinctive group of organic associations.
Pseudoplanktonic   planktonic by means of attachment to a floating organism or other floating material.
Quadrat   a standard area, commonly 1 sq m, used in studying the composition of an organic assemblage.
Quaquaversal   sloping outward in all directions (especially of reefs).
Range   the stratigraphical spread of a form. Cf. *distribution*.
Region   a primary division of the earth.

Relict   pertaining to a community or fragment of one that has survived some major change.

Riparian   living by rivers or streams.

Rupestral   living in meadowland.

Saprophytic   pertaining to plants growing on dead organic matter.

Savannah or *parkland*   grassland with occasional trees.

Scavenger   animal feeding on dead organic matter.

Sere   succession of communities leading to climax community *q.v.*

Sessile   sedentary, or attached in one place.

Steno-   prefix denoting limited range of tolerance. Cf. *eury-*.

Sublittoral (*neritic* of some authors)   pertaining to the sea floor from low tide to the edge of the continental shelf, i.e., to about 200 m depth.

Substratum   the surface to which a fixed organism is attached.

Supralittoral   above high tide level.

Symbiosis   relationship between two or more species in which one or more benefit and none suffers.

Synecology   the ecology of communities, as distinct from that of individual species or groups.

Taphocoenose   burial assemblage.

Taphonomy   the study of burial.

-taxis   suffix denoting movement; e.g., *phototaxis* = movement in relation to light.

Teratological   pertaining to monstrosities.

Thanatocoenose   death assemblage.

-thermal   suffix pertaining to heat.

Tiphic   pertaining to ponds.

Transect   line or belt selected for study of the composition of a particular assemblage.

-tropism   suffix denoting movement in response to stimuli, particularly pertaining to growth; e.g., *phototropism* = growth movement in response to light.

Ultrahaline   having a salinity of more than 30.0‰.

Vagile   moving about, wandering.

Xero-   prefix denoting dryness; e.g., *xerophyte* = plant adapted to dry conditions.

Zoo-   prefix denoting animals; e.g., *zooplankton* = floating animals.

APPENDIX 2

Field questionnaire

The questions should be answered, as far as possible, for each separate rock unit.

Distribution

1. Are the fossils evenly distributed throughout the rock unit?
2. Are they in pockets, lenses, bands, or nodules?
3. Are they more abundant at any particular level in the unit?
4. Do they occur in reefs or shell banks?
5. Are the various kinds of fossils distributed in the same way?
6. Are the same fossils present as are seen in the same bed elsewhere?
7. Are any of the species present unusual in the studied area but more common elsewhere?
8. Approximately how many species are present?

Associations

1. What, very roughly, is the relative abundance of the different groups of fossils present?
2. Are there any obvious close associations, e.g., crinoids with wood fragments?
3. Are there any obvious abstentees, e.g., no ammonoids in a Cretaceous marine shale?
4. Are there any obvious derived fossils?
5. Are all growth stages present for each species? If not, which stages are present for which?
6. Are any of the fossils encrusted or bored? If so, how (e.g., bryozoans inside and/or outside pelecypod shells)?
7. Are any of the other fossils attached to one another in any way?
8. Is there any evidence of the mixing of organisms from different environments, e.g., land plants and echinoderms?

Preservation

1. Are there any unusual features about the preservation, e.g., color banding on nautiloids?
2. Are all the fossils preserved in the same way?
3. Are there any traces of "soft" parts?
4. Are any delicate structures preserved, e.g., spines on productoids?
5. Are the fossils worn or broken, and are some species more so than others?
6. Are the valves of bivalves separated (mollusks, brachiopods, and/or arthropods)? If so, are both valves present in equal numbers?

317

7. If the valves of bivalves are still joined together, are they tightly closed, partly open, or wide open?
8. If there are crinoid or other pelmatozoan stems present, are the ossicles separated, in short lengths, or in long lengths?
9. If higher-plant remains are present, which parts of the plants are they, (e.g., roots, stem, leaves, fruits)?

Relation to sediment

1. What is the nature of the enclosing sediment?
2. Are there any sedimentation structures, such as false bedding, slumps, ripple marks, and scour marks?
3. Is there any obvious relationship between the fossils and the nature and/ or grade of the sediment (e.g., larger forams in coarser-grained sands)?
4. Are any of the fossils obviously out of place in the sediment, e.g., reef corals in shale?
5. Are the fossils in nodules, if any, preserved in the same way as those in the surrounding sediment?
6. What is the nature of the infilling of any closed shells?
7. Are there any signs of a general disturbance of the sediment by organisms?
8. Are any of the fossils in position of life? If so, what percentage of each species?
9. Are any of the other fossils oriented in a particular way, e.g., belemnite rostra lying parallel to one another?

Form

1. Are there any noteworthy growth forms, e.g., delicately branched corals?
2. Are there any possible pecularities of adaptation, e.g., expanded glabella on trilobites?
3. Are there any obviously pathological specimens or any that have been damaged during life?
4. Are there any cemented forms, e.g., oysters, or forms requiring a firm substratum for anchorage?
5. Are there any borings, burrows, tracks, or trails?
6. Are there any other signs of organic activity, e.g., coprolites?
7. Are the fossils highly ornamented or smooth, or are there some of each?
8. Are there any signs of stunting or gigantism?
9. Are there any signs of unusual thickness of shell or excessive ornamentation?
10. Are there any signs of seasonal growth or of general change in growth rate or direction during life?

General

1. Are there any other phenomena of paleoecological interest in the assemblage?
2. Give a title to the indigenous part (if any) of the assemblage in terms of its dominant members (e.g., the *Choristites*-mollussan assemblage of the top bed in Figure 13.2, the lycopod-equisetalean assemblage of the Pentre seam in Figure 14.9, and the *Receptaculites*–solitary-coral assemblage of the bottom of zone II in Figure 16.5).

Bibliography

ABEL, O. 1935. Vorzeitliche Lebensspuren. 644 pp. Jena, Gustav Fischer.

AGER, D. V. 1954. The Genus *Gibbirhynchia* in the British Domerian. *Proc. Geol. Assoc., London*, vol. 65, pp. 25–51.

——. 1956a. The Geographical Distribution of Brachiopoda in the British Middle Lias. *Quart. Jour. Geol. Soc., London*, vol. 112, pp. 157–187.

——. 1956b. "Geographical Factors in the Definition of Fossil Species" *in* P. C. Sylvester-Bradley (ed.), The Species Concept in Palaeontology. Systematics Assoc., Publ. no. 2, pp. 105–109.

——. 1960. Brachiopod Distributions in the European Mesozoic. *Rept. XXIst Internat. Geol. Cong., Copenhagen*, part 22, pp. 20–25.

——. 1961a. Introducing Geology. 230 pp. London, Faber.

——. 1961b. The Epifauna of a Devonian Spiriferid. *Quart. Jour. Geol. Soc., London*, vol. 117, pp. 1–10.

——. 1961c. "La répartition géographique des brachiopodes dans le lias français" *in* Colloque sur le Lias français. *Bur. Recherches Géol. Min.*, Mém. no. 4, pp. 209–211.

——. 1962. The Occurrence of Pedunculate Brachiopods in Soft Sediments. *Geol. Mag.*, vol. 99, pp. 184–186.

—— AND E. A. RIGGS. 1963. The Internal Anatomy, Shell Growth and Asymmetry of a Devonian Spiriferid. *Jour. Paleont.* In press.

ALLAN, R. S. 1937. On a Neglected Factor in Brachiopod Migration. *Rec. Canterbury Mus. N.Z.*, vol. 4, pp. 157–165.

——. 1948. Geological Correlation and Paleoecology. *Bull. Geol. Soc. Amer.*, vol. 59, pp. 1–10.

ANDERSON, R. V. V. 1933. The Diatomaceous and Fish-bearing Beida Stage of Algeria. *Jour. Geol.*, vol. 41, pp. 673–698.

ANDERSON, R. Y. 1960. Evidence of Seasonal Lamination. *Program Geol. Soc. Amer. Ann. Mtg.*, p. 48.

ANDRICHUK, J. M. 1958. Stratigraphy and Facies Analysis of Upper Devonian Reefs in Leduc, Stettler and Redwater Areas, Alberta. *Bull. Amer. Assoc. Petroleum Geologists*, vol. 42, pp. 1–93.

ARIÇ, C. 1955. Istanbul paleozoik arazisinde bulunan oolitli ve fosilli demir madeni. Teknik Univ. Istanbul, Matbaasi, pp. 1–2. (In Turkish.)

ARKELL, W. J. 1928. Aspects of the Ecology of Certain Fossil Coral Reefs. *Jour. Ecol.*, vol. 16, pp. 134–149.

———. 1933. The Jurassic System in Great Britain. 681 pp. Oxford, Clarendon Press.

———. 1935. On the Nature, Origin and Climatic Significance of the Coral Reefs in the Vicinity of Oxford. *Quart. Jour. Geol. Soc., London*, vol. 91, pp. 77–110.

———. 1956a. Jurassic Geology of the World. 806 pp. Edinburgh and London, Oliver & Boyd.

———. 1956b. "Species and Species" *in* P. C. Sylvester-Bradley (ed.), The Species Concept in Palaeontology. *Systematics Assoc.*, Publ. no. 2, pp. 97–99.

BARBOUR, E. H. 1894. Additional Notes on the New Fossil, *Daimonelix:* Its Mode of Occurrence, Its Gross and Minute Structure. *Univ. Studies, Univ. Nebraska*, vol. 2, pp. 1–16.

BARTLEY, J. H. 1951. Pennsylvanian Reef and Non-reef Development in West Texas. *World Oil*, vol. 133, no. 4, pp. 142–145.

BASS, N. W. 1936. Origin of the Shoestring Sands of Greenwood and Butler Counties, Kansas. *Bull. Kansas State Geol. Survey*, no. 23, pp. 1–135.

BATHER, F. A. 1911. Upper Cretaceous Terebelloids from England. *Geol. Mag.*, vol. 8, pp. 481–487, 549–556.

BEECHER, C. E. 1894. On the Mode of Occurrence and the Structure and Development of *Triarthrus becki*. *Amer. Geol.*, vol. 13, pp. 38–43.

BEER, G. DE. 1958. The Darwin-Wallace Centenary. *Endeavour*, vol. 17, pp. 61–76.

BENTHEM JUTTING, W. S. S. VAN. 1946. Marine Organisms in the Island of Walcheren (Netherlands) during the Inundation, October 1944–October 1945. *Arch. Zeeuwsch. Genoot. Wetensch.*, pp. 1–7.

BERRY, E. W. 1914. The Upper Cretaceous and Eocene Floras of South Carolina and Georgia. *U.S. Geol. Survey*, Prof. Paper, no. 84, 200 pp.

BETTS, M. M. 1955. The Food of Titmice in Oak Woodland. *Jour. Animal Ecol.*, vol. 24, pp. 282–323.

BIERNAT, G. 1957. On *Peregrinella multicarinata* (Lamarck) (Brachiopoda). *Acta Palaeont. Polon.*, vol. 2, pp. 19–50.

———. 1961. *Diorygma atrypophilia* n. gen., n. sp.: A Parasitic Organism of *Atrypa zonata* Schnur. *Acta Palaeont. Polon.*, vol. 6, pp. 17–28.

BILLINGS, E. 1858. On the Asteriadae of the Lower Silurian Rocks of Canada. *Geol. Survey Canada. Figs. & Descr. Canad. Organic Remains*, Dec. 3, pp. 75–85.

BOOTH, A. H. 1958. The Niger, the Volta and the Dahomey Gap as Geographic Barriers. *Evolution*, vol. 12, pp. 48–62.

BORMANN, F. H. 1953. The Statistical Efficiency of Sample Plot Size and Shape in Forest Ecology. *Ecology*, vol. 34, pp. 474–487.

BOUCOT, A. J. 1953. Life and Death Assemblages among Fossils. *Amer. Jour. Sci.*, vol. 251, pp. 25–40; errata, p. 248.

———, W. BRACE, AND R. DEMAR. 1958. Distribution of Brachiopod and Pelecypod Shells by Currents. *Jour. Sed. Petrology*, vol. 28, pp. 321–332.

BOWEN, R. 1961a. Paleotemperature Analyses of Mesozoic Belemnoidea from Germany and Poland. *Jour. Geol.*, vol. 69, pp. 75–83.

————. 1961*b*. Paleotemperature Analyses of Belemnoidea and Jurassic Paleoclimatology. *Jour. Geol.*, vol. 69, pp. 309–320.

BRADLEY, W. H. 1946. Coprolites from the Bridger Formation of Wyoming: Their Composition and Micro-organisms. *Amer. Jour. Sci.*, vol. 244, pp. 215–239.

BRANDT, K. 1897. Die Fauna der Ostsee, insbesondere die der Kieler Bucht. *Verh. deutsch. zool. Gesell. siebenten Jahresvers. zu Kiel*, pp. 10–34.

BROADHURST, F. M. 1959. *Anthraconaia pulchella* sp. nov. and a Study of Palaeoecology in the Coal Measures of the Oldham Area of Lancashire. *Quart. Jour. Geol. Soc., London*, vol. 114, pp. 523–545.

BRONGERSMA-SANDERS, M. 1948. The Importance of Upwelling Water to Vertebrate Paleontology and Oil Geology. *Verh. Koninkl. Ned. Akad. Wetensch. Natuurk.*, sec. 2, vol. 45, pp. 1–112.

————. 1949. On the Occurrence of Fish Remains in Fossil and Recent Marine Deposits. *Bijdragen tot de Dierkunde*, vol. 28, pp. 65–76.

————. 1957. Mass Mortality in the Sea. *Geol. Soc. Amer.*, Mem. 67, vol. 1, pp. 941–1010.

BROWN, R. W. 1941. The Comb of a Wasp Nest from the Upper Cretaceous of Utah. *Amer. Jour. Sci.*, vol. 239, pp. 54–56.

BUCHANAN, G. D. 1958. The Current Range of the Armadillo *Dasypus novemcinctus mexicanus* in the United States. *Texas Jour. Sci.*, vol. 10, pp. 349–351.

———— AND R. V. TALMAGE. 1954. The Geographical Distribution of the Armadillo in the United States. *Texas Jour. Sci.*, vol. 6, pp. 142–150.

BUCHER, W. H. 1928. Observations on Organisms and Sedimentation on Shallow Sea-bottoms. (Review of work by R. Richter.) *Amer. Midland Naturalist*, vol. 11, pp. 236–242.

————. 1938. A Shell-boring Gastropod in a *Dalmanella* Bed of Upper Cincinnatian Age. *Amer. Jour. Sci.*, vol. 36, pp. 1–7.

BUCHER, W. S. 1929. Tetractinellid Sponge in the Sunbury Shale of Ohio. *Bull. Geol. Soc. Amer.*, vol. 40, p. 222.

BUCKMAN, S. S. 1906. Brachiopod Homeomorphy: *Pygope, Antinomia, Pygites. Quart. Jour. Geol. Soc., London*, vol. 62, pp. 433–455.

————. 1907. Some Species of the Genus *Cincta*. *Proc. Cotteswold Naturalists' Field Club*, vol. 16, pp. 41–63.

————. 1919. Type Ammonites. London. Vol. 3, part 20, pp. 7–8.

————. 1920. Jurassic Chronology. I. Lias: Supplement I. *Quart. Jour. Geol. Soc., London*, vol. 76, pp. 62–103.

————. 1922. Type Ammonites. London. Vol. 4, part 37, pp. 21–28.

BURLING, L. D. 1917. Was the Lower Cambrian Trilobite Supreme? *Ottawa Naturalist*, vol. 31, pp. 77–79.

CAILLEUX, A. 1951. Récifs coralliness et paléoclimats. *Comptes Rendus Soc. Biogéographie, Paris*, no. 239, pp. 21–23.

CAIN, S. A. 1938. The Species-Area Curve. *Amer. Midland Naturalist*, vol. 19, pp. 573–581.

CARPENTER, G. D. H. 1919. Third Report on the Bionomics of *Glossina palpalis* on Shores of Lake Victoria. *Rept. Sleeping Sickness Comm. Royal Soc.*, no. 17 (for 1914), pp. 3–66.

CARTER, D. J. 1951. Indigenous and Exotic Foraminifera in the Coralline Crag of Sutton, Suffolk. *Geol. Mag.*, vol. 88, pp. 236–248.

CASTER, K. E. 1944. Limuloid Tracks from the Upper Triassic (Chinle) of the Petrified Forest National Monument, Arizona. *Amer. Jour. Sci.*, vol. 242, pp. 74–84.

———. 1957. Problematica. *Geol. Soc. Amer.*, Mem. 67, vol. 2, pp. 1025–1032.

CAVE, A. J. E. 1959. Posture of Neanderthal Man. *Proc. XVth Internat. Cong. Zool.*, London, pp. 431–432.

CHALONER, W. G. 1958. The Carboniferous Upland Flora. *Geol. Mag.*, vol. 95, pp. 261–262.

CHANDLER, M. E. J. 1951. Note on the Occurrence of Mangroves in the London Clay. *Proc. Geol. Assoc.*, London, vol. 62, pp. 271–272.

———. 1961. The Lower Tertiary Floras of Southern England. I. Palaeocene Floras, London Clay Flora (supplement). *Brit. Mus. (Nat. Hist.) Monogr.*, 354 pp., atlas.

CHANEY, R. W. 1924. Quantitative Studies of the Bridge Creek Flora. *Amer. Jour. Sci.*, vol. 8, pp. 127–144.

———. 1940. Tertiary Forests and Continental Drift. *Bull. Geol. Soc. Amer.*, vol. 51, pp. 469–488.

CHAPMAN, F. 1929. On a New Species of *Capulus* Found Attached to a *Pterygotus* Carapace. *Proc. Royal Soc., Victoria*, vol. 41, pp. 217–219.

CHAPPELL, W. M., J. W. DURHAM, AND D. E. SAVAGE. 1951. Mold of a Rhinoceros in Basalt, Lower Grand Coulee, Washington. *Bull. Geol. Soc. Amer.*, vol. 62, pp. 907–918.

CHATWIN, C. P. 1923. Geology at the British Association. *Naturalist*, no. 803, pp. 398–402.

CHERNYSHEV, B. I. 1930. *Calceola* from the Devonian Beds of Salair Range. *Annals Soc. paléont. Russie*, vol. 8, pp. 91–97.

CLARKE, G. L. 1954. Elements of Ecology. 534 pp. New York and London, Wiley.

CLARKE, J. M. 1908. The Beginnings of Dependent Life. *Bull. New York State Mus.*, no. 121, pp. 146–169.

———. 1912. Early Adaptation in the Feeding Habits of Starfishes. *Jour. Acad. Nat. Sci.*, ser. 2, vol. 15, pp. 113–118.

———. 1921. Organic Dependence and Disease. 113 pp. *Bull. New York State Mus.*, nos. 221, 222.

CLAY, T. 1947. The Systematic Position of the Musophagi as Indicated by Their Mallophagan Parasites. *Ibis*, vol. 89, pp. 645–656.

CLEMENTS, F. E., AND V. E. SHELFORD. 1939. Bio-ecology. 425 pp. New York and London, Wiley.

CLOUD, P. E. 1948. Assemblages of Diminutive Brachiopods and Their Paleoecological Significance. *Jour. Sed. Petrology*, vol. 18, pp. 56–60.

———. 1959. Geology of Saipan Mariana Islands. Part 4. Submarine Topography and Shoal-water ecology. *U.S. Geol. Survey*, Prof. paper no. 280-K, pp. 361–445.

Bibliography

COLEMAN, P. J. 1957. Permian Productacea of Western Australia. 189 pp. *Bull. Bur. Min. Res., Geol. Geophys.*, no. 40.

CONDRA, G. E., AND M. K. ELIAS. 1944. Study and Revision of *Archimedes* (Hall). 243 pp. *Geol. Soc. Amer.*, Spec. paper no. 53.

COOPE, G. R. 1962. A Pleistocene Coleopterous Fauna with Arctic Affinities from Fladbury, Worcestershire. *Quart. Jour. Geol. Soc., London*, vol. 118, pp. 103–123.

————, F. W. SHOTTON, AND I. STRACHAN. 1961. A Late Pleistocene Fauna and Flora from Upton Warren, Worcestershire. *Philos. Trans. Royal Soc., London*, ser. B, vol. 244, pp. 379–421.

COTTAM, G., J. T. CURTIS, AND B. W. HALE. 1953. Some Sampling Characteristics of a Population of Randomly Dispersed Individuals. *Ecology*, vol. 34, pp. 741–757.

CRAIG, G. Y. 1952. A Comparative Study of the Ecology and Palaeoecology of *Lingula*. *Trans. Edinburgh Geol. Soc.*, vol. 15, pp. 110–120.

————. 1953. Fossil Communities and Assemblages. (Discussion of Boucot, 1953.) *Amer. Jour. Sci.*, vol. 251, pp. 547–548.

————. 1954. The Palaeoecology of the Top Hosie Shale (Lower Carboniferous) at a Locality near Kilsyth. *Quart. Jour. Geol. Soc., London*, vol. 110, pp. 103–119.

————. 1956. Mode of Life of Certain Carboniferous Animals from West Kirkton Quarry, near Bathgate. *Trans. Edinburgh Geol. Soc.*, vol. 16, pp. 272–279.

CRISP, D. J., AND A. J. SOUTHWARD. 1953. Isolation of Intertidal Animals by Sea Barriers. *Nature*, vol. 172, pp. 208–209.

———— AND H. G. STUBBINGS. 1957. The Orientation of Barnacles to Water Currents. *Jour. Animal Ecol.*, vol. 26, pp. 179–196.

CROSFIELD, M. C., AND M. S. JOHNSTON. 1914. A Study of Ballstone and the Associated Beds in the Wenlock Limestone of Shropshire. *Proc. Geol. Assoc., London*, vol. 25, pp. 193–224.

CROUCH, R. W. 1954. Paleontology and Paleoecology of the San Pedro Shelf and Vicinity. *Jour. Sed. Petrology*, vol. 24, pp. 182–190.

DACQUÉ, E. 1915. Grundlagen und Methoden der Palaeogeographie. 499 pp. Jena, Gustav Fischer.

DAPPLES, E. C. 1942. The Effect of Macro-organisms upon Near-shore Marine Sediments. *Jour. Sed. Petrology*, vol. 12, pp. 118–126.

DAVIES, A. M. 1937. Evolution and Its Modern Critics. 277 pp. London, Thomas Murby.

DAVIES, D. 1921. The Ecology of the Westphalian and the Lower Part of the Staffordian Series of Clydach Vale and Gilfach Goch (East Glamorgan). *Quart. Jour. Geol. Soc., London*, vol. 77, pp. 30–74.

DAVIS, A. G., AND G. F. ELLIOTT. 1957. The Palaeogeography of the London Clay Sea. *Proc. Geol. Assoc., London*, vol. 68, pp. 255–277.

DEGENS, E. T., A. PRASHNOWSKY, K. O. EMERY, AND J. PIMENTA. 1961. Organic Materials in Recent and Ancient Sediments. Part II. Amino Acids in Marine Sediments of Santa Barbara Basin, California. *Neues Jahrb. Geol. Paläont.*, vol. 8, pp. 413–426.

DELO, D. M. 1935. Locomotive Habits of Some Trilobites. *Amer. Midland Naturalist*, vol. 16, pp. 406–409.

DEXTER, R. W. 1947. The Marine Communities of a Tidal Inlet at Cape Ann, Massachusetts: A Study in Bio-ecology. *Ecol. Monogr.*, vol. 17, pp. 261–294.

DIENER, C. 1895. The Cephalopods of the Triassic Limestone-crags of Chitichun. *Palaeontologia Indica*, ser. 15, vol. 2, pp. 101–118.

DOLLO, L. 1910. La paléontologie ethologique. *Bull. Soc. Belge Géol. Paléont. Hydrol.*, vol. 23, pp. 377–421.

DROST-HANSEN, W., AND H. W. NEILL. 1955. Temperature Anomalies in the Properties of Liquid Water. *Phys. Rev.*, vol. 100, p. 1800.

DUBAR, G. 1942. Études paléontologiques sur le Lias du Maroc, Brachiopodes térébratules et zeilléries multiplissées. 103 pp. *Notes et Mém. Serv. Min. Maroc*, no. 57.

DU BOIS, E. P. 1943. Evidence on the Nature of Conodonts. *Jour. Paleont.*, vol. 17, pp. 155–159.

DU BOIS, H. M. 1916. Variation Induced in Branchiopods by Environmental Conditions. *Puget Sound Marine Sta. Publ.*, vol. 1, pp. 177–183.

DUNBAR, C. O. 1924. Was There Pennsylvanian-Permian Glaciation in the Arbuckle and Wichita Mountains of Oklahoma? *Amer. Jour. Sci.*, ser. 5, vol. 8, pp. 241–248.

DURHAM, J. W. 1942. Eocene and Oligocene Coral Faunas of Washington. *Jour. Paleont.*, vol. 16, pp. 84–104.

———. 1950. Cenozoic Marine Climates of the Pacific Coast. *Bull. Geol. Soc. Amer.*, vol. 61, pp. 1243–1264.

———. 1952. Early Tertiary Marine Faunas and Continental Drift. *Amer. Jour. Sci.*, vol. 250, pp. 321–343.

DU TOIT, A. L. 1954. The Geology of South Africa (3d edition). 611 pp. Edinburgh and London, Oliver & Boyd.

EAGAR, R. M. C. 1952. Growth and Variation in the Non-marine Lamellibranch Fauna above the Sand Rock Mine of the Lancashire Millstone Grit. *Quart. Jour. Geol. Soc., London*, vol. 107, pp. 339–373.

———. 1953. Variation with Respect to Petrological Differences in a Thin Band of Upper Carboniferous Non-marine Lamellibranchs. *Liverpool & Manchester Geol. Jour.*, vol. 1, pp. 161–190.

———. 1960. A Summary of the Results of Recent Work on the Palaeoecology of Carboniferous Non-marine Lamellibranchs. *Comptes Rendus IVe Cong. Av. Étud. strat. géol. Carbonifére, Maastricht*, pp. 137–149.

EDWARDS, W., AND C. J. STUBBLEFIELD. 1948. Marine Bands and Other Faunal Marker-horizons in Relation to the Sedimentary Cycles of the Middle Coal Measures of Nottinghamshire and Derbyshire. *Quart. Jour. Geol. Soc., London*, vol. 103, pp. 209–260.

EDWARDS, W. N. 1936. The Flora of the London Clay. *Proc. Geol. Assoc., London*, vol. 47, pp. 22–31.

———. 1955. The Geographical Distribution of Past Floras. *Adv. Sci., London*, no. 46, pp. 1–12.

EFREMOV, I. A. 1940. Taphonomy, a New Branch of Palaeontology. *Biul. Akad. Nauk. S.S.S.R.* (*Biol. Ser.*), no. 3, pp. 405–413. (In Russian.)

———. 1950. Taphonomy and the Geological Record. Part 1. 178 pp. *Trud. Paleont. Inst. Akad. Nauk. S.S.S.R.*, vol. 24. (In Russian.)

EKMAN, S. 1953. Zoogeography of the Sea. 417 pp. London, Sidgwick & Jackson.

ELLENBERGER, F., AND P. ELLENBERGER. 1960. Sur une nouvelle dalle à pistes de vertébrés, découverte au Basutoland (Afrique du Sud). *Comptes Rendus Soc. géol. France*, fasc. 9, pp. 236–238.

ELLES, G. L. 1939. Factors Controlling Graptolite Succession and Assemblages. *Geol. Mag.*, vol. 76, pp. 181–187.

———. 1940. Graptogonophores. *Geol. Mag.*, vol. 77, pp. 283–288.

ELLIOTT, G. F. 1948. Palingenesis in Thecidea. *Annals Mag. Nat. Hist.*, ser. 12, vol. 1, pp. 1–30.

———. 1950. The Genus *Hamptonina* (Brachiopoda). *Annals Mag. Nat. Hist.*, ser. 12, vol. 2, pp. 429–446.

———. 1953. The Conditions of Formation of the Lower Rhaetic at Blue Anchor, Somerset, and the Western European Rhaetic Generally. *Proc. Geol. Soc., London*, no. 1494, pp. xxxii–xxxv.

———. 1956a. Post-Palaeozoic Brachiopod Ecology: A Re-assessment. *Geol. Mag.*, vol. 93, pp. 196–200.

———. 1956b. On Tertiary Transarctic Brachiopod Migration. *Annals Mag. Nat. Hist.*, ser. 12, vol. 9, pp. 280–286.

———. 1958. Algal Debris-facies in the Cretaceous of the Middle East. *Palaeontology*, vol. 1, pp. 254–259.

ELLISON, S. P. 1955. Economic Applications of Paleoecology. *Econ. Geol.*, 50th anniv. vol., Part 2, pp. 867–884.

ELTON, C. 1956. Animal Ecology (7th impression). 209 pp. London, Sidgwick & Jackson.

EMILIANI, C. 1950. Introduction to a Method for Determining the Physical Characters of Fossil Environments. *Jour. Paleont.*, vol. 24, pp. 485–491.

ENDO, S. 1934. The Pleistocene Flora of Japan and Its Climatic Significance. *Johns Hopkins Univ., Studies Geol.*, Baltimore, vol. 11, pp. 251–267.

ERICSON, D. B., G. WOLLIN, AND J. WOLLIN. 1954. Coiling Direction of *Globorotalia truncatulinoides* in Deep-sea Cores. *Deep Sea Research*, vol. 2, pp. 152–158.

ERNST, W., K. KREJCI-GRAF, AND H. WERNER. 1958. Parallelisierung von Leithorizonten in Ruhrkarbon mit Hilfe von Bor-Gehaltes. *Geochim. Cosmochim. Acta*, vol. 14, pp. 211–222.

ETHERIDGE, R. 1876. On an Adherent Form of *Productus* and a Small *Spiriferina* from the Lower Carboniferous Limestone Group of the East of Scotland. *Quart. Jour. Geol. Soc., London*, vol. 32, pp. 454–465.

EVANS, R. G. 1948. The Lethal Temperatures of Some Common British Littoral Molluscs. *Jour. Animal Ecol.*, vol. 17, pp. 165–173.

FELL, H. B.   1953.   The Origin and Migrations of Australian Echinoderm Faunas since the Mesozoic. *Trans. Royal Soc. N.Z.*, vol. 81, pp. 245–255.

FENTON, C. L.   1935.   Viewpoints and Objects of Paleoecology. *Jour. Paleont.*, vol. 9, pp. 63–78.

—— AND M. A. FENTON.   1932*a*.   Boring Sponges in the Devonian of Iowa. *Amer. Midland Naturalist*, vol. 13, pp. 42–54.

—— AND ——.   1932*b*.   Orientation and Injury in the Genus *Atrypa*. *Amer. Midland Naturalist*, vol. 13, pp. 63–74.

—— AND ——.   1934*a*.   *Arthraria*-like Markings Made by Annelids and Snails. *Pan-Amer. Geol.*, vol. 61, pp. 264–266.

—— AND ——.   1934*b*.   *Lumbricaria:* A Holothuroid Casting? *Pan-Amer. Geol.*, vol. 61, pp. 291–292.

—— AND —— (*initials reversed*).   1934*c*.   *Scolithus* as a Fossil Phoronid. *Pan-Amer. Geol.*, vol. 61, pp. 341–348.

—— AND ——.   1937.   Trilobite "Nests" and Feeding Burrows. *Amer. Midland Naturalist*, vol. 18, pp. 446–451.

FEOFILOVA, A. P.   1959.   Facies Environments of Lower Carboniferous Coal Measures in the Donetz Basin. *Izv. Akad. Nauk. S.S.S.R.* (*Geol. Ser.*), no. 5. (In Russian.)

FINCH, G. E.   1904.   Notes on the Position of the Individuals in a Group of *Nileus vigilans* Found at Elgin, Iowa. *Proc. Iowa Acad. Sci.*, vol. 11, pp. 179–181.

FISCHER, A. G.   1961.   Latitudinal Variations in Organic Diversity. *Amer. Scientist*, vol. 49, pp. 50–74.

FISCHER-PIETTE, E.   1935.   Systématique et Biogéographie: Les Patelles d'Europe et d'Afrique du Nord. *Jour. Conchyl.*, ser. 4, vol. 79, pp. 5–66.

FLEMING, C. A.   1944.   Molluscan Evidence of Pliocene Climatic Change in New Zealand. *Trans. Royal Soc. N.Z.*, vol. 74, pp. 207–220.

FLOWER, R. H.   1939.   Study of the Pseudorthoceratidae. 214 pp. *Palaeontographica Americana*, vol. 2, no. 10.

——.   1942*a*.   An Arctic Cephalopod Fauna from the Cynthiana of Kentucky. 50 pp. *Bull. Amer. Paleont.*, vol. 27, no. 103.

——.   1942*b*.   Environment of Early Paleozoic Nautiloids. *Rept. Natl. Research Council Comm. Marine Ecol. Paleont.*, no. 2, pp. 37–41.

——.   1957.   Nautiloids of the Paleozoic. *Geol. Soc. Amer.*, Mem. 67, vol. 2, pp. 829–852.

FOERSTE, A. F.   1930.   The Color Patterns of Fossil Cephalopods and Brachiopods, with Notes on Gastropods and Pelecypods. *Contr. Mus. Geol. Univ. Michigan*, vol. 3, pp. 109–150.

——.   1936.   Cephalopods from the Upper Ordovician of Percé, Quebec. *Jour. Paleont.*, vol. 10, pp. 373–384.

FORBES, E.   1843.   Report on the Mollusca and Radiata of the Aegean Sea, and on Their Distribution, Considered as Bearing on Geology. *Rept. Brit. Assoc. Adv. Sci.*, pp. 130–193.

FRANKS, J. W., A. J. SUTCLIFFE, M. P. KERNEY, AND G. R. COOPE.   1958. Haunt of Elephant and Rhinoceros: The Trafalgar Square of 100,000 Years Ago—New Discoveries. *Illus. London News*, June 14, pp. 1011–1013.

FRENTZEN, K. 1932. Palaeobiologisches über die Korallen-vorkommen in oberen Weissen Jura bei Nattheim. *Badische Geol. Abh.,* vol. 4, pp. 43–57.

FRIANT, M. 1952. Quelques caracteres d'evolution de l'ours des cavernes (*Ursus spelaeus* Rosenm.). *Annals Soc. roy. Zool. Belge,* vol. 83, pp. 189–194.

FRITEL, P. H. 1903. Histoire naturelle de la France. Part 24. Paléobotanique (Plantes fossiles). 325 pp. Paris, E. Deyrolle.

FRIZZELL, D. L., AND H. EXLINE. 1958. Crustacean Gastroliths from the Claiborne Eocene of Texas. *Micropaleontology,* vol. 4, pp. 273–280.

——— AND W. C. HORTON. 1961. Crustacean Gastroliths from the Jackson Eocene of Louisiana. *Bull. Univ. Michigan School Min. Metal.,* no. 99, pp. 3–6.

FRYE, J. C., AND A. B. LEONARD. 1957. Ecological Interpretations of Pliocene and Pleistocene Stratigraphy in the Great Plains Region. *Amer. Jour. Sci.,* vol. 255, pp. 1–11.

FRYER, G. 1959. The Trophic Interrelationships and Ecology of Some Littoral Communities of Lake Nyasa with Especial Reference to the Fishes, and a Discussion of the Evolution of a Group of Rock-frequenting Cichlidae. *Proc. Zool. Soc., London,* vol. 132, pp. 153–281.

FUCHS, T. 1895. Studien über Fucoiden und Hieroglyphen. 80 pp. *Denkschr. k. Akad. Wiss., Wien,* vol. 62.

GÉCZY, B. 1954. Cyclolites (Anth.) tanulmányok. 180 pp. *Geol. Hungarica, Ser. Palaeont.,* vol. 24. (In Hungarian with German translation.)

GEKKER, R. F. 1935. The Phenomena of Adherence and Attachment among the Upper Devonian Fauna and Flora of the Main Outcrop. *Trud. Paleont. Inst. Moskva,* vol. 4, pp. 149–280. (In Russian.)

———. 1955. Instructions for Palaeoecological Investigations. 38 pp. *Izdat. Akad. Nauk. S.S.S.R.* (In Russian.)

———. 1957. Introduction to Paleoecology. 83 pp. Moscow. (In Russian. French translation (slightly expanded), Bases de la Paléoécologie, by J. Roger, 1960. Paris. *Bur. Recherches Géol. Min.*)

———. 1960. Fossil Facies of Smooth Rocky Sea-floors. *Trud. geol. Inst. Akad. Nauk. Est. S.S.R.,* vol. 5, pp. 199–227.

———, A. N. RIABININE, E. S. RAMMELMEYER, AND M. F. FILIPPOVA. 1948. A Fossil Jurassic Lake in the Kara-Tau Chain. *Trud. Paleont. Inst. Akad. Nauk. S.S.S.R.,* vol. 15. (In Russian.)

GOLDFUSS, G. A. 1826–1844. Petrefacta Germaniae tam ea quae Museo Universitatis Regiae Borussicae Fredericiae Wilhelmiae Rhenanae quam alia in Museis Hoeninghusiaso, Münsteriano, aliisque, iconibus et descriptionibus illustrata. 3 vols. 1604 pp. Düsseldorf.

GORJANOVIĆ-KRAMBERGER, K. 1901. Über die Gattung *Valenciennesia* und einige unterpontische Limnaeen. *Beitr. Paläont. Oesterreich.-Ungarns. Orients.,* vol. 13, pp. 121–140.

———. 1923. Ueber die Bedeutung der Valenciennesiiden in stratigraphischer und genetischer Hinsicht. *Paläont. Zeitsch.,* vol. 5, pp. 339–344.

GORVETT, H. 1958. Animal Life on Wave-beaten Rocks. *Nature,* vol. 182, pp. 1652–1653.

GRANT, R. E. 1963. Unusual Attachment of a Permian Linoproductid Brachiopod. *Jour. Paleont.*, vol. 37, pp. 134–140.

GRÖNWALL, K. A. 1912. Maskrör från Köpingesandstenen. *Geol. Fören. Stockholm Förh.*, vol. 34, pp. 215–220.

GUILLAUME, L. 1927. Revision des Posidonomyes jurassiques. *Bull. Soc. géol. France*, vol. 27, pp. 217–234.

GUNTER, G. 1957. Temperature. *Geol. Soc. Amer.*, Mem. 67, vol. 1, pp. 159–184.

HALLAM, A. 1955. The Palaeontology and Stratigraphy of the Marlstone Rock-bed in Leicestershire. *Trans. Leicestershire Lit. Philos. Soc.*, vol. 49, pp. 17–35.

————. 1960a. A Sedimentary and Faunal Study of the Blue Lias of Dorset and Glamorgan. *Philos. Trans. Royal Soc., London*, ser. B, No. 698, vol. 243, pp. 1–44.

————. 1960b. *Kulundrichnus langi*, a New Trace-fossil from the Lias. *Palaeontology*, vol. 3, pp. 64–68.

————. 1962. Brachiopod Life Assemblages from the Marlstone Rock-bed of Leicestershire. *Palaeontology*, vol. 4, pp. 653–659.

HALLE, T. G. 1937. The Relation between the Late Palaeozoic Floras of Eastern and Northern Asia. *Comptes rendus Cong. Strat. Carb., Heerlen*, vol. 1, pp. 237–245.

HAMILTON, E. L. 1956. Sunken Islands of the Mid-Pacific Mountains. *Geol. Soc. Amer.*, Mem. 64, pp. 1–97.

HÄNTZSCHEL, W. 1955. Rezente und fossile Lebensspuren, ihre Deutung und geologische Auswertung. *Experientia*, vol. 11, pp. 373–382.

————. 1956. Rückschau auf die paläontologischen und neontologischen Ergebnisse der Forschungsanstalt "Senkenberg am Meer." *Senckenbergiana Lethaea*, vol. 37, pp. 319–330.

HANZLÍKOVÁ, E. 1953. Mikropaleontologicko-stratigrafické zhodnocení vrtby Žukov NP 15. *Sborník Ústred. ústav. geol. (pal.), Praha*, vol. 20, pp. 85–168. (In Czech, with English and Russian summaries.)

————. 1956. "Mikrobiostratigrafický výzkum popisovaného území a Jeho oklí" *in* A. Matejka and Z. Roth, Geologie magurského flyše v severím povodí Váhu mezi Bytčou a Trenčinem. *Rozpravy Ústred. ústav. geol., Praha*, vol. 22, pp. 207–220. (In Czech, with English and Russian summaries.)

————. 1959. Mikrobiostratigrafické poměry Čerhovských hor a západní bardějovské části Ondavskej vrchoviny. *Zprávy o geol. výzhumech, Praha*, vol. for 1957, pp. 57–64.

HARRINGTON, H. J. 1959. "General Description of Trilobita" *in* R. C. Moore (ed.), Treatise on Invertebrate Paleontology. Part O, Arthropoda I, pp. O38–O117. Lawrence, Kans., Univ. Kansas Press and *Geol. Soc. Amer.*

HARRIS, T. M. 1958. Forest Fire in the Mesozoic. *Jour. Ecol.*, vol. 46, pp. 447–453.

HARTLEY, P. H. T. 1953. An Ecological Study of the Feeding Habits of the English Titmice. *Jour. Animal Ecol.*, vol. 53, pp. 261–288.

HAUFF, B. 1953. Das Holzmadenbuch. 54 pp. Öhringen, Germany.

HAYASAKA, S. 1960. Large-sized Oysters from the Japanese Pleistocene and Their Paleoecological Implications. *Sci. Rept. Tohoku Univ., Ser. 2* (*Geol.*), Spec. vol. 4, pp. 356–370.

HECKER, R. Th. *See* GEKKER, R. F.

HEDGPETH, J. W. (ed.). 1957. Treatise on Marine Ecology and Paleoecology. Vol. 1. Ecology. 1296 pp. *Geol. Soc. Amer.*, Mem. 67.

HEER, O. 1865. Die Urwelt der Schweiz. 652 pp. Zurich. (Reprint, shortened by L. Mazurczak, 1946.)

———. 1876. The Primaeval World of Switzerland. 2 vols., 717 pp. London. (Translated by W. S. Dallas.)

HENBEST, L. G. 1960. Fossil Spoor and Their Environmental Significance in Morrow and Atoka Series, Pennsylvanian, Washington County, Arkansas. *U.S. Geol. Survey* Prof. paper no. 400-B, pp. B383–B385.

HENNIG, E. 1923. Geologie von Württemburg nebst Hohenzollern. *Handb. Geol. Bodensch. Deutsch.* (vol. 2, *Regionale Geol. Deutsch.*) 383 pp. Berlin.

HEWATT, W. G. 1937. Ecological Studies on Selected Marine Intertidal Communities of Monterey Bay, California. *Amer. Midland Naturalist,* vol. 18, pp. 161–206.

HILL, D. 1938. A Monograph on the Carboniferous Rugose Corals of Scotland. Part I. *Palaeontog. Soc. Monogr.*, pp. 1–78.

HOFFMEISTER, W. S. 1955. Microfossil Prospecting for Petroleum. *Amer. Geol. Inst. Newsletter,* vol. 6, no. 6, p. 1.

HOPPE, K. H. 1932. Die Coelolepiden und Acanthodien des Obersilurs der Insel Oesel. *Paleontographica,* vol. 76, pp. 35–94.

HOWELL, B. F., AND C. E. RESSER. 1933. Habitats of the Agnostid Trilobites. (Abstract only.) *Proc. Geol. Soc. Amer.*, pp. 360–361.

HUDSON, R. G. S., AND R. P. S. JEFFERIES. 1961. Upper Triassic Brachiopods and Lamellibranchs from the Oman Peninsula, Arabia. *Paleontology,* vol. 4, pp. 1–41.

HUENE, F. VON. 1928. Lebensbild des Saurischier-Vorkommens im Obersten Keuper von Trossingen in Württemberg. *Palaeobiologica,* vol. 1, pp. 103–116.

HUPÉ, P. 1953. "Classe des Trilobites" *in* J. Piveteau (ed.), Traité de Paléontologie. Vol. 3, pp. 44–246. Paris, Masson.

HUTCHINSON, G. E. 1957. Future of Marine Paleoecology. *Geol. Soc. Amer.*, Mem. 67, vol. 2, pp. 683–690.

ILLING, M. 1950. The Mechanical Distribution of Recent Foraminifera in Bahamas Banks Sediments. *Annals Mag. Nat. Hist.*, ser. 12, vol. 3, pp. 757–761.

IMBRIE, J. 1955. Quantitative Lithofacies and Biofacies Study of Florena Shale (Permian) of Kansas. *Bull. Amer. Assoc. Petroleum Geologists,* vol. 39, pp. 649–670.

IREDALE, T. 1942. Report on Molluscan Content of Heron Island Reef Boring Samples. *Rept. Great Barrier Reef Comm.*, vol. 5, appendix 1, pp. 120–122.

IVANOVA, E. A., AND I. V. KHVOROVA. 1955. Stratigraphy of the Middle and Upper Carboniferous in the Eastern Part of the Moscow Syneclise. *Trud. Paleont. Inst. Akad. Nauk. S.S.S.R.*, vol. 53, pp. 1–282.

IVERSEN, J. 1956. *in* J. Troels-Smith, Vandstands-svinginger i indsøbassiner og havtransgressioner og-regressioner. *Medd. Dansk Geol. Foren.*, vol. 13, p. 127.

JAEKEL, O. M. 1918. Phylogenie und System der Pelmatozoen. *Paläont. Zeitschr.*, vol. 3, pp. 1–128.

JEFFERIES, R. P. S. 1960. Photonegative Young in the Triassic Lamellibranch *Lima lineata* (Schlotheim). *Palaeontology*, vol. 3, pp. 362–369.

———. 1962. The Palaeoecology of the *Actinocamax plenus* Subzone (Lowest Turonian) in the Anglo-Paris Basin. *Palaeontology*, vol. 4, pp. 609–647.

JELETZKY, J. A. 1948. Zur Kenntnis der Oberkreide des Dnjepr-Donetz-Senke und boralen Oberkreide mit derjenigen Polen und nordwest Europas. *Geol. Fören. Förh.*, *Stockholm*, vol. 70, no. 455, pp. 583–602.

JOHNSON, J. H., AND K. KONISHI. 1960. An Interesting Late Cretaceous Calcareous Alga from Guatemala. *Jour. Paleont.*, vol. 34, pp. 1099–1105.

JOHNSON, R. G. 1957. Experiments on the Burial of Shells. *Jour. Geol.*, vol. 65, pp. 527–535.

———. 1960*a*. Models and Methods for Analysis of the Mode of Formation of Fossil Assemblages. *Bull. Geol. Soc. Amer.*, vol. 71, pp. 1075–1086.

———. 1960*b*. Pennsylvanian Life Assemblages, Western Illinois. (Abstract only.) *Program Geol. Soc. Amer. Ann. Mtg.*, pp. 130–131.

———. 1962*a*. Interspecific Associations in Pennsylvanian Fossil Assemblages. *Jour. Geol.*, vol. 70, pp. 32–55.

———. 1962*b*. Mode of Formation of Marine Fossil Assemblages of the Pleistocene Millerton Formation of California. *Bull. Geol. Soc. Amer.*, vol. 73, pp. 113–130.

JORDAN, D. S. 1920. A Miocene Catastrophe. *Nat. Hist.*, vol. 20, pp. 18–22.

JOYSEY, K. A. 1959. Probable Cirripede, Phoronid, and Echiuroid Burrows within a Cretaceous Echinoid Test. *Palaeontology*, vol. 1, pp. 397–400.

JURAVLEV, K. J. 1943. The Remains of Upper Jurassic Sea Reptiles at the Seveljevka Shale Mine. *Biul. Akad. Nauk. S.S.S.R.* (*Biol. Ser.*), no. 5, pp. 293–306.

KAUFFMAN, E. G., AND R. V. KESLING. 1960. An Upper Cretaceous Ammonite Bitten by a Mosasaur. *Contr. Mus. Paleont. Univ. Michigan*, vol. 15, no. 9, pp. 193–248.

KAY, M. 1945. Paleogeographic and Palinspastic Maps. *Bull. Amer. Assoc. Petroleum Geologists*, vol. 29, pp. 426–440.

KERNEY, M. P. 1958. On the Occurrence of *Margaritifera auriculiaria* (Spengler) in the English Pleistocene. *Jour. Conchology*, vol. 24, p. 250.

KETTLEWELL, H. B. D. 1957. The Contribution of Industrial Melanism in the Lepidoptera to Our Knowledge of Evolution. *Adv. Sci.*, *London*, vol. 13, pp. 245–252.

KINDLE, E. M. 1938. A Pteropod Record of Current Direction. *Jour. Paleont.*, vol. 12, pp. 515–516.

KING, P. B. 1942. Permian of West Texas and Southeastern New Mexico. *Bull. Amer. Assoc. Petroleum Geologists,* vol. 26, pp. 535–763.

KNOX, G. A. 1954. The Intertidal Flora and Fauna of the Chatham Islands. *Nature,* vol. 174, pp. 871–873.

KOBAYASHI, T. 1954. A Contribution towards Paleoflumenology, Science of the Oceanic Currents in the Past, with a Description of a New Miocene *Aturia* from Central Japan. *Jap. Jour. Geol. Geog.,* vol. 25, pp. 35–56.

KOHN, A. J. 1959. The Ecology of *Conus* in Hawaii. *Ecol. Monogr.,* vol. 29, pp. 1–90.

KOLESNIKOV, V. P. 1949. On Some Problems of Paleontology. *Biul. Moskov. Obshch. Ispyt. Prirody* (N.S.), vol. 54, geol. sec., no. 24, part 3.

KORNICKER, L. S., AND H. T. ODUM. 1958. Characterization of Modern and Ancient Environments by Species Diversity. (Abstract only.) *Bull. Geol. Soc. Amer.,* vol. 69, p. 1599.

KREJCI-GRAF, K. 1932. Definition der Begriffe Marken, Spuren, Fährten, Bauten, Hieroglyphen und Fucoiden. *Senckenbergiana,* vol. 14, pp. 19–39.

KRINSLEY, D. 1960. Orientation of Orthoceracone Cephalopods at Lemont, Illinois. *Jour. Sed. Petrology,* vol. 30, pp. 321–323.

KUENEN, P. H. 1961. Some Arched and Spiral Structures in Sediments. *Geol. Mijnbouw,* vol. 40, pp. 71–74.

KULP, J. L., K. K. TUREKIAN, AND D. W. BOYD. 1952. Strontium Content of Limestones and Fossils. *Bull. Geol. Soc. Amer.,* vol. 63, pp. 701–716.

KUMMEL, B. 1948. Environmental Significance of Dwarfed Cephalopods. *Jour. Sed. Petrology,* vol. 18, pp. 61–64.

———— AND R. M. LLOYD. 1955. Experiments on Relative Streamlining of Coiled Cephalopod Shells. *Jour. Paleont.,* vol. 29, pp. 159–170.

KURTÉN, B. 1958. Life and Death of the Pleistocene Cave Bear: A Study in Paleoecology. *Acta Zool. Fennica,* no. 95, pp. 1–59.

KUYL, O. S., J. MULLER, AND H. T. WATERBOLK. 1955. The Application of Palynology to Oil Geology, with Special Reference to Western Venezuela. *Geol. Mijnbouw,* vol. 17, pp. 49–75.

KUŹNIAR, W. 1910. Eocen Tatr i Podhala, I. *Spraw. Akad. Um., Cracow,* vol. 44, pp. 26–76.

LACK, D. 1954. The Natural Regulation of Animal Numbers. 343 pp. Oxford, Clarendon Press.

LADD, H. S. 1934. Geology of Vitilevu, Fiji. *Bull. Bernice P. Bishop Mus.,* vol. 119, pp. 1–263.

———— (ed.). 1957a. Treatise on Marine Ecology and Paleoecology. Vol. 2. Paleoecology. 1077 pp. *Geol. Soc. Amer.,* Mem. 67.

————. 1957b. Paleoecological Evidence. *Geol. Soc. Amer.,* Mem. 67, vol. 2, pp. 31–66.

————. 1959. Ecology, Paleontology, and Stratigraphy. *Science,* vol. 129, no. 3341, pp. 69–78.

LALICKER, C. G. 1948. Dwarfed Protozoan Faunas. *Jour. Sed. Petrology,* vol. 18, pp. 51–55.

LAMONT, A.   1934.   Lower Palaeozoic Brachiopoda of the Girvan District. *Annals Mag. Nat. Hist.*, ser. 10, vol. 14, pp. 161–184.

———.   1952.   Ecology and Correlation of the Pentlandian—a New Division of the Silurian System in Scotland. *Rept. XVIIIth Internat. Geol. Cong., London*, part 10, pp. 27–32.

LAUGHBAUM, L. R.   1960.   A Paleoecologic Study of the Upper Denton Formation, Tarrant, Denton, and Cooke Counties, Texas. *Jour. Paleont.*, vol. 34, pp. 1183–1197.

LECOMPTE, M.   1958.   Les recifs paleozoiques en Belgique. *Geol. Rundschau*, vol. 47, pp. 384–401.

LLOYD, E. R.   1929.   Capitan Limestone and Associated Formations of New Mexico and Texas. *Bull. Amer. Assoc. Petroleum Geologists*, vol. 13, pp. 645–658.

LOCHMAN-BALK, C., AND J. L. WILSON.   1958.   Cambrian Biostratigraphy in North America. *Jour. Paleont.*, vol. 32, pp. 312–350.

LOOMIS, F. B.   1903.   The Dwarf Fauna of the Pyrite Layer of the Horizon of the Tully Limestone in Western New York. *Bull. Univ. State New York*, no. 303 (*Bull. New York State Mus.*, vol. 69), pp. 892–920.

LOWENSTAM, H. A.   1948.   Biostratigraphic Studies of the Niagaran Inter-reef Formations in North-eastern Illinois. *Sci. Papers Illinois State Mus.*, vol. 4, pp. 1–146.

———.   1950.   Niagaran Reefs of the Great Lakes Area. *Jour. Geol.*, vol. 58, pp. 430–487.

———.   1954.   Factors Affecting the Aragonite-Calcite Ratios in Carbonate-secreting Marine Organisms. *Jour. Geol.*, vol. 62, pp. 284–322.

———.   1957.   Niagaran Reefs in the Great Lakes Area. *Geol. Soc. Amer.*, Mem. 67, vol. 2, pp. 215–248.

———.   1960. O^{18}/O^{16} Ratios and Sr and Mg Contents in Recent and Fossil Articulate Brachiopods and Their Relationship to the Water Chemistry. (Abstract only.) *Bull. Geol. Soc. Amer.*, vol. 71, pp. 2065–1066.

———.   1961.   Mineralogy, O^{18}/O^{16} Ratios, and Strontium and Magnesium Contents of Recent and Fossil Brachiopods and Their Bearing on the History of the Oceans. *Jour. Geol.*, vol. 69, pp. 241–260.

——— AND S. EPSTEIN.   1954.   Paleotemperatures of the Post-Aptian Cretaceous as Determined by the Oxygen Isotope Method. *Jour. Geol.*, vol. 62, pp. 207–248.

——— AND ———.   1959.   Cretaceous Paleotemperatures as Determined by the Oxygen Isotope Method, Their Relations to and the Nature of Rudistid Reefs. *Rept. XXth Internat. Geol. Cong., Mexico*, El Sistemo Cretacico, part 1, pp. 65–76.

———, H. B. WILLMAN, AND D. H. SWANN.   1956.   The Niagaran Reef at Thornton, Illinois. *Guidebook Amer. Assoc. Petroleum Geologists & Soc. Econ. Paleont. Min.*, Urbana, Ill., pp. 1–19.

LOWMAN, S. W.   1949.   Sedimentary Facies in Gulf Coast. *Bull. Amer. Ass. Petroleum Geologists*, vol. 33, pp. 1939–1997.

MA, T. Y. H.   1933.   On the Seasonal Change of Growth in Some Palaeozoic Corals. *Proc. Imp. Acad. Japan*, vol. 9, no. 8, pp. 407–409.

————. 1937. On the Seasonal Growth in Palaeozoic Tetracorals and the Climate during the Devonian Period. *Palaeontologia Sinica,* ser. B, vol. 2, fasc. 3, pp. 1–106.

————. 1954. Climate and the Relative Positions of the Continents during the Lower Carboniferous Period. *Acta Geol. Taiwanica,* no. 6, pp. 1–86.

————. 1957. Climate and the Relative Positions of Continents during the Upper Cretaceous. 70 pp. Taipei, Taiwan.

MacGinitie, G. E., and N. MacGinitie. 1949. Natural History of Marine Animals. 473 pp. New York, McGraw-Hill.

McGinity, T. L. 1955. *Spirula spirula* Linné, a Remarkable Find. *The Nautilus,* vol. 69, p. 35.

McIntyre, G. A. 1953. Estimation of Plant Density Using Line Transects. *Jour. Ecol.,* vol. 41, pp. 319–330.

McKee, E. D. 1947. Experiments on the Development of Tracks in Fine Cross-bedded Sand. *Jour. Sed. Petrology,* vol. 17, pp. 23–28.

————. 1960. Spatial Relations of Fossils and Bedded Cherts in the Redwall Limestone, Arizona. *U.S. Geol. Survey,* Prof. paper no. 400-B, pp. B461–B463.

McKerrow, W. S. 1953. Variation in the Terebratulacea of the Fuller's Earth Rock. *Quart. Jour. Geol. Soc.,* London, vol. 109, pp. 97–124.

Maclennan, R. M. 1943. The Association of *Naiadites* and *Carbonicola* in a Part of the Central Coalfield of Scotland. *Geol. Mag.,* vol. 80, pp. 52–55.

Makowski, H. 1962. Recherches sur le dimorphisme sexuel chez les Ammonoidés. *Polska Akad. Nauk., Kom. Geol., Ksiega Pamiatkowa Prof. J. Samsonowicza,* pp. 31–56.

Matley, C. A. 1939. On Some Coprolites from the Maleri Beds of India. *Rec. Geol. Survey India,* vol. 74, pp. 530–534.

Matteson, M. R. 1955. Studies on the Natural History of the Unionidae. *Amer. Midland Naturalist,* vol. 53, pp. 126–145.

Mayr, E. 1951. Bearing of Some Biological Data on Geology. *Bull. Geol. Soc. Amer.,* vol. 62, pp. 537–546.

Menard, H. W., and A. J. Boucot. 1951. Experiments on the Movement of Shells by Water. *Amer. Jour. Sci.,* vol. 249, pp. 131–151.

Miller, A. K., and W. M. Furnish. 1937. Paleoecology of the Paleozoic Cephalopoda. *Rept. Natl. Research Council Comm. Paleoecol.* (for 1936–1937), pp. 54–63.

Miyaji, D., and T. Habe. 1947. On Thanatocoenoses of Bays. *Physiology & Ecology, Tokyo,* vol. 1, pp. 110–124. (In Japanese, with English abstract.)

Mojsisovics, E. 1882. Die Cephalopoden der Mediterranean Triasprovinz. *Abh. Geol. Reichsanst., Wien,* vol. 10, pp. 1–322.

————. 1899. Upper Triassic Cephalopoda Faunae of the Himalaya. *Palaeontologia Indica,* ser. 15, vol. 3, pp. 1–157.

Moodie, R. L. 1916. The Coal Measures Amphibia of North America. 222 pp. *Carnegie Inst., Washington,* Publ. no. 238.

————. 1923. Paleopathology: An Introduction to the Study of Ancient Evidences of Disease. 568 pp. Urbana, Ill., University of Illinois Press.

MOORE, H. B. 1934. The Relation of Shell Growth to Environment in *Patella vulgata*. *Proc. Malac. Soc.*, vol. 21, pp. 217–222.

————. 1939. "Faecal Pellets in Relation to Marine Deposits" *in* P. D. Trask (ed.), Recent Marine Sediments: A Symposium. London, American Association of Petroleum Geologists. pp. 516–524 (2d edition, 1955).

MOORE, R. C. 1957. Modern Methods of Paleoecology. *Bull. Amer. Assoc. Petroleum Geologists*, vol. 41, pp. 1775–1801.

MORISHIMA, M. 1948. Foraminiferal Thanatocoenoses of Ago Bay, Kii Peninsula, Japan. *Rept. Natl. Research Council Comm. Marine Ecol. Paleoecol.*, no. 8, pp. 111–117.

MOSELEY, H. N. 1892. Notes by a Naturalist on the "Challenger" (2d edition). 540 pp. London.

MUIR-WOOD, H. M. 1959. Report on the Brachiopoda of the John Murray Expedition. *Brit. Mus. (Nat. Hist.) John Murray Exped. 1933–1934. Sci. Rept.*, vol. 10, pp. 283–317.

MÜLLER, K. J. 1959. Kambrische Conodonten. *Zeitschr. Deutsch. geol. Gesell.*, vol. 111, pp. 434–485.

MUNIER-CHALMAS, E. C. P. A. 1892. Sur la possibilité d'admettre un dimorphisme sexual chez les Ammonitidés. *Comptes Rendus Soc. géol. France*, ser. 3, vol. 20, pp. 170–174.

NATIONAL RESEARCH COUNCIL. 1941–1951. Reports of Committee on a Treatise on Marine Ecology and Paleoecology, Division of Geology and Geography. Nos. 1–11, Washington.

NATLAND, M. L. 1933. The Temperature- and Depth-distribution of some Recent and Fossil Foraminifera in the Southern California Region. *Bull. Scripps Inst. Oceanog.*, vol. 3, pp. 225–230.

NEVES, R. 1958. Upper Carboniferous Plant Spore Assemblages from the *Gastrioceras subcrenatum* Horizon, North Staffordshire. *Geol. Mag.*, vol. 95, pp. 1–19.

NEWELL, N. D., J. IMBRIE, E. G. PURDY, AND D. L. THURBER. 1959. Organic Communities and Bottom Facies, Great Bahaman Bank. *Bull. Amer. Mus. Nat. Hist.*, vol. 117, pp. 183–228.

————, J. K. RIGBY, A. G. FISCHER, A. J. WHITEMAN, J. E. HICKOK, AND J. S. BRADLEY. 1953. The Permian Reef Complex of the Guadalupe Mountains Region, Texas and New Mexico: A Study in Paleoecology. 236 pp. San Francisco, Freeman.

NICHOLS, D. 1959. Changes in the Chalk Heart-urchin *Micraster* Interpreted in Relation to Living Forms. *Philos. Trans. Royal Soc., London*, ser. B, vol. 242, pp. 347–437.

NICHOLSON, A. J. 1933. The Balance of Animal Populations. *Jour. Animal Ecol.*, vol. 2, pp. 132–178.

NICOL, D. 1962. The Biotic Development of Some Niagaran Reefs: An Example of an Ecological Succession or Sere. *Jour. Paleont.*, vol. 36, pp. 172–176.

NOBLE, E. R. 1959. The Ecology of Parasitism. *Proc. XVth Internat. Cong. Zool., London,* pp. 654–657.

NORDENG, S. C. 1959. Possible Use of Precambrian Calcareous Algal Colonies as Indicators of Polar Shifts. *Abs. 5th Ann. Mtg. Inst. Lake Superior Geol., Minneapolis,* p. 9.

OAKLEY, K. P. 1937. Cretaceous Sponges: Some Biological and Geological Considerations. *Proc. Geol. Assoc., London,* vol. 48, pp. 330–348.

ODUM, H. T. 1950. Strontium Biochemistry, Ecosystems, and Paleoecological Tools. *Rept. Natl. Research Council Comm. Marine Ecol. Paleoecol.,* no. 10, pp. 55–58.

———. 1951*a*. Notes on the Strontium Content of Sea Water. *Science,* vol. 114, p. 214.

———. 1951*b*. The Stability of the World Strontium Cycle. *Science,* vol. 114, pp. 407–411.

OHLE, E. L., AND J. S. BROWN. 1954. Geologic Problems in the Southeast Missouri Lead District. *Bull. Geol. Soc. Amer.,* vol. 65, pp. 201–221.

OLSON, E. C. 1952. The Evolution of a Permian Vertebrate Chronofauna. *Evolution,* vol. 6, pp. 181–196.

ORTON, J. H. 1914. On Ciliary Mechanisms in Brachiopods and Some Polychaetes, with a Comparison of the Ciliary Mechanisms on the Gills of Molluscs, Protochordata, Brachiopods and Crytocephalous Polychaetes, and an Account of the Endostyle of *Crepidula* and Its Allies. *Jour. Marine Biol. Assoc.,* vol. 10, pp. 283–311.

OSBORNE, H. F. 1935. The Ancestral Tree of the Proboscidea, Discovery, Evolution, Migration and Extinction over a 50,000,000-year period. *Proc. Natl. Acad. Sci.,* vol. 21, pp. 404–412.

———. 1942. Proboscidea: A Monograph of the Discovery, Evolution, Migration and Extinction of the Mastodonts and Elephants of the World. Vol. II. Stegodontoidea, Elephantoidea. 873 pp. New York, American Museum Press.

PARKER, F. L., F. B. PHLEGER, AND J. F. PEIRSON. 1953. Ecology of Foraminifera from San Antonio Bay and Environs, Southwest Texas. *Cushman Found.,* Spec. Publ. no. 2, pp. 1–75.

PARKER, R. H. 1956. Macro-invertebrate Assemblages as Indicators of Sedimentary Environments in East Mississippi Delta Region. *Bull. Amer. Assoc. Petroleum Geologists,* vol. 40, pp. 295–376.

———. 1959. Macro-invertebrate Assemblages of Central Texas Coastal Bays and Laguna Madre. *Bull. Amer. Assoc. Petroleum Geologists,* vol. 43, pp. 2100–2166.

PAUČA, M. 1934. Die Fossile Fauna und Flora aus dem Oligocän von Suslănești-Muscel in Rumänien. *Anuar. Inst. Geol. Român.,* vol. 16, pp. 575–668.

PERCIVAL, E. 1944. A Contribution to the Life-history of the Brachiopod, *Terebratella inconspicua* Sowerby. *Trans. Royal Soc. N.Z.,* vol. 74, pp. 1–23.

PÉRÈS, J. 1957. Le problème de l'étagement des formations benthiques. *Rec. Trav. Sta. marine Endoume,* fasc. 21, pp. 4–21.

Petersen, C. G. J. 1913. Valuation of the Sea. II. The Animal Communities of the Sea Bottom and Their Importance for Marine Geography. *Rept. danish biol. Sta.*, no. 21, pp. 1–44.

———. 1914. Appendix to Report 21: On the Distribution of the Animal Communities of the Sea Bottom. *Rept. danish biol. Sta.*, no. 22, pp. 1–7.

———. 1915. On the Animal Communities of the Sea Bottom in the Skagerrak, the Christiana Fjord and the Danish Waters. *Rept. danish biol. Sta.*, no. 23, pp. 3–28.

———. 1918. The Sea Bottom and Its Production of Fish-food: A Survey of the Work Done in Connection with the Valuation of the Danish Waters from 1883–1917. *Rept. danish biol. Sta.*, no. 25, pp. 1–62.

———. 1924. A Brief Survey of the Animal Communities in Danish Waters, Based upon Quantitative Samples Taken with the Bottom Sampler. *Amer. Jour. Sci.*, vol. 7, pp. 343–354.

Petránek, J., and E. Kómárkova. 1953. Orientace schránek hlavonožců ve vapencich Barrandienu a její paleogeografický význam. *Sborník Ústřed. ústav. geol.*, vol. 20, pp. 129–148. (In Czech. English summary in *Geol. Soc. Amer.*, Mem. 67, vol. 2, pp. 850–851.)

Phleger, F. B. 1951. Ecology of Foraminifera, Northwest Gulf of Mexico. Part I. Foraminifera Distribution. *Geol. Soc. Amer.*, *Mem.* 46, pp. 1–88.

———. 1960. Ecology and Distribution of Recent Foraminifera. 297 pp. Baltimore, Johns Hopkins.

Popovici, Z. 1940. Messensterben von *Upogebia littoralis* an der Westkuste des schwarzen Meeres. *Mem. Acad. Roumaine, Sec. Sci.*, ser. 3, vol. 22, pp. 420–422.

Prashnowsky, A., E. T. Degens, K. O. Emery, and J. Pimenta. 1961. Organic Materials in Recent and Ancient Sediments. Part I. Sugars in Marine Sediment of Santa Barbara Basin, California. *Neues Jahrb. Geol. Paläont.*, vol. 8, pp. 400–413.

Pruvost, R. 1930. La faune continentale du terrain houiller de la Belgique. *Mém. Mus. roy. Hist. nat. Belge*, no. 44, pp. 103–283.

Pryor, W. A., and H. D. Glass. 1961. Cretaceous-Tertiary Clay Mineralogy of the Upper Mississippi Embayment. *Jour. Sed. Petrology*, vol. 31, pp. 38–51.

Purchon, R. D. 1939. The Effect of the Environment on the Shell of *Cardium edule*. *Proc. Malac. Soc.*, vol. 23, pp. 256–267.

Puri, G. S. 1943. The Occurrence of *Woodfordia fruticosa* (Linn.) S. Kurz in the Karewa Deposits of Kashmir, with Remarks on Changes of Altitude and Climate during the Pleistocene. *Jour. Indian Bot. Soc.*, vol. 22, pp. 125–131.

———. 1945. Some Fossil Leaves of the Salicaceae from Ningal Nullah and Laredura, Pir Panjal, with a Note on the Significance of Temperate Species in the Pleistocene Flora of Kashmir. *Proc. Indian Acad. Sci.*, sec. B, vol. 22, pp. 87–112.

——— (*anonymous communication on his work.*). 1946. Fossil Floras of the Karewa Series. *Nature*, vol. 157, p. 491.

———. 1947a. Some Fossil Leaves of *Mallotus phillippinensis* Muell. from the Karewa Beds at Laredura and Liddamarg, Pir Panjal, Kashmir. *Jour. Indian Bot. Soc.*, vol. 26, pp. 125–128.

———. 1947*b*. The Occurrence of a Tropical Fig (*Ficus cunia* Buch-Ham.) in the Karewa Beds at Laredura and Liddamarg, Pir Panjal, Kashmir, with Remarks on the Sub-tropical Forests of the Kashmir Valley during the Pleistocene. *Jour. Indian Bot. Soc.*, vol. 26, pp. 131–135.

———. 1948. The Flora of the Karewa Series of Kashmir and its Phytogeographical Affinities, with Chapters on the Methods Used in Identification. *Indian Forester*, vol. 74, pp. 105–122.

RAMSAY, J. G. 1961. The Effects of Folding upon the Orientation of Sedimentation Structures. *Jour. Geol.*, vol. 69, pp. 84–100.

RANKAMA, K. 1954. The Isotopic Constitution of Carbon in Ancient Rocks as an Indicator of Its Biogenic or Nonbiogenic Origin. *Geochim. Cosmochim. Acta*, vol. 5, pp. 142–152.

RÁSKY, K. 1948. *Nipadites burtini* Brong. Termése Dudarról. *Földt. Közl., Budapest*, vol. 78, pp. 130–134.

RAYMOND, P. E. 1920. The Appendages, Anatomy and Relationships of Trilobites. *Mem. Connecticut Acad. Arts Sci.*, vol. 7, pp. 1–169.

REID, D. M. 1935. The Range of the Sea-urchin *Echinus esculentus*. *Jour. Animal Ecol.*, vol. 4, pp. 7–16.

REID, E. M., AND M. E. J. CHANDLER. 1933. The London Clay Flora. 561 pp. London, Brit. Mus. (Nat. Hist.).

REID, R. E. H. 1958. Remarks on the Upper Cretaceous Hexactinellida of County Antrim. *Irish Naturalist Jour.*, vol. 12, pp. 236–268.

———. 1962. Sponges and the Chalk Rock. *Geol. Mag.*, vol. 99, pp. 271–278.

RENZ, C. 1932. Brachiopoden des südschweizerischen und westgrieschischen Lias. *Abh. schweiz. palaeont. Gesell.*, vol. 52, pp. 1–61.

RESSER, C. E. 1939. The Ptarmigania Strata of the Northern Wasatch Mountains. *Smithsonian Misc. Colln.*, vol. 98, no. 24, pp. 1–72.

REZAK, R. 1959. Permian Algae from Saudi Arabia. *Jour. Paleont.*, vol. 33, pp. 531–539.

RHODES, F. H. T. 1952. A Classification of Pennsylvanian Conodont Assemblages. *Jour. Paleont.*, vol. 26, pp. 886–901.

RICHARDS, P. W. 1952. The Tropical Rain Forest. 450 pp. Cambridge, Cambridge University Press.

RICHARDSON, E. S. 1956. Pennsylvanian Invertebrates of the Mazon Creek Area, Illinois: Introduction. *Fieldiana Geol.*, vol. 12, pp. 1–12.

——— AND R. ZANGERL. 1957. Postulates Employed in a Pennsylvanian Paleoecological Study. (Abstract only.) *Program Amer. Assoc. Adv. Sci., Sec. E*, Indianapolis.

RICHTER, R. 1915. Neue Beobachtungen für den Bau der Trilobiten Gattung *Harpes*. *Zool. Anz.*, vol. 45, pp. 146–152.

———. 1919. Von Bau und Leben der Trilobiten. I. Der Schwimmen. *Senckenbergiana*, vol. 1, pp. 213–238.

———. 1920*a*. Von Bau und Leben der Trilobiten. II. Die Aufenthalt auf dem Boden. Der Schutz. Die Ernährung. *Senckenbergiana*, vol. 2, pp. 23–43.

————. 1920*b*. Ein devonischer "Pfeifenquarzit" vergleichen mit der heutigen "Sandkoralle" (*Sabellaria,* Annelidae). *Senckenbergiana,* vol. 2, pp. 215–235.

————. 1923*a*. Von Bau und Leben der Trilobiten. III. Die Beiziehungen von Glatze und Magen. *Palaeontologica Hungarica,* vol. 1, pp. 77–89.

————. 1923*b*. Von Bau und Leben der Trilobiten. IV. Die Versteifungen der Schale und daraus hervorgehende Konvergenzen. *Palaeontologica Hungarica,* vol. 1, pp. 90–108.

————. 1925. Von Bau und Leben der Trilobiten. V. Die Segmentbildung der Trilobiten, vergleichen mit anderen Tiergruppen. *Centralbl. f. Min.,* ser. B, pp. 104–122.

————. 1926. Von Bau und Leben der Trilobiten. VI. Paläozoologische Bermerkungen zu Storch's Phyllopoden-Fanggerät "bei den Trilobiten." *Zool. Anz.,* vol. 65, pp. 297–311.

————. 1927*a*. Die fossilen Fährten und Bauten der Würmer: Ein Ueberblick überihre biologischen Grundformen und deren geologische Bedeutung. *Paläont. Zeitschr.,* vol. 9, pp. 193–235.

————. 1927*b*. "Sandkorallen": Riffe in der Nordsee. *Natur u. Mus.,* pp. 49–62.

————. 1928. Aktuopaläontologie und Paläobiologie: Eine Abgrenzung. *Senckenbergiana,* vol. 10, pp. 285–292. (*See also* W. H. Bucher, 1928.)

————. 1929. Das Verhältnis von Funktion und Form bei den Deckelkorallen. *Senckenbergiana,* vol. 11, pp. 57–94.

————. 1931. Tierwelt und Umwelt im Hunsrück-Schiefer, zur Enstehung eines schwarzen schlammsteins. *Senckenbergiana,* vol. 13, pp. 299–342.

————. 1934. Von Bau und Leben der Trilobiten. VII. Missbildungen bei Scutellidae und konstruktive Konvergenzen. *Senckenbergiana,* vol. 16, pp. 155–160.

————. 1936. Marken und Spuren im Hunsrück-Schiefer. II. Schichtung und Grund-Leben. *Senckenbergiana,* vol. 18, pp. 215–244.

————. 1937. Von Bau und Leben der Trilobiten. VIII. Die "Salter'sche Einbettung" als Folge und Kennzeichen des Häutungs-Vorgangs. *Senckenbergiana,* vol. 19, pp. 413–431.

————. 1941. Marken und Spuren im Hunsrück-Schiefer. III. Fährten als Zeugnisse des Lebens am Meeres-Grunde. *Senckenbergiana,* vol. 23, pp. 218–260.

———— AND E. RICHTER. 1939. Die Kot-Schnur *Tomaculum* Groom (= *Syncoprulus* Rud. und E. Richter), ähnliche Scheitel-Platten und beider stratigraphische Bedeutung. *Senckenbergiana,* vol. 21, pp. 278–291.

RINGUEBERG, E. N. S. 1886. A Trilobite Track Illustrating One Mode of Progression of the Trilobites. (Abstract only.) *Proc. Amer. Assoc. Adv. Sci.,* vol. 35, p. 228.

RIOULT, M. 1958. Phénomènes de dissolution bio-chimique datant du Jurassique inférieur sur les grès et quartzites du synclinal de May. *Bull. Soc. Linné Normandie,* vol. 9, pp. 48–54.

ROMER, A. S. 1945. Vertebrate Paleontology (2d edition). 687 pp. Chicago, University of Chicago Press.

—— AND L. W. PRICE. 1940. Review of the Pelycosauria. 538 pp. *Geol. Soc. Amer.*, Spec. paper no. 28.

ROSA, D. 1931. L'Ologénèse: Nouvelle théorie de l'évolution et de la distribution géographique des êtres vivants. 368 pp. Paris, Félix Alcan.

ROSENKRANTZ, A., AND H. W. RASMUSSEN. 1960. South-eastern Sjaelland and Mön, Denmark. 17 pp. *Excursion Guide, XXIst Internat. Geol. Cong., Copenhagen.*

ROTHPLETZ, A. 1909. Über die Einbettung von Ammoniten in die Solnhofener Schichten. *Abh. k. bayer. Akad. Wiss., München*, vol. 24, pp. 313–337.

ROWE, A. W. 1899. An Analysis of the Genus *Micraster,* as Determined by Rigid Zonal Collecting from the Zone of *Rhynchonella Cuvieri* to That of *Micraster cor-anguinem. Quart. Jour. Geol. Soc.,* London, vol. 55, pp. 494–547.

RÓZYCKI, S. Z. 1948. Remarks about Upper Jurassic Rhynchonellidae of the Cracow-Czestochowa Chain. *Bull. Inst. géol. Pologne,* vol. 42, pp. 16–40.

RUDWICK, M. J. S. 1958. Protective Devices in Fossil Brachiopods. *New Scientist,* Sept. 11th, pp. 799–801.

——. 1961*a.* The Feeding Mechanism of the Permian Brachiopod *Prorichthofenia. Palaeontology,* vol. 3, pp. 450–471.

——. 1961*b.* The Anchorage of Articulate Brachiopods on Soft Sediments. *Palaeontology,* vol. 4, pp. 475–476.

RUEDEMANN, R. 1897. Evidence of Current Action in the Ordovician of New York. *Amer. Geol.,* vol. 19, pp. 367–391.

——. 1921. On Color Bands in *Orthoceras. Bull. New York State Mus.,* no. 227–228, pp. 79–88.

——. 1926. Faunal Facies Differences of the Utica and Lorraine Shales. *Bull. New York State Mus.,* no. 267, pp. 61–78.

——. 1934. Paleozoic Plankton of North America. *Geol. Soc. Amer.,* Mem. 2, pp. 1–141.

——. 1935. Ecology of Black Mud Shales of Eastern New York. *Jour. Paleont.,* vol. 9, pp. 79–91.

SAID, R. 1950. The Distribution of Foraminifera in the Northern Red Sea. *Contr. Cushman Lab. Foram. Research,* vol. 1, no. 3, pp. 9–29.

SARDESON, F. W. 1924. Habit of an Ordovicic Pelecypod. *Pan-Amer. Geol.,* vol. 42, pp. 345–356.

——. 1926*a.* Beloit Formation and Bentonite. *Pan-Amer. Geol.,* vol. 46, pp. 11–24.

——. 1926*b.* Pioneer Re-population of Devastated Sea-bottoms. *Pan-Amer. Geol.,* vol. 46, pp. 273–288.

——. 1929. Ordovicic Brachiopod Habit. *Pan-Amer. Geol.,* vol. 51, pp. 23–40.

SARTENAER, P. 1959*a.* Premieres recherches taphonomiques, en scaphandre autonome, sur le facies à *Turritella tricarinata* forme *communis* de la vase molle terrigene du Golfe de Fos (1). *Rec. Trav. Sta. Marine Endoume*, fasc. 26, bull. 16, pp. 15–38.

——. 1959*b*. La plongée en scaphandre autonome au service de la taphonomie. *Bull. Inst. Océanog.*, Monaco, no. 1159, pp. 1–14.

SCHÄFER, W. 1956. Wirkungen der Benthos-Organismen auf den jungen Schichtverband. *Senckenbergiana Lethaea*, vol. 37, pp. 183–263.

——. 1962. Akuto-Paläontologie nach Studien in der Nordsee. 666 pp. Frankfurt-am-Main, Waldemar Kramer.

SCHLAUDT, C. M., AND K. YOUNG. 1960. Acrothoracic Barnacles from Texas Permian and Cretaceous. *Jour. Paleont.*, vol. 34, pp. 903–907.

SCHMIDT, HERMAN. 1930. Über die Bewegungsweise der Schalencephalopoden. *Paläont. Zeitschr.*, vol. 12, pp. 194–207.

SCHMIDT, HERTA. 1937. Zur Morphogenie der Rhynchonelliden. *Senckenbergiana*, vol. 19, pp. 22–60.

SCHOTT, W. 1935. Die Foraminiferen in dem aequatorialen Teil des Atlantischen Ozeans. *Deutsche Atlantische Exped. Meteor 1925–1927*, vol. 3, pp. 43–134.

SCOTT, G. 1940. Paleoecological Factors Controlling the Distribution and Mode of Life of Cretaceous Ammonoids in the Texas Area. *Jour. Paleont.*, vol. 14, pp. 299–323.

SCOTT, H. W. 1942. Conodont Assemblages from the Heath Formation, Montana. *Jour. Paleont.*, vol. 16, pp. 293–300.

——. 1948. Significance of Crustaceans in Dwarfed Faunas. *Jour. Sed. Petrology*, vol. 18, pp. 65–70.

SEILACHER, A. 1953. Studien zur Palichnologie. I. Ueber die Methoden der Palichnologie. *Neues Jahrb. Geol. Paläont.*, vol. 96, pp. 421–452.

——. 1954. Ökologie der triassichen Muschel *Lima lineata* (Schloth.) und ihrer Epöken. *Neues Jahrb. Geol. Paläont. Mh. H.* 4, pp. 163–183.

——. 1958. Zur ökologischen Characteristik von Flysch und Molasse. *Eclog. Geol. Helvet.*, vol. 51, pp. 1062–1078.

——. 1960. Epizoans as a Key to Ammonoid Ecology. *Jour. Paleont.*, vol. 34, pp. 189–193.

——. 1962. Paleontological Studies on Turbidite Sedimentation and Erosion. *Jour. Geol.*, vol. 70, pp. 227–234.

SEWELL, R. B. S. 1940. The Extent to Which the Distribution of Marine Organisms Can Be Explained by, and Is Dependent on, the Hydrographic Conditions in the Great Oceans, with Special Reference to Plankton. *Proc. Linn. Soc., London*, vol. 152, pp. 256–286.

SHAVER, R. H. 1960. The Pennsylvanian Ostracode *Bairdia oklahomaensis* in Indiana. *Jour. Paleont.*, vol. 34, pp. 656–670.

SHIMER, H. V. 1908. Dwarf-faunas. *Amer. Naturalist*, vol. 42, pp. 472–490.

SHOTWELL, J. A. 1955. An Approach to the Paleoecology of Mammals. *Ecology*, vol. 36, pp. 327–337.

SHOU-HSIN, C. 1959. Note on the Paleoecological Relation between *Aulopora* and *Mucrospirifer*. *Acta Paleont. Sinica*, vol. 7, pp. 502–504.

SHROCK, R. R. 1935. Probable Worm Castings ("coprolites") in the Salem Limestone of Indiana. *Proc. Indiana Acad. Sci.*, vol. 44, pp. 174–175.

Simpson, E. H. 1949. Measurement of Diversity. *Nature,* vol. 163, p. 688.

Simpson, G. G. 1940. Mammals and Land Bridges. *Jour. Washington Acad. Sci.,* vol. 30, pp. 137–163.

———. 1953. Evolution and Geography. 64 pp. Eugene, Ore., Oregon State System of Higher Education.

Simpson, S. 1957. On the Trace-fossil *Chondrites. Quart. Jour. Geol. Soc., London,* vol. 112, pp. 475–499.

Skellam, J. G. 1952. Studies in Statistical Ecology. I. Spatial Pattern. *Biometrika,* vol. 39, pp. 346–362.

Smith, J. P. 1927. Upper Triassic Marine Invertebrate Faunas of North America. *U.S. Geol. Survey,* Prof. paper no. 141, pp. 1–262.

Smith, W. E. 1961. The Cenomanian Deposits of South-east Devonshire. *Proc. Geol. Assoc., London,* vol. 72, pp. 91–134.

Smoot, T. W. 1958. Relation of Silurian Reefs to Ordovician Structure in the Patoka Oil Area. *Illinois State Geol. Survey,* Circ. no. 258, pp. 1–20.

Sokolova, M. N. 1959. On the Distribution of Deep-water Bottom Animals in Relation to Their Feeding Habits and the Character of Sedimentation. *Deep Sea Research,* vol. 6, pp. 1–4.

Sorby, H. C. 1908. On the Application of Quantitative Methods to the Study of the Structure and History of Rocks. *Quart. Jour. Geol. Soc., London,* vol. 64, pp. 171–233.

Sorgenfrei, T. 1958. Molluscan Assemblages from the Marine Middle Miocene of South Jutland and Their Environments. 2 vols., 503 pp. Copenhagen, Reitzel.

Staff, H. von, and H. Reck. 1911. Ueber die Lebensweise der Trilobiten: Eine Entwicklungs mechanische Studie. *Sitz. Gesell. Naturforsch. Freunde,* pp. 130–146.

Stefanini, G. 1924. Relations between American and European Tertiary Echinoid Faunas. *Bull. Geol. Soc. Amer.,* vol. 35, pp. 827–846.

Stehli, F. G. 1957. Possible Permian Climatic Zonation and Its Implications. *Amer. Jour. Sci.,* vol. 255, pp. 607–618.

Stenzel, H. B. 1948. Ecology of Living Nautiloids. *Rept. Natl. Research Council Comm. Marine Ecol. Paleoecol.,* no. 8, pp. 84–90.

———, F. E. Turner, and C. J. Hesse. 1944. Brackish and Non-marine Miocene in Southeastern Texas. *Bull. Amer. Assoc. Petroleum Geologists,* vol. 28, pp. 977–1011.

Stephenson, L. W. 1933. The Zone of *Exogyra cancellata* Traced Twenty-five Hundred Miles. *Bull. Amer. Assoc. Petroleum Geologists,* vol. 17, pp. 1351–1361.

Stewart, W. N. 1950. Report on the Carr and Daniels Collections of Fossil Plants from Mazon Creek. *Trans. Illinois Acad. Sci.,* vol. 43, pp. 41–45.

Stock, C. 1935. Exiled Elephants of the Channel Islands, California. *Science Monthly,* vol. 41.

Stockdale, P. B. 1931. Bioherms in the Borden Group of Indiana. *Bull. Geol. Soc. Amer.,* vol. 42, pp. 707–718.

Størmer, L. 1940. Studies on Trilobite Morphology. Part I. The Thoracic

Appendages and Their Phylogenetic Significance. *Norsk Geol. Tidsskrift*, vol. 19, pp. 143–276.

STRAATEN, L. M. J. U. VAN. 1952. Biogene Textures and the Formation of Shell Beds in the Dutch Wadden Sea. *Koninkl. Ned. Akad. Wetensch.*, ser. B, vol. 55, pp. 500–516.

———. 1956. Composition of Shell Beds Formed in Tidal Flat Environment in the Netherlands and in the Bay of Arcachon (France). *Geol. Mijnbouw*, N.S., Jaargang 18, pp. 209–226.

———. 1960. Marine Mollusc Shell Assemblages of the Rhône Delta. *Geol. Mijnbouw*, N.S., Jaargang 39, pp. 105–129.

STRAELEN, V. VAN. 1925. The Microstructure of the Dinosaurian Eggshells from the Cretaceous Beds of Mongolia. *Amer. Mus. Novitates New York*, no. 173, p. 4.

———. 1928. Les oeufs de reptiles fossiles. *Palaeobiologica, Wien*, vol. 1, pp. 295–312.

STUBBLEFIELD, C. J. 1939. Some Aspects of the Distribution and Migration of Trilobites in the British Lower Palaeozoic Faunas. *Geol. Mag.*, vol. 76, pp. 49–72.

SWAIN, F. W. 1961. Stratigraphic Distribution of Furfurals and Amino Compounds in Jurassic Rocks of Gulf of Mexico Region. *Bull. Amer. Assoc. Petroleum Geologists*, vol. 45, pp. 1713–1720.

SWAN, E. F. 1952. The Growth of the Clam *Mya arenaria* as Affected by the Substratum. *Ecology*, vol. 33, pp. 530–534.

SWINTON, W. E. 1934. The Dinosaurs. 233 pp. London, Thomas Murby.

SYLVESTER-BRADLEY, P. C. 1959. Iterative Evolution in Fossil Oysters. *Proc. XVth Internat. Zool. Cong., London*, pp. 193–197.

TANAI, T. 1961. Neogene Floral Change in Japan. *Jour. Fac. Sci. Hokkaido Univ.*, ser. 4, vol. 11, pp. 119–398.

TAPPAN, H. 1960. Cretaceous Biostratigraphy of Northern Alaska. *Bull. Amer. Assoc. Petroleum Geologists*, vol. 44, pp. 273–297.

TASCH, P. 1953. Causes and Paleoecological Significance of Dwarfed Fossil Marine Invertebrates. *Jour. Paleont.*, vol. 27, pp. 356–444.

———. 1957. Fauna and Paleoecology of the Pennsylvanian Dry Shale of Kansas. *Geol. Soc. Amer.*, Mem. 67, vol. 2, pp. 365–406.

TASNADI-KUBACSKA, A. 1962. Pathologie der vorzeitlichen Tiere. 269 pp. Budapest, Akad. Kiadó.

TAYLOR, B. W. 1954. An Example of Long Distance Dispersal. *Ecology*, vol. 35, pp. 569–572.

TERMIER, H., AND G. TERMIER. 1948. Les phénomènes de spéciation dans le genre *Halorella*. *Notes et Mém. Serv. géol. Maroc*, no. 71, vol. 1, pp. 47–63.

THOMAS, A. O. 1911. A Fossil Burrowing Sponge from the Iowa Devonian. *Bull. Univ. Iowa*, vol. 6, pp. 165–166.

THORSON, G. 1946. Reproduction and Larval Development of Danish Marine Bottom Invertebrates with Special Reference to the Planktonic Larvae in the Sound (Øresund). *Medd. Komm. Dan. Fisk.-Havunders. Plankton*, vol. 4, pp. 1–523.

————. 1950. Reproduction and Larval Ecology of Marine Bottom Invertebrates. *Biol. Rev.*, vol. 25, pp. 1–45.

————. 1957. Bottom Communities (Sublittoral or Shallow Shelf). *Geol. Soc. Amer.*, Mem. 67, vol. 1, pp. 461–534.

TILLYARD, R. J. 1924. Kansas Permian Insects. Part 3. The New Order Protohymenoptera. *Amer. Jour. Sci.*, vol. 8, pp. 111–122.

TRECHMANN, C. T. 1913. On a Mass of Anhydrite in the Magnesian Limestone of Hartlepool, and on the Permian of South-eastern Durham. *Quart. Jour. Geol. Soc.*, London, vol. 69, pp. 184–218.

————. 1921. Some Remarkably Preserved Brachiopods from the Lower Magnesian Limestone of Durham. *Geol. Mag.*, vol. 58, pp. 538–543.

————. 1925. The Permian Formation in Durham. *Proc. Geol. Assoc.*, London, vol. 36, pp. 135–145.

————. 1945. On Some New Permian Fossils from the Magnesian Limestone near Sunderland. *Quart. Jour. Geol. Soc.*, London, vol. 100, pp. 333–354.

TROELS-SMITH, J. 1960. Ivy, Mistletoe and Elm: Climate Indicators—Fodder Plants. (*Publ.*) *Geol. Survey Denmark*, ser. 4, vol. 4, pp. 1–32.

TRUEMAN, A. E. 1940. The Ammonite Body-chamber, with Special Reference to the Buoyancy and Mode of Life of the Living Ammonite. *Quart. Jour. Geol. Soc.*, London, vol. 96, pp. 339–383.

————. 1942. Supposed Commensalism of Carboniferous Spirorbids and Certain Non-marine Lamellibranchs. *Geol. Mag.*, vol. 79, pp. 312–320.

————. 1947. Stratigraphical Problems in the Coal Measures of Europe and North America. *Quart. Jour. Geol. Soc.*, London, vol. 102, pp. xlix–xciii.

TUREKIAN, K. 1955. Paleoecological Significance of the Strontium-Calcium Ratio in Fossils and Sediments. *Bull. Geol. Soc. Amer.*, vol. 66, pp. 155–158.

————. 1956. Significance of Trace Elements in Carbonate Sediments. (Abstract only.) *Prog. Ann. Mtg. Geol. Soc. Amer. & Amer. Assoc. Adv. Sci.* (*Sec. E*), New York, p. 21.

UNKLESBAY, A. G., AND W. B. NIEWOEHNER. 1959. Attachment Loops on Infant Brachiopods from the Louisiana Limestone in Missouri. *Jour. Paleont.*, vol. 33, pp. 547–549.

UREY, H. C., H. A. LOWENSTAM, S. EPSTEIN, AND C. R. MCKINNEY. 1951. Measurement of Paleotemperatures and Temperatures of the Upper Cretaceous of England, Denmark and the Southeastern United States. *Bull. Geol. Soc. Amer.*, vol. 62, pp. 399–416.

VANDERCAMMEN, A. 1959. Essai d'étude statistique des *Cyrtospirifer* du Frasnian de la Belgique. *Inst. roy. Sci. nat. Belg.*, Mem. 145, pp. 1–175.

VAUGHAN, T. W. 1911. Physical Conditions under Which the Paleozoic Coral Reefs Were Formed. *Bull. Geol. Soc. Amer.*, vol. 22, pp. 238–252.

————. 1940. Ecology of Modern Marine Organisms with Reference to Paleogeography. *Bull. Geol. Soc. Amer.*, vol. 51, pp. 433–468.

VAUGHAN, T. W., AND J. W. WELLS. 1943. Revision of the Suborders, Families and Genera of the Scleractinia. *Spec. Paper Geol. Soc. Amer.*, no. 44, pp. 1–363.

VEEVERS, J. 1959. Size and Shape Variation in the Brachiopod *Schizophoria* from the Devonian of Western Australia. *Jour. Paleont.*, vol. 33, pp. 888–901.

VOKES, H. E., AND B. BROWN. 1944. (Trails in the Cretaceous Mowry Shale of Montana). *Rept. Natl. Research Comm. Marine Ecol. Paleoecol.*, no. 4, pp. 11–12.

VYALOV, O. S., AND N. L. ZENKEVICH. 1961. Trail of a Crawling Animal on the Floor of the Pacific Ocean. *Izv. Akad. Nauk. S.S.S.R.* (Ser.), *Geol.* no. 1, pp. 52–58. (In Russian.)

WALCOTT, C. D. 1881. The Trilobite: New and Old Evidence Relating to Its Organization. *Bull. Mus. Comp. Zool., Harvard*, vol. 8, pp. 191–230.

WALTHER, J. 1904. Die Fauna der Solnhofener Plattenkalk. *Haeckel Festschr.-Denkschr. Medd. nat. Gesell., Jena*, vol. 11, pp. 133–214.

WATSON, D. M. S. 1951. Paleontology and Modern Biology. 216 pp. New Haven, Conn., Yale University Press.

———. 1957. The Two Great Breaks in the History of Life. *Quart. Jour. Geol. Soc., London*, vol. 92, pp. 435–444.

WELLS, H. W. 1957. Abundance of the Hard Clam *Mercenaria mercenaria* in Relation to Environmental Factors. *Ecology*, vol. 38, pp. 123–128.

WELLS, J. W. 1937. Individual Variation in the Rugose Coral Species *Heliophyllum halli* E. & H. *Palaeontographica Americana*, vol. 2, pp. 1–23.

———. 1944. Middle Devonian Bone Beds of Ohio. *Bull. Geol. Soc. Amer.*, vol. 55, pp. 273–302.

———. 1957a. Corals. *Geol. Soc. Amer.*, Mem. 67, vol. 1, pp. 1087–1104.

———. 1957b. Corals. *Geol. Soc. Amer.*, Mem. 67, vol. 2, pp. 773–782.

WELLS, P. V. 1959. Comments on "Plant Ecology as a Branch of Botany." *Ecology*, vol. 40, p. 153.

WESTOLL, T. S. 1950. Some Aspects of Growth Studies in Fossils. *Proc. Royal Soc., London*, ser. B, vol. 137, no. 889, pp. 490–509.

WETMORE, A. 1943. The Occurrence of Feather Impressions in the Miocene Deposits of Maryland. *The Auk*, vol. 60, pp. 440–441.

WHITTARD, W. F. 1934. A Revision of the Trilobite Genera *Deiphon* and *Onychopyge*. *Annals Mag. Nat. Hist.*, ser. 10, vol. 14, pp. 505–533.

WILLIAMS, C. B. 1946. Yule's "Characteristic" and the Index of Diversity. *Nature*, vol. 157, p. 482.

———. 1951. Diversity as a Measurable Character of an Animal or Plant Population. *Année Biol.*, vol. 27, pp. 129–141.

———. 1954. The Statistical Outlook in Relation to Ecology. *Jour. Ecol.*, vol. 42, pp. 1–13.

WILLIAMS, E. G. 1960. Marine and Fresh Water Fossiliferous Beds in the Pottsville and Allegheny Groups of Western Pennsylvania. *Jour. Paleont.*, vol. 34, pp. 908–922.

WILLIS, J. C. 1922. Age and Area: A Study in Geographic Distribution and Origin of Species. 259 pp. Cambridge, Cambridge University Press.

WILLS, L. J. 1951. A Palaeogeographical Atlas of the British Isles and Adjacent Parts of Europe. 64 pp. Glasgow and London, Blackie.

WILSON, J. L. 1951. Paleoecology. *Texas Jour. Sci.*, vol. 3, pp. 58–65.

WOLFF, J. A., AND E. S. BARGHOORN. 1960. Generic Changes in Tertiary Floras in Relation to Age. *Amer. Jour. Sci.*, vol. 258A, pp. 388–399.

WOOD, A. 1942. The Lower Carboniferous Calcareous Algae *Mitcheldeania* Wethered and *Garwoodia* gen nov. *Proc. Geol. Assoc., London*, vol. 52, pp. 216–226.

———. 1946. Probable Sponge Embryos in a Rock of Arenig Age. *Proc. Geol. Assoc., London*, vol. 57, pp. 19–21.

———. 1948. "*Sphaerocodium*," a Misinterpreted Fossil from the Wenlock Limestone. *Proc. Geol. Assoc., London*, vol. 59, pp. 9–22.

WOOD, H. E., AND A. E. WOOD. 1933. *Daemonhelix* in the Pleistocene of Texas. *Jour. Geol.*, vol. 41, pp. 824–833.

WOODRING, W. P. 1928. Miocene Mollusks from Bowden, Jamaica: Part III. Gastropods and Discussion of Results. 564 pp. *Carnegie Inst., Washington*, Publ. no. 385.

———. 1960. Paleoecologic Dissonance: *Astarte* and *Nipa* in the Early Eocene London Clay. "*Bradley Vol.*," *Amer. Jour. Sci.*, vol. 258-A, pp. 418–419.

WRIGLEY, A. 1936. An "Aenigma" of the London Clay. *Proc. Malac. Soc., London*, vol. 22, pp. 23–26.

———. 1945. Tertiary Turridae as Horizon-indicators. *Proc. Geol. Assoc., London*, vol. 56, pp. 149–150.

WURSTER, P. 1958. Geometrie und Geologie von Kreuzschichtungskörpern. *Geol. Rundschau*, vol. 47, pp. 322–359.

YABE, H., AND S. TOYAMA. 1928. On Some Rock-forming Algae from the Younger Mesozoic of Japan. *Sci. Rept. Tohoku Imp. Univ.*, ser. 2, vol. 12, pp. 141–152.

YAKOVLEV, N. N. 1926. The Phenomena of Parasitism, Commensalism and Symbiosis in the Paleozoic Invertebrata. *Annals Soc. paléont. Russie*, vol. 4, pp. 113–124.

YOCHELSON, E. L. 1961. The Operculum and Mode of Life of *Hyolithes*. *Jour. Paleont.*, vol. 35, pp. 152–161.

ZANGERL, R., AND E. S. RICHARDSON. 1955. Ecologic History of a Transgressing Pennsylvanian Sea near Mecca, Indiana. (Preliminary Report.) *Bull. Geol. Soc. Amer.*, vol. 66, p. 1639.

ZAPFE, H. 1937. Paläobiologische Untersuchungen an Hippuritenvorkommen der nordalpen Gosauschichten. *Verh. zool.-bot. Gesell., Wien*, vol. 86–7, pp. 73–124.

———. 1957. Dachsteinkalk und "Dachsteinmuscheln." *Natur u. Volk, Wien*, vol. 87, pp. 87–94.

ZENKEVICH, L. A. 1951. "Fauna and Biological Productivity of the Sea" *in* The World Ocean, vol. 1. 506 pp. Leningrad, Sovyet. Nauk. (In Russian.)

———. 1959. Certain Zoological Problems Connected with the Study of the Abyssal and Ultra-abyssal Zones in the Ocean. *Proc. XVth Internat. Cong. Zool., London*, pp. 215–218.

ZEUNER, F. E. 1946. Dating the Past. 444 pp. London, Methuen.

Index

Numbers in **boldface** type refer to illustrations